THE NOTEBOOKS OF
LEONARDO DA VINCI

THE
NOTEBOOKS
OF
LEONARDO
DA VINCI

Abridged from the translation by
EDWARD MacCURDY

Edited, with an Introduction, by
ROBERT N. LINSCOTT

THE MODERN LIBRARY · NEW YORK

First Modern Library Edition, 1957

© *Copyright, 1957, by Random House, Inc.*

All rights reserved under International and
Pan-American Copyright Conventions.

Library of Congress Catalog Card Number: 57-11170

Published by arrangement with Harcourt, Brace and Company.

CONTENTS

I   Observations and Aphorisms   1

II   On Painting: Comparison of the Arts; Precepts of the Painter; Color; Landscape; Light and Shade; Perspective; Artists' Materials; Notes for The Last Supper   35

III   Sculpture, Architecture and Music   155

IV   Anatomy: Human Anatomy; Comparative Anatomy; Human Proportions   171

V   Flight: Of Birds; Of Man   219

VI   Warfare: On Land; On Sea   253

VII   Experiments and Inventions   273

VIII   Earth, Air and Water: Physical Geography; The Atmosphere; The Nature of Water; Canals   291

IX   Physics and Other Sciences: Movement and Weight; Mathematics; Astronomy; Botany   339

X   Sight and Sound: Optics; Acoustics   393

XI   Tales, Fables and Prophecies   415

XII   Personalia and Letters   439

INTRODUCTION

THE richest gifts sometimes congregate in one sole person; beauty, grace and talent being united in such a manner that his every action is so divine as to leave all other men far behind him. This was seen and acknowledged in the case of Leonardo da Vinci in whom, to say nothing of his beauty of person, there was a grace beyond expression, and so rare a gift of talent and ability that to whatsoever subject he turned his attention, however difficult, he presently made himself absolute master of it.   —GIORGIO VASARI,

LEONARDO DA VINCI was born near Florence, Italy, in 1452, and died in France in 1519. During these sixty-seven years he painted a few superb pictures and modeled one colossal statue, but by far the greater part of his time and energy was spent in observing the world around him, and in filling some twenty notebooks with the results of his observations.

Most men see much but comprehend little. Leonardo burned with desire to observe, to deduce and to understand. If he lifted a finger he had to analyze the mechanism of the movement even though it meant the dissection of a human body. If he noticed that a swallow held its tail in a certain way at the instant of alighting, then he must check the flight of hundreds of other birds in order to establish a principle of landing techniques and the laws that govern them. An eddy in running water was an invitation to study the nature of the flow and the contours of banks and bottom for an explanation of why the water was whirled clockwise or counterclockwise.

To him a landscape was not only a thing of beauty but a problem in optics: how could its image enter the eye and be recorded by the brain? And always, when he had observed, analyzed and drawn his conclusions, down would go the results haphazard in his notebooks.

These notebooks, then, are the testament of a man who sought knowledge as a mystic seeks God; the record of a lifetime of observation and speculation, set down in five thousand manuscript pages, illustrated with hundreds of sketches, and containing some of the most brilliant and far-ranging deductions that the mind of man has ever conceived.

The price Leonardo paid for his curiosity was high. To gratify it he sacrificed the full flower of his career as painter and sculptor, perhaps the greatest the world has ever known. There is on record a letter to the Marchioness Isabella d'Este from an emissary she had sent to Florence to persuade Leonardo to paint a picture for her (in vain, as it turned out). The letter says, "He is working hard at geometry and is very impatient of painting. . . . In short his mathematical experiments have so estranged him from painting that he cannot bear to take up a brush." And this is typical, for Leonardo's career is one long record of commissions refused; of paintings unfinished.

Why did Leonardo thus sacrifice his greatest talent? To answer this question one turns first to the notebooks for whatever light they may throw on this most enigmatic of all great men. But Leonardo's thirst was for knowledge of things and forces; never of people and events. In the whole vast manuscript there is virtually no mention of his outward life or the world in which he lived; of friends, of women, of fellow artists, or of the men for and with whom he worked. In short, these are laboratory notes set down with a minimum of comment by a genius with a complex for secrecy, and whatever light they throw on his life and times is incidental and

inferential. Moreover, to appraise even this fitful illumination it will be necessary to review first the known facts of
Leonardo's career.

He was born out of wedlock, the son of a peasant girl and
a prosperous lawyer. His earliest years were spent with his
mother; then his father adopted him and he was brought up
by a kindly and childless stepmother, the first of his father's
four wives. Freud, in his study of Leonardo, surmises that
"The accident of his illegitimate birth and the pampering of
his mother exerted the most decisive influence on his character" and helped to explain, not only why Leonardo
"sublimated his libido into a thirst for knowledge," but also
why he never married, and, so far as can be determined, was
sexually inactive throughout his life.

Having as a child shown a natural talent for drawing,
Leonardo was apprenticed to a painter at the age of eighteen
and soon achieved a reputation for his skill in uniting precision of line with rhythm of movement, and for his technical
innovations in the representation of light and shade. Already
his passion for knowledge had begun to curtail his artistic
career as he immersed himself more and more in scientific
studies and experiments. During these early years he was
designing buildings, machines and canals, devising engines
for moving earth and drawing water, and studying botany
and astronomy. In a city and a period glittering with the
vitality of the high Renaissance, he was outstanding, not only
for his manifold talents, but no less for his beauty, his charm,
his strength, and for the brilliance of his conversation.

At the age of thirty, Leonardo left Florence for Milan,
then ruled by Lodovico Sforza, who was attempting to secure
more firmly the throne his family had usurped, by subsidizing
poets and artists to celebrate his magnificence.

As usual with Leonardo, the reason for his change of
scene can only be conjectured. Vasari, in his *Lives of the*

Italian Painters, written about thirty years after Leonardo's death, says: "He was invited with great honor to Milan by the Duke who delighted in the music of the lute, to the end that the master might play before him; Leonardo, therefore, took with him a certain instrument which he himself had constructed almost wholly of silver and in the shape of a horse's head. Here Leonardo surpassed all the musicians . . . and the Duke was so charmed by his varied gifts that he delighted beyond measure in his society." And now, as an example of the inconsistencies that baffle the biographer, turn to page 445 of this book, and compare Vasari's romantic statement with the curious and childishly boastful letter in which Leonardo attempts to sell his services to the Duke, not primarily as an artist, and certainly not as a musician, but as a military engineer and inventor of engines of destruction.

In Milan, Leonardo was employed by Sforza to devise and carry out elaborate pageants with ingenious mechanical accompaniments. He also made studies for completing the cathedral and modernizing the city, designed improvements and decorations for the palace, planned canals and irrigation projects, modeled a huge equestrian statue of Sforza's father and completed his *Cenacolo* or *Last Supper* in which he brought the art of painting to a point never before and scarcely since achieved.

Four years were spent on this magnificent picture, and the only authentic glimpse we have of Leonardo at work was given by Bandello, a contemporary novelist, who wrote: "It was his habit often, and I have frequently seen him, to go early in the morning and mount upon the scaffolding as the *Cenacolo* is some distance from the ground; it was his habit, I say, from sunrise until dusk never to lay down his brush, but, forgetful alike of eating and drinking, to paint without intermission. At other times two, three or four days would pass without his touching the fresco, but he would remain before it for an hour or two at a time merely looking at it, considering, examining the figures. I have also seen him, as the caprice or whim took him, set out at midday from the Corte Vecchia, where he was at work on the clay model of the great horse, and go straight to the Grazie and there mount on the scaffolding and take up the brush and give one or two touches to one of the figures and suddenly give up and go away again."

Characteristically, the statue was so large that it was never cast, and the painting began almost at once to flake from the wall, due to Leonardo's insistence on experimenting with new techniques.

To this period also is attributed the exquisite *Virgin of the Rocks,* with its glittering technique and romantic background of rocks and water.

Sforza was eventually involved in war and appointed Leonardo his chief military engineer. When Milan was captured by the French, Leonardo fled to Venice and then to Florence, where he drew up plans for the control of the river Arno, and sketched (but never completed) his famous *Virgin and St. Anne.* Next he served for two years as engineer for Cesare Borgia, most ruthless of the Renaissance princelings, returning to Florence in 1502 at the age of fifty. Here we find him at work on a flying machine, and painting a battle scene to adorn the new council chamber. The flying machine failed to fly; the painting created an immense sensation but was never transferred to the wall.

One painting of this period which he did finish (though not, it is reported, to his own satisfaction) was the world's most famous portrait, *Mona Lisa,* or *La Gioconda.* This he loitered over, as Vasari says, for four years, taking the precaution, meanwhile, "of keeping someone constantly near her to sing, or play on instruments, or to jest and otherwise amuse her, to the end that she might continue cheerful." The celebrated and mysterious smile that plays upon the lips, not only of Mona Lisa, but of other women whom Leonardo painted, was, in Freud's opinion, a memory of his peasant mother.

In 1506, Leonardo was again in Milan and serving under the French. Six years later he moved to Rome, but there the younger generation in the persons of Raphael and Michelangelo dominated the world of art, and after two years he left Rome, struck up a friendship with the new French king, Francis I, and accepted his offer of a generous pension and the use of his castle of Cloux in France. There he died two and a half years later at the age of sixty-seven. His epitaph was pronounced by the king, who said that "he did not believe there had ever been another man born into the world who had known as much as Leonardo, and this not only in matters concerning sculpture, painting and architecture, but because he was a great philosopher."

The notebooks were bequeathed by Leonardo to his friend and disciple, Francesco Melzi, treasured by him, dispersed by his descendants, and, centuries later, reunited in printed form, after prolonged research and study, by many devoted scholars.

These are the outward facts of a life that would seem to have been a miracle of inconsistency. Two questions are especially perplexing: first, why a man uniquely gifted as an artist and with a reputation that made him sought after by kings and princes should have spent the greater part of his life in study and have written down his findings in code and without organization so that succeeding generations had no opportunity to profit from his discoveries; second, why a man who hated war (he called it bestial madness) and loved liberty (he would buy caged birds in order to set them free) should have served the tyrants of the period and expended such ingenuity in devising more lethal weapons of destruction. Vasari says he kept many servants and horses, but moneymaking could not have interested him or he would never have spent so many years in abstract studies. One might imagine that he passed through life as in a trance, following his fancies, and unaware of, or indifferent to, the forces of good and evil, if it were not for the high moral tone of the philosophic maxims that are scattered through his manuscripts.

And the questions raised by the notebooks are no less baffling. Consider, first of all, that the whole vast manuscript was written backward; i.e., from right to left. One would infer from this and from the occasional use of rebuses and anagrams (Amor, for example, instead of Roma) that Leonardo had a passion for concealment, but the labor of writing backward would surely have been out of all proportion to the secrecy value, since the script could be read by anyone with a mirror. Consider also the extraordinary and extraneous material which he copied into his notebooks. This includes an apparently meaningless list of nearly eight thousand words; parts of a Latin grammar; a large collection of popular superstitions about animals, some taken from Pliny and some from medieval bestiaries; hundreds of quotations or paraphrases from other writers, unmarked and with no clue to their origin, so that in reading his aphorisms one never knows whether to pay tribute to Leonardo as a thinker or as an appropriator; and finally a section of excessively dull jokes. Are the letters that purport to describe events in Asia Minor evidence that he actually traveled in the East as some commentators believe, or are they the beginnings of an attempt at fiction?

One can answer these questions only by affirming that Leonardo was unique, conforming to no pattern, and can be comprehended only in the context of his time, as an intermediary between the Middle Ages and the modern world. Harvey had yet to discover the circulation of the blood; Newton the law of gravitation; Galileo the movements of the heavenly bodies. Leonardo half anticipated these discoveries but lacked the accumulated knowledge to define his surmises. If, now and then, his conclusions seem childlike or absurd, it must be remembered that he was still partly in the medieval night of the mind, attempting by faulty reasoning based on erroneous premises to understand phenomena dependent on principles beyond the comprehension of the age in which he lived.

What must amaze every reader of these notebooks is the precision of Leonardo's observations and the brilliance of the deductions which enabled him to anticipate so many of the discoveries of modern science. In anatomy, physics, geology, mathematics and other sciences he was centuries ahead of his time. He was the first since the ancient Greeks seriously to probe the mysteries of the universe; the first to understand the earth's motion, the laws of friction, of velocities, of combustion, of respiration, and the true nature of fossils. He was the first to grasp the principles of the camera obscura, screw propulsion, the parachute, underwater swimming, the use of tanks in warfare and mines to destroy forts. He restored the laws of the lever and may be said almost to have originated the science of hydraulics, and he invented or improved many labor-saving devices, from the door spring to the wheelbarrow. By patient dissection he uncovered the workings of the human body. By observing the flight of birds he deduced the principles of human flight but lacked the motive power to put them into practice. Considering the times, and the tools with which he worked, his instruments and inventions were incredibly ingenious. He was the only man in history equally and prodigiously gifted both in science and in art. As Rachel Taylor aptly says in *Leonardo the*

Florentine, "Because of his isolation he remains the most brilliant and versatile of all amateurs, lost in fascinating experiments, making wonderful guesses, handling all problems with originality and dexterity . . . inventing many things that have been reinvented since. Without the notebooks we would hardly have suspected the radiating energy that maintained this life of laborious research parallel with the mystical and absorbed existence of the great artist, so different is the psychology revealed."

Many different subjects are covered in Leonardo's notebooks, and the scientific value of what he wrote can be appraised only by specialists in each of these fields. To the layman they offer an absorbing record of the thoughts and speculations, the observations and philosophy, of "the most gifted of all the sons of men."

ROBERT N. LINSCOTT

HISTORY OF THE NOTEBOOKS

After Leonardo's death, this "collection without order," as its author called it, was taken to Milan by Francesco Melzi, and kept, for the most part, intact during his lifetime. When Melzi died, the manuscripts were gradually dispersed. Some disappeared and have never been traced. Thirteen of the volumes were given to a tutor in the Melzi family. One of these was eventually acquired by the Ambrosian Library at Milan, two were lost and ten came into the possession of a sculptor named Pompeo Leoni, who cut them up and pasted them together into one large volume of 402 sheets and 1700 drawings, known as the Codice Atlantico. Part of this collection, after many vicissitudes, was acquired by the Ambrosian Library. Two sections disappeared during the years it was in the library; the rest was seized by Bonaparte in 1796 and deposited in the Bibliothèque Nationale and the Institut de France.

After the downfall of Napoleon, the notebooks which were in the Bibliothèque Nationale were returned to the Ambrosian Library, but those in the Institut de France were overlooked and are still there, except for two sections which were stolen more than a century ago, one eventually ending up in the Royal Library of Turin, the other in the Bibliothèque Nationale.

There are also manuscripts by Leonardo in the Royal Library at Windsor and in the British Museum, probably purchased by the Earl of Arundel early in the seventeenth century; in the Victoria and Albert Museum, purchased in Vienna by the Earl of Lytton; and in the Morgan Library in New York, purchased from the Earl of Leicester, whose ancestors acquired them two centuries ago.

Towards the end of the last century the first serious attempts were made to coordinate and transcribe the Notebooks, notably by Dr. J. P. Richter in The Literary Works of Leonardo da Vinci (1883). The first complete translation of the Notebooks into English was made by Edward Mac-Curdy, and it is from his translation that this Modern Library edition has been made. Readers who wish to pursue the subject further are referred to the complete edition of the Notebooks published in America in 1939; also to Leonardo the Florentine, by R. A. Taylor, and The Mind of Leonardo da Vinci, by Edward MacCurdy.

R.N.L.

I

Observations and Aphorisms

BEGUN in Florence in the house of Piero di Braccio Martelli, on the 22nd day of March, 1508. This will be a collection without order, made up of many sheets which I have copied here, hoping afterwards to arrange them in order in their proper places according to the subjects of which they treat; and I believe that before I am at the end of this I shall have to repeat the same thing several times; and therefore, O reader, blame me not, because the subjects are many, and the memory cannot retain them and say: "This I will not write because I have already written it." And if I wished to avoid falling into this mistake, it would be necessary, in order to prevent repetition, that on every occasion when I wished to transcribe a passage I should always read over all the preceding portion, and this especially because long periods of time elapse between one time of writing and another.

Seeing that I cannot choose any subject of great utility or pleasure, because my predecessors have already taken as their own all useful and necessary themes, I will do like one who, because of his poverty, is the last to arrive at the fair, and not being able otherwise to provide himself, chooses all the things which others have already looked over and not taken, but refused as being of little value. With these despised and rejected wares—the leavings of many buyers—I will load my modest pack, and therewith take my course, distributing, not indeed amid the great cities, but among the mean hamlets, and taking such reward as befits the things I offer.

I am fully aware that the fact of my not being a man of letters may cause certain arrogant persons to think that they may with reason censure me, alleging that I am a man ignorant of book-learning. Foolish folk! Do they not know that I might retort by saying, as did Marius to the Roman Patricians: "They who themselves go about adorned in the labor of others will not permit me my own"? They will say that because of my lack of book learning, I cannot properly express what I desire to treat of. Do they not know that my subjects require for their exposition experience rather than the words of others? And since experience has been the mistress of whoever has written well, I take her as my mistress, and to her in all points make my appeal.

If indeed I have no power to quote from authors, as they have, it is a far bigger and more worthy thing to read by the light of experience, which is the instructress of their masters. They strut about puffed up and pompous, decked out and adorned not with their own labors but by those of others, and they will not even allow me my own. And if they despise me who am an inventor, how much more should blame be given to themselves, who are not inventors but trumpeters and reciters of the works of others?

Those who are inventors and interpreters between nature and man, as compared with the reciters and trumpeters of the works of others, are to be considered simply as is an object in front of a mirror in comparison with its image when seen in the mirror, the one being something in itself, the other nothing: people whose debt to nature is small, for it seems only by chance that they wear human form, and but for this one might class them with the herds of beasts.

Many will believe that they can with reason censure me, alleging that my proofs are contrary to the authority of certain men who are held in great reverence by their inexperienced judgments, not taking into account that my conclusions were arrived at as a result of simple and plain experience, which is the true mistress.

These rules enable you to discern the true from the false, and thus to set before yourselves only things possible and of more moderation; and they forbid you to use a cloak of ignorance, which will bring about that you attain to no result and in despair abandon yourself to melancholy.

The natural desire of good men is knowledge.

I know that many will call this a useless work, and they will be those of whom Demetrius said that he took no more account of the wind that produced the words in their mouths than of the wind that came out of their hinder parts: men whose only desire is for material riches and luxury and who are entirely destitute of the desire of wisdom, the sustenance and the only true riches of the soul. For as the soul is more worthy than the body, so much are the soul's riches more worthy than those of the body. And often when I see one of these men take this work in hand, I wonder whether he will not put it to his nose like the ape, and ask me whether it is something to eat.

We have no lack of system or device to measure and to parcel out these poor days of ours; wherein it should be our pleasure that they be not squandered or suffered to pass away in vain, and without reward to honor, leaving no record of themselves in the minds of men; to the end that this our poor course may not be sped in vain.

Our judgment does not reckon in their exact and proper order things which have come to pass at different periods of time; for many things which happened many years ago will seem nearly related to the present, and many things that are recent will seem ancient, extending back to the far-off period of our youth. And so it is with the eye, with regard to distant things, which when illumined by the sun seem near to the eye, while many things which are near seem far off.

Supreme happiness will be the greatest cause of misery, and the perfection of wisdom the occasion of folly.

Every part is disposed to unite with the whole, that it may thereby escape from its own incompleteness.

The soul desires to dwell with the body because without the members of that body it can neither act nor feel.

[*Drawing: bird sitting in cage*]
The thoughts turn towards hope.[1]

O Time, thou that consumest all things! O envious age, thou destroyest all things and devourest all things with the hard teeth of the years, little by little, in slow death! Helen, when she looked in her mirror and saw the withered wrinkles which old age had made in her face, wept, and wondered to herself why ever she had twice been carried away.[2]

---

[1] The sketch at the side of this sentence serves to recall the fact that, as Vasari states, Leonardo was in the habit of paying the price demanded by the owners of captive birds simply for the pleasure of setting them free.

[2] Gerolamo Calvi has shown in an article in the *Archivio Storico Lombardo,* Anno XLIX (1916), Fasc. III, that the source of this passage is to be found in Ovid's *Metamorphoses,* Book XV, lines 232-6:

> Flet quoque, ut in speculo rugas aspexit aniles
> Tyndaris, et secum, cur sit bis rapta, requirit.
> Tempus edax rerum, tuque, invidiosa vetustas,
> Omnia destruitis, vitiataque dentibus aevi
> Paulatim lenta consumitis omnia morte.

"Helen also weeps when she sees her aged wrinkles in the looking glass, and tearfully asks herself why she should twice have been a lover's prey. O Time, thou great devourer, and thou, envious Age, together

Observations

The age as it flies glides secretly and deceives one and another; nothing is more fleeting than the years, but he who sows virtue reaps honor.

Wrongfully do men lament the flight of time, accusing it of being too swift, and not perceiving that its period is yet sufficient; but good memory wherewith nature has endowed us causes everything long past to seem present.

Whoever would see in what state the soul dwells within the body, let him mark how this body uses its daily habitation, for if this be confused and without order the body will be kept in disorder and confusion by the soul.

O thou that sleepest, what is sleep? Sleep is an image of death. Oh, why not let your work be such that after death

---

you destroy all things; and, slowly gnawing with your teeth, you finally consume all things in lingering death!"

The passage as it appears in the *Codice Atlantico* serves to show how Leonardo in borrowing enriched the Roman poet's thought with the melody of music by introducing the apostrophe to time and envious age as prelude as well as finale:

"O tempo, consumatore delle cose, e o invidiosa antichità, tu distruggi tutte le cose e consumi tutte le cose da duri denti della vecchiezza a poco a poco con lenta morte!

"Elena quando si specchiava, vedendo le vizze grinze del suo viso, fatte per la vecchiezza, piagnie e pensa seco, perchè fu rapita due volte.

"O tempo, consumatore delle cose, e o invidiosa antichità, per la quale tutte le cose sono consumate."

Immediately below this passage Leonardo wrote these words: "This book belongs to Michele di Francesco Bernabini and his family." It is a reasonable inference that they refer to the copy of Ovid from which the lines were taken. Farther below in writing of the same time is a fragment: "Tell, tell me how things are passing yonder and whether Caterina wishes to make . . ."

Caterina was the name of Leonardo's mother. He wrote the name when his thoughts had just been turning to the poet's description of the changes that time had made in Helen's beauty. From this has arisen the conjecture—it is nothing more!—that the sentence refers to her and that he was making some provision for her in her old age.

you become an image of immortality; as in life you become when sleeping like unto the hapless dead.

Man and the animals are merely a passage and channel for food, a tomb for other animals, a haven for the dead, giving life by the death of others, a coffer full of corruption.

Behold a thing which the more need there is of it is the more rejected: this is advice, listened to unwillingly by those who have most need of it, that is, by the ignorant. Behold a thing which the more you have fear of it and the more you flee from it comes the nearer to you: this is misery, which the more you flee from it makes you the more wretched and without rest.

Experience, the interpreter between resourceful nature and the human species, teaches that that which this nature works out among mortals constrained by necessity cannot operate in any other way than that in which reason, which is its rudder, teaches it to work.

To the ambitious, whom neither the boon of life nor the beauty of the world suffice to content, it comes as penance that life with them is squandered, and that they possess neither the benefits nor the beauty of the world.

The air as soon as there is light is filled with innumerable images to which the eye serves as a magnet.

In youth acquire that which may requite you for the deprivations of old age; and if you are mindful that old age has wisdom for its food, you will so exert yourself in youth, that your old age will not lack sustenance.

Nothing is superfluous and nothing is lacking in any species of animal or product of nature unless the defect comes from the means which produce it.

There is no result in nature without a cause; understand the cause and you will have no need of the experiment.

Experience is not at fault; it is only our judgment that is in error in promising itself from experience things which are not within her power.

Wrongly do men cry out against experience and with bitter reproaches accuse her of deceitfulness. Let experience alone, and rather turn your complaints against your own ignorance, which causes you to be so carried away by your vain and insensate desires as to expect from experience things which are not within her power!

O mathematicians, throw light on this error.

The spirit has no voice, for where there is voice, there is a body, and where there is a body, there is occupation of space which prevents the eye from seeing things situated beyond this space; consequently this body of itself fills the whole surrounding air, that is, by its images.

The body of the earth is of the nature of a fish, a grampus or sperm whale, because it draws water as its breath instead of air.

How the movements of the eye, of the ray of the sun, and of the mind are the swiftest that can be:

The sun so soon as ever it appears in the east instantly proceeds with its rays to the west; and these are made up of three incorporeal forces, namely, radiance, heat and the image of the shape which produces these.

The eye so soon as ever it is opened beholds all the stars of our hemisphere.

The mind passes in an instant from the east to the west; and all the great incorporeal things resemble these very closely in their speed.

When you wish to produce a result by means of an instrument, do not allow yourself to complicate it by introducing many subsidiary parts but follow the briefest way possible, and do not act as those do who, when they do not know how to express a thing in its own proper vocabulary, proceed by a method of circumlocution and with great prolixity and confusion.

Two weaknesses leaning together create a strength. Therefore the half of the world leaning against the other half becomes firm.

While I thought that I was learning how to live, I have been learning how to die.

Every part of an element separated from its mass desires to return to it by the shortest way.

Nothingness has no center, and its boundaries are nothingness.

My opponent says that nothingness and a vacuum are one and the same thing, having indeed two separate names by which they are called, but not existing separately in nature.

The reply is that whenever there exists a vacuum, there will also be the space which surrounds it, but nothingness exists apart from occupation of space; it follows that nothingness and a vacuum are not the same, for the one is divisible to infinity, and nothingness cannot be divided because nothing can be less than it is; and if you were to take part from it this part would be equal to the whole, and the whole to the part.

Aristotle in the Third [Book] of the Ethics: man is worthy of praise and blame solely in respect of such actions as it is within his power to do or to abstain from.

He who expects from experience what she does not possess takes leave of reason.

For what reason do such animals as sow their seed sow with pleasure, and the one who awaits receives with pleasure and brings forth with pain?

Intellectual passion drives out sensuality.

The knowledge of past time and of the position of the earth is the adornment and the food of human minds.

Among the great things which are found among us the existence of Nothing is the greatest. This dwells in time, and stretches its limbs into the past and the future, and with these takes to itself all works that are past and those that are to come, both of nature and of the animals, and possesses nothing of the indivisible present. It does not, however, extend to the essence of anything.

The lover is drawn by the thing loved, as the sense is by that which it perceives, and it unites with it, and they become one and the same thing. The work is the first thing born of the union; if the thing that is loved be base, the lover becomes base. When the thing taken into union is in harmony

9

with that which receives it, there follow rejoicing and pleasure and satisfaction. When the lover is united to that which is loved, it finds rest there; when the burden is laid down there, it finds rest. The thing is known with our intellect.

As a well-spent day brings happy sleep, so life well used brings happy death.

Where there is most power of feeling, there of martyrs is the greatest martyr.

All our knowledge originates in our sensibilities.

Science, knowledge of the things that are possible present and past; prescience, knowledge of the things which may come to pass.

To enjoy—to love a thing for its own sake and for no other reason.

The senses are of the earth, the reason stands apart from them in contemplation.

Life well spent is long.

In rivers, the water that you touch is the last of what has passed and the first of that which comes: so with time present.

Every action must necessarily find expression in movement.

To know and to will are two operations of the human mind.

To discern, to judge, to reflect are actions of the human mind.

Our body is subject to heaven, and heaven is subject to the spirit.

Observations

Many times one and the same thing is drawn by two violences, namely, necessity and power.

Water falls in rain; the earth absorbs it from necessity of moisture; and the sun raises it up not from necessity but by its power.

The soul can never be infected by the corruption of the body, but acts in the body like the wind which causes the sound of the organ, wherein if one of the pipes becomes spoiled, no good effect can be produced because of its emptiness.

If you kept your body in accordance with virtue, your desires would not be of this world.

You grow in reputation like bread in the hands of children.

There cannot be any sound where there is no movement or percussion of the air. There cannot be any percussion of the air where there is no instrument. There cannot be any instrument without a body. This being so, a spirit cannot have either sound or form or force, and if it should assume a body it cannot penetrate or enter where the doors are shut. And if any should say that through air being collected together and compressed a spirit may assume bodies of various shapes, and by such instrument may speak and move with force, my reply to this would be that where there are neither nerves nor bones there cannot be any force exerted in any movement made by imaginary spirits. Shun the precepts of those speculators whose arguments are not confirmed by experience.

Force I define as a spiritual power, incorporeal and invisible, which with brief life is produced in those bodies which as the result of accidental violence are brought out of their natural state and condition.

I have said spiritual because in this force there is an active, incorporeal life; and I call it invisible because the body in which it is created does not increase either in weight or in size; and of brief duration because it desires perpetually to subdue its cause, and when this is subdued it kills itself.

One ought not to desire the impossible.

Conception: Necessity wills that the corporeal agent be in contact with that which employs it.

Observe the light and consider its beauty. Blink your eye and look at it. That which you see was not there at first, and that which was there is no more.
Who is it who makes it anew if the maker dies continually?

Man has great power of speech, but the greater part thereof is empty and deceitful. The animals have little, but that little is useful and true; and better is a small and certain thing than a great falsehood.

You who speculate on the nature of things, I praise you not for knowing the processes which nature ordinarily effects of herself, but rejoice if so be that you know the issue of such things as your mind conceives.

Words which fail to satisfy the ear of the listener always either fatigue or weary him; and you may often see a sign of this when such listeners are frequently yawning. Consequently, when addressing men whose good opinion you desire, either cut short your speech when you see these evident signs of impatience, or else change the subject; for if you take any other course, then in place of the approbation you desire you will win dislike and ill will.

And if you would see in what a man takes pleasure without hearing him speak, talk to him and change the subject of your discourse several times, and when it comes about that you see him stand fixedly without either yawning or knitting his brows or making any other movement, then be sure that the subject of which you are speaking is the one in which he takes pleasure.

Every evil leaves a sorrow in the memory except the supreme evil, death, and this destroys memory itself together with life.

Though nature has given sensibility to pain to such living organisms as have the power of movement—in order thereby to preserve the members which in this movement are liable to diminish and be destroyed—the living organisms which have no power of movement do not have to encounter opposing objects, and plants consequently do not need to have a sensibility to pain, and so it comes about that if you break them they do not feel anguish in their members as do the animals.

Water struck by water creates circles at a great distance round the spot where it is struck; the voice in the air goes further, in fire further still; mind ranges over the universe, but being finite it does not extend into infinity.

The water which rises in the mountains is the blood which keeps the mountain in life. If one of its veins be open either internally or at the side, nature, which assists its organisms, abounding in increased desire to overcome the scarcity of moisture thus poured out, is prodigal there in diligent aid, as also happens with the place at which a man has received a blow. For one sees then how, as help comes, the blood increases under the skin in the form of a swelling in order to open the infected part. Similarly, life being severed at the topmost extremity [of the mountain], nature sends her fluid from its lowest foundations up to the greatest height of the severed passage, and as this is poured out there, it does not leave it bereft of vital fluid down to the end of its life.

Movement is the cause of all life.

He who does not value life does not deserve it.

Nature is full of infinite causes which were never set forth in experience.

What is it that is much desired by men, but which they know not while possessing? It is sleep.

Wine is good, but water is preferable at table.

Science is the captain, practice the soldiers.

Flax is dedicated to death and human corruption: to death by the lakes with nets for birds, beasts and fishes; to corruption by the linen cloths in which the dead are wrapped when they are buried, for in these cloths they suffer corruption.
And moreover this flax does not become separated from its stalks until it commences to soften and become corrupt; and it is this which one should use to make garlands and adornments for funeral processions.

Truth alone was the daughter of time.

Small rooms or dwellings set the mind in the right path, large ones cause it to go astray.

Just as eating contrary to the inclination is injurious to the health, so study without desire spoils the memory, and it retains nothing that it takes in.

Call not that riches which may be lost; virtue is our true wealth, and the true reward of its possessor. It cannot be lost; it will not abandon us unless life itself first leaves us. As for property and material wealth, these you should ever hold in fear; full often they leave their possessor in ignominy, mocked at for having lost possession of them.

The earth is moved from its position by the weight of a tiny bird resting upon it.
The surface of the sphere of the water is moved by a tiny drop of water falling upon it.

Every action done by nature is done in the shortest way.

Where the descent is easier, there the ascent is more difficult.

It is possible to conceive everything that has substance as divisible into an infinite number of parts.
Amid the greatness of the things around us the existence of nothingness holds the first place, and its function extends among the things which have no existence, and its essence dwells as regards time between the past and the future, and possesses nothing of the present. This nothingness has the part equal to the whole and the whole to the part, the divisible to the indivisible, and it comes to the same amount whether we divide it or multiply it or add to it or subtract

from it, as is shown by the arithmeticians in their tenth sign which represents this nothingness. And its power does not extend among the things of nature.

[*Of the end of the world*]

The watery element remaining pent up within the raised banks of the rivers and the shores of the sea, it will come to pass with the upheaval of the earth that as the encircling air has to bind and circumscribe the complicated structure of the earth, its mass which was between the water and the fiery element will be left narrowly compassed about and deprived of the necessary supply of water.

The rivers will remain without their waters; the fertile earth will put forth no more her budding branches; the fields will be decked no more with waving corn. All the animals will perish, failing to find fresh grass for fodder; and the ravening lions and wolves and other beasts which live by prey will lack sustenance; and it will come about after many desperate shifts that men will be forced to abandon their life and the human race will cease to be.

And in this way the fertile fruitful earth being deserted will be left arid and sterile, and through the pent-up moisture of the water enclosed within its womb and by the activity of its nature, it will follow in part its law of growth until having passed through the cold and rarefied air it will be forced to end its course in the element of fire. Then the surface of it will remain burned to a cinder, and this will be the end of all terrestrial nature.

[*A disputation*]

Against. Why nature did not ordain that one animal should not live by the death of another.

For. Nature, being capricious and taking pleasure in creating and producing a continuous succession of lives and forms because she knows that they serve to increase her terrestrial substance, is more ready and swift in creating than time is in destroying, and therefore she has ordained that many animals shall serve as food one for the other; and as this does not satisfy her desire, she sends forth frequently certain noisome and pestilential vapors and continual plagues upon the vast accumulations and herds of animals and especially upon human beings, who increase very rapidly because other animals do not feed upon them; and if the causes are taken away the results will cease.

Against. Therefore this earth seeks to lose its life while desiring continual reproduction for the reason brought forth, and demonstrated to you. Effects often resemble their causes. The animals serve as a type of the life of the world.

For. Behold now the hope and desire of going back to one's own country or returning to primal chaos, like that of the moth to the light, of the man who with perpetual longing always looks forward with joy to each new spring and each new summer, and to the new months and the new years, deeming that the things he longs for are too slow in coming; and who does not perceive that he is longing for his own destruction. But this longing is in its quintessence the spirit of the elements, which finding itself imprisoned within the life of the human body desires continually to return to its source.

And I would have you to know that this same longing is in its quintessence inherent in nature, and that man is a type of the world.

The end of nothingness and the beginning of the line are in contact one with another, but they are not joined together, and in such contact is the point which divides the continuation of nothingness and the line.

It follows that the point is less than nothing, and if all

the parts of nothingness are equal to one we may the more conclude that all the points also are equal to one single point and one point is equal to all.

And from this it follows that many points imagined in continuous contact do not constitute the line, and as a consequence many lines in continuous contact as regards their sides do not make a surface, nor do many surfaces in continuous contact make a body, because among us bodies are not formed of incorporeal things.

The point is that which has no center because it is all center, and nothing can be less.

The contact of the liquid with the solid is a surface common to the liquid and to the solid, and the lighter liquids with the heavier have the same.

All the points are equal to one and one to all.

Nothingness has a surface in common with a thing, and the thing has a surface in common with nothingness, and the surface of a thing is not part of this thing. It follows that the surface of nothingness is not part of this nothingness; it must needs be therefore that a mere surface is the common boundary of two things that are in contact; thus the surface of water does not form part of the water nor consequently does it form part of the atmosphere, nor are any other bodies interposed between them. What is it, therefore, that divides the atmosphere from the water? It is necessary that there should be a common boundary which is neither air nor water but is without substance, because a body interposed between two bodies prevents their contact, and this does not happen in water with air because they are in contact without the interposition of any medium.

Therefore they are joined together and you cannot raise up or move the air without the water, nor will you be able to raise up the flat thing from the other without drawing it back through the air. Therefore a surface is the common boundary of two bodies which are not continuous, and does not form part of either one or the other, for if the surface formed part of it, it would have divisible bulk, whereas, however, it is not divisible and nothingness divides these bodies the one from the other.

Although time is numbered among continuous quantities, yet through its being invisible and without substance it does not altogether fall under the category of geometrical terms, which are divided in figures and bodies of infinite variety, as may constantly be seen to be the case with things visible and things of substance; but it harmonises with these only as regards its first principles, namely, as to the point and the line. The point as viewed in terms of time is to be compared with the instant, and the line resembles the length of a quantity of time. And just as points are the beginning and end of the said line, so instants form the end and the beginning of a certain given space of time. And if a line be divisible to infinity, it is not impossible for a space of time to be so divided. And if the divided parts of a line may bear a certain proportion one to another, so also may the parts of time.

Given the cause, nature produces the effect in the briefest manner that it can employ.

Write of the nature of time as distinct from its geometry.

Every continuous quantity is infinitely divisible; therefore the division of this quantity will never result in a point which is given as the extremity of a line. It follows that the breadth and depth of the natural line is divisible to infinity.

It is asked whether all the infinites are equal or whether they are greater the one than the other. The answer is that

every infinite is eternal and eternal things are of equal permanence but not of equal length of existence. For that which
functioned first commenced to divide and has passed a longer
existence, but the periods to come are equal.

No element has in itself gravity or levity unless it moves.
The earth is in contact with the water and with the air and
has of itself neither gravity nor levity. It has no consciousness
of the water or air which surrounds it except by accident
which arises from their movement. And this we learn from
the leaves of plants which grow upon the earth when it is in
contact with water or air, for they do not bend except by
the movement of the air or water.

From the foregoing we should say that gravity is an incident created by the movement of the lower elements in the
higher.

Levity is an incident created when the thinner element is
drawn beneath the less thin which then moves, being unable
to resist, and then acquires weight, this being created so soon
as the element lacks the power of resistance; which resistance
being subdued by weight it does not change without change
of substance; and in changing it acquires the name of levity.

Levity is not produced except together with gravity, nor
gravity without levity: this may be produced: for let air be
suspended under water by blowing through a pipe, then this
air will acquire levity from being beneath the water and the
water will acquire gravity from having beneath it the air
which is a body thinner and lighter than itself.

Therefore levity is born of weight and weight of lightness,
and they give birth one to another at the same time repaying
the boon of their existence, and at the same instant they
destroy one another as the avengers of their death.

Levity and gravity are caused by immediate movement.
Movement is created by heat and cold.

Movement is an incident created by inequality of weight and force.

The atmosphere has not of itself a natural position and always closes up over a body that is thicker than itself, never over the lighter when it is in contact with it, except by violence.

The movement of the elements arises from the sun.

The heat of the universe is produced by the sun.

The light and heat of the universe come from the sun and its cold and darkness from the withdrawal of the sun.

Every movement of the elements arises from heat and cold.

Gravity and levity are created in the elements.

Why does the eye see a thing more clearly in dreams than the imagination when awake?

And this man excels in folly in that he continually stints himself in order that he may not want, and his life slips away while he is still looking forward to enjoying the wealth which by extreme toil he has acquired.

Here nature seems in many or for many animals to have been rather a cruel stepmother than a mother, and for some not a stepmother but a compassionate mother.

I obey thee, O Lord, first because of the love which I ought reasonably to bear thee; secondly, because thou knowest how to shorten or prolong the lives of men.

Shun those studies in which the work that results dies with the worker.

Lo, some who can call themselves nothing more than a passage for food, producers of dung, fillers up of privies, for of them nothing else appears in the world, nor is there any virtue in their work, for nothing of them remains but full privies.

And thou, man, who by these my labors dost look upon the marvelous works of nature, if thou judgest it to be an atrocious act to destroy the same, reflect that it is an infinitely atrocious act to take away the life of man. For thou shouldst be mindful that though what is thus compounded seem to thee of marvelous subtlety, it is as nothing compared with the soul that dwells within this structure; and in truth, whatever this may be, it is a divine thing which suffers it thus to dwell within its handiwork at its good pleasure, and wills not that thy rage or malice should destroy such a life, since in truth he who values it not does not deserve it.

For we part from the body with extreme reluctance, and I indeed believe that its grief and lamentation are not without cause.

The idea or the faculty of imagination is both rudder and bridle to the senses, inasmuch as the thing imagined moves the sense.

Pre-imagining is the imagining of things that are to be.

Post-imagining is the imagining of things that are past.

Neither promise yourself things nor do things if you see that when deprived of them they will cause you material suffering.

Of all human discourses that must be considered as most foolish which affirms a belief in necromancy, which is the sister of alchemy, the producer of simple and natural things, but is so much the more worthy of blame than alchemy, because it never gives birth to anything whatever except to things like itself, that is to say, lies; and this is not the case with alchemy, which works by the simple products of nature, but whose function cannot be exercised by nature herself, because there are in her no organic instruments with which she might be able to do the work which man performs with his hands, by the use of which he has made glass, etc. But this necromancy, an ensign or flying banner, blown by the wind, is the guide of the foolish multitude, which is a continual witness by its clamor to the limitless effects of such an art. And they have filled whole books in affirming that enchantments and spirits can work and speak without tongues, and can speak without any organic instrument—without which speech is impossible—and can carry the heaviest weights, and bring tempests and rain, and that men can be changed into cats and wolves and other beasts, although those first become beasts who affirm such things.

And, undoubtedly if this necromancy did exist, as is believed by shallow minds, there is nothing on earth that would have so much power either to harm or to benefit man; if it were true, that is, that by such an art one had the power to disturb the tranquil clearness of the air, and transform it into the hue of night, to create coruscations and tempests with dreadful thunderclaps and lightning flashes rushing through the darkness, and with impetuous storms to overthrow high buildings and uproot forests, and with these to encounter armies and break and overthrow them, and—more important even than this—to make the devastating tempests, and thereby rob the husbandmen of the reward of their labors. For what method of warfare can there be which can inflict such damage upon the enemy as the exercise of the power to deprive him of his crops? What naval combat could there be which should compare with that which he would wage who has command of the winds and can create ruinous tempests that would submerge every fleet whatsoever? In truth, whoever has control of such irresistible forces will be lord over all nations, and no human skill will be able to resist his destructive power. The buried treasures, the jewels that lie in the body of the earth will all become manifest to him; no lock, no fortress, however impregnable, will avail to save anyone against the will of such a necromancer. He will cause himself to be carried through the air from east to west, and through all the uttermost parts of the universe. But why do I thus go on adding instance to instance? What is there which could not be brought to pass by a mechanician such as this? Almost nothing, except the escaping from death.

We have therefore ascertained in part the mischief and the usefulness that belong to such an art, if it is real; and if it is real, why has it not remained among men who desire so much, not having regard to any deity, merely because there are an infinite number of persons who in order to gratify one of their appetites would destroy God and the whole universe?

If then it has never remained among men, although so necessary to them, it never existed, and never can exist, as follows from the definition of a spirit, which is invisible and incorporeal, for within the elements there are no incorporeal things, because where there is not body there is a vacuum, and the vacuum does not exist within the elements, because it would be instantly filled up by the element.

Therefore, O students, study mathematics and do not build without foundations.

Mental things which have not passed through the under-standing are vain and give birth to no truth other than what is harmful. And because such discourses spring from poverty of intellect, those who make them are always poor, and if they have been born rich they shall die poor in their old age. For nature, as it would seem, takes vengeance on such as would work miracles and they come to have less than other men who are more quiet. And those who wish to grow rich in a day shall live a long time in great poverty, as happens and will to all eternity happen to the alchemists, the would-be creators of gold and silver, and to the engineers, who think to make dead water stir itself into life with perpetual motion, and to those supreme fools, the necromancer and the enchanter.

He who blames the supreme certainty of mathematics feeds on confusion, and will never impose silence upon the contradictions of the sophistical sciences, which occasion a perpetual clamor.

The abbreviators of works do injury to knowledge and to love, for love of anything is the offspring of knowledge, love being more fervent in proportion as knowledge is more certain; and this certainty springs from a thorough knowledge of all those parts which united compose the whole of that thing which ought to be loved.

Of what use, pray, is he who, in order to abridge the part of the things of which he professes to give complete information, leaves out the greater part of the matters of which the whole is composed?

True it is that impatience, the mother of folly, is she who praises brevity; as though such folk had not a span of life that would suffice to acquire complete knowledge of one particular subject such as the human body. And then they think to comprehend the mind of God which embraces the whole universe, weighing and dissecting it as though they were making an anatomy. O human stupidity! Do you not perceive that you have spent your whole life with yourself and yet are not aware of that which you have most in evidence, and that is your own foolishness? And so with the crowd of sophists you think to deceive yourself and others, despising the mathematical sciences in which is contained true information about the subjects of which they treat! Or you would fain range among the miracles and give your views upon those subjects which the human mind is incapable of comprehending and which cannot be demonstrated by any natural instance. And it seems to you that you have performed miracles when you have spoiled the work of some ingenious mind, and you do not perceive that you are falling into the same error as does he who strips a tree of its adornment of branches laden with leaves intermingled with fragrant flowers or fruits, in order to demonstrate the suitability of the tree for making planks. Even as did Justinus, maker of an epitome of the histories of Trogus Pompeius, who had written an elaborate account of all the great deeds of his ancestors which lent themselves to picturesque description, for by so doing he composed a bald work fit only for such impatient minds as conceive themselves to be wasting time when they spend it usefully in study of the works of nature and of human things.

Let such as these remain in the company of the beasts, and let their courtiers be dogs and other animals eager for prey and let them keep company with them; ever pursuing whatever takes flight from them, they follow after the inoffensive animals who in the season of the snowdrifts are impelled by hunger to approach your doors to beg alms from you as from a guardian.

If you are, as you have described yourself, the king of the animals—it would be better for you to call yourself king of the beasts, since you are the greatest of them all!—why do you not help them so that they may presently be able to give you their young in order to gratify your palate, for the sake of which you have tried to make yourself a tomb for all the animals? Even more I might say if to speak the entire truth were permitted me.

But do not let us quit this subject without referring to one supreme form of wickedness which hardly exists among the animals, among whom are none that devour their own species except for lack of reason (for there are insane among them as among human beings though not in such great numbers). Nor does this happen except among the voracious animals, as in the lion species and among leopards, panthers, lynxes, cats and creatures like these, which sometimes eat their young. But not only do you eat your children, but you eat father, mother, brothers and friends; and this even not sufficing you, you make raids on foreign islands and capture men of other races and then after mutilating them in a shameful manner you fatten them up and cram them down your gullet. Say, does not nature bring forth a sufficiency of simple things to produce satiety? Or if you cannot content yourself with simple things, can you not by blending these together make an infinite number of compounds as did Platina and other authors who have written for epicures?

And if any be found virtuous and good, drive them not away from you but do them honor, lest they flee from you and take refuge in hermitages and caves or other solitary places in order to escape from your deceits. If any such be found, pay him reverence, for as these are as gods upon the earth they deserve statues, images and honors. But I would impress upon you that their images are not to be eaten by you, as happens in a certain district of India; for there, when in the judgment of the priests these images have worked some miracle, they cut them in pieces, being of wood, and distribute them to all the people of the locality—not without payment.

And each of them then grates his portion very fine and spreads it over the first food he eats; and so they consider that symbolically by faith they have eaten their saint, and they believe that he will then guard them from all dangers.

What think you, man, of your species? Are you as wise as you set yourself up to be? Are acts such as these things that men should do, Justinus?

Let no one read me who is not a mathematician in my beginnings.

Every action of nature is made along the shortest possible way.

Thou, O God, dost sell unto us all good things at the price of labor.

Falsehood is so utterly vile that though it should praise the great works of God it offends against His divinity. Truth is of such excellence that if it praise the meanest things they become ennobled.

Without doubt truth stands to falsehood in the relation of light to darkness, and truth is in itself of such excellence that even when it treats of humble and lowly matters it yet immeasurably outweighs the sophistries and falsehoods which are spread out over great and high-sounding discourses; for though we have set up falsehood as a fifth element in our mental state, it yet remains that the truth of things is the chief food of all finer intellects—though not indeed of wandering wits.

But you who live in dreams, the specious reasonings, the feints which *palla* players might use, if only they treat of things vast and uncertain, please you more than do the things which are sure and natural and of no such high pretension.

Whoever in discussion adduces authority uses not intellect but rather memory.

Good literature proceeds from men of natural probity, and since one ought rather to praise the inception than the result, you should give greater praise to a man of probity unskilled in letters than to one skilled in letters but devoid of probity.

As courage endangers life even so fear preserves it.
Threats only serve as weapons to the threatened.
Who walks rightly seldom falls.
You do ill if you praise, but worse if you censure what you do not rightly understand.

To devise is the work of the master, to execute the act of the servant.

A thing that moves acquires as much space as it loses.

The acquisition of any knowledge whatever is always useful to the intellect, because it will be able to banish the useless things and retain those which are good. For nothing can be either loved or hated unless it is first known.

Iron rusts from disuse; stagnant water loses its purity and in cold weather becomes frozen; even so does inaction sap the vigor of the mind.

This by experience is proved, that he who never puts his trust in any man will never be deceived.

The memory of benefits is frail as against ingratitude.

Reprove a friend in secret but praise him before others.

Nothing is more to be feared than ill fame.

Toil flees away bearing in its arms fame almost hidden.

We make our life by the death of others.

Lust is the cause of generation.
Appetite is the stay of life.
Fear or timidity is the prolongation of life.
Deceit is the preservation of the instrument.

The ermine would rather die than soil itself.

The cock does not crow until he has flapped his wings three times. The parrot passing from branch to branch never puts his foot where he has not first fixed his beak.

Vows begin when hope dies.

It is by testing that we discern fine gold.

As is the mold so will the cast be.

Ask counsel of him who governs himself well.

You can have neither a greater nor a less dominion than that over yourself.

It is easier to resist at the beginning than at the end.

No counsel is more trustworthy than that which is given upon ships that are in peril.

Let him expect disaster who shapes his course on a young man's counsel.

Consider the end first.

Fear springs to life more quickly than anything else.

He who injures others does not safeguard himself.

Give to your master the example of the captain, for it is not he who conquers but the soldiers by means of his counsel and yet he deserves the reward.

It is as great an error to speak well of a worthless man as to speak ill of a good man.

Necessity is the theme and artificer of nature—the bridle, the law and the theme.

Poor is the pupil who does not surpass his master.

Death rather than weariness.

Hands into which fall like snow ducats and precious stones, these never tire of serving, but such service is only for its usefulness and not for our own advantage.

I never weary of being useful.

He who wishes to become rich in a day is hanged in a year.

The wine consumed by the drunkard, this wine revenges itself upon the drinker.

The paper on seeing itself all spotted by the murky blackness of the ink grieves over it; and this ink shows it that by the words which it composes upon it, it becomes the cause of its preservation.

The bee may be likened to deceit, for it has honey in its mouth and poison behind.

Fame should be represented in the shape of a bird, but with the whole figure covered with tongues instead of feathers.

The evil that does not harm me is as the good that does not help me.

Wood feeds the fire that consumes it.

When fortune comes seize her with a firm hand. In front, I counsel you, for behind she is bald.

Patience serves as a protection against wrongs as clothes do against cold. For if you put on more clothes as the cold increases, it will have no power to hurt you. So in like manner you must grow in patience when you meet with great wrongs, and they will then be powerless to vex your mind.

In the moment when virtue is born she gives birth to envy against herself, and a body shall sooner exist without a shadow than virtue without envy.

Oh, human misery! Of how many things do you make yourself the slave for money!

If you shall choose pleasure, know that he has behind him one who will deal out to you tribulation and repentance.
This is pleasure together with pain, and they are represented as twins because the one is never separated from the other.

Every man desires to acquire wealth in order that he may give it to the doctors, the destroyers of life; therefore they ought to be rich.

Strive to preserve your health; and in this you will the better succeed in proportion as you keep clear of the physicians, for their drugs are a kind of alchemy concerning which there are no fewer books than there are medicines.

You know that medicines when well used restore health to the sick: they will be well used when the doctor together with his understanding of their nature shall understand also what man is, what life is, and what constitution and health are. Know these well and you will know their opposites; and when this is the case you will know well how to devise a remedy.

The act of procreation and the members employed therein are so repulsive, that if it were not for the beauty of the faces and the adornments of the actors and the pent-up impulse, nature would lose the human species.

Methinks that coarse men of bad habits and little power of reason do not deserve so fine an instrument or so great a variety of mechanism as those endowed with ideas and with great reasoning power, but merely a sack wherein their food is received, and from whence it passes away.

For in truth one can only reckon them as a passage for food; since it does not seem to me that they have anything in common with the human race except speech and shape, and in all else they are far below the level of the beasts.

II

On Painting

I · COMPARISON OF THE ARTS

How painting surpasses all human works by reason of the subtle possibilities which it contains:

The eye, which is called the window of the soul, is the chief means whereby the understanding may most fully and abundantly appreciate the infinite works of nature; and the ear is the second, inasmuch as it acquires its importance from the fact that it hears the things which the eye has seen. If you historians, or poets or mathematicians had never seen things with your eyes, you would be ill able to describe them in your writings. And if you, O poet, represent a story by depicting it with your pen, the painter with his brush will so render it as to be more easily satisfying and less tedious to understand. If you call painting "dumb poetry," then the painter may say of the poet that his art is "blind painting." Consider then which is the more grievous affliction, to be blind or to be dumb! Although the poet has as wide a choice of subjects as the painter, his creations fail to afford as much satisfaction to mankind as do paintings, for while poetry attempts to represent forms, actions and scenes with words, the painter employs the exact images of these forms in order to reproduce them. Consider, then, which is more fundamental to man, the name of man or his image? The name changes with change of country; the form is unchanged except by death.

And if the poet serves the understanding by way of the ear, the painter does so by the eye, which is the nobler sense.

I will only cite as an instance of this how if a good painter represents the fury of a battle and a poet also describes one, and the two descriptions are shown together to the public, you will soon see which will draw most of the spectators, and where there will be most discussion, to which most praise will be given and which will satisfy the more. There is no doubt that the painting, which is by far the more useful and beautiful, will give the greater pleasure. Inscribe in any place the name of God and set opposite to it His image, you will see which will be held in greater reverence!

Since painting embraces within itself all the forms of nature, you have omitted nothing except the names, and these are not universal like the forms. If you have the results of her processes we have the processes of her results.

Take the case of a poet describing the beauties of a lady to her lover and that of a painter who makes a portrait of her; you will see whither nature will the more incline the enamored judge. Surely the proof of the matter ought to rest upon the verdict of experience!

You have set painting among the mechanical arts! Truly, were painters as ready equipped as you are to praise their own works in writing, I doubt whether it would endure the reproach of so vile a name. If you call it mechanical because it is by manual work that the hands represent what the imagination creates, your writers are setting down with the pen by manual work what originates in the mind. If you call it mechanical because it is done for money, who fall into this error—if indeed it can be called an error—more than you yourselves? If you lecture for the schools, do you not go to whoever pays you the most? Do you do any work without some reward?

And yet I do not say this in order to censure such opinions, for every labor looks for its reward. And if the poet should say, "I will create a fiction which shall express great things," so likewise will the painter also, for even so Apelles made the Calumny. If you should say that poetry is more enduring —to this I would reply that the works of a coppersmith are more enduring still, since time preserves them longer than either your works or ours; nevertheless they show but little imagination; and painting, if it be done upon copper in enamel colors, can be made far more enduring.

In art we may be said to be grandsons unto God. If poetry treats of moral philosophy, painting has to do with natural philosophy; if the one describes the workings of the mind, the other considers what the mind effects by movements of the body; if the one dismays folk by hellish fictions, the other does the like by showing the same things in action. Suppose the poet sets himeslf to represent some image of beauty or terror, something vile and foul, or some monstrous thing, in contest with the painter, and suppose in his own way he makes a change of forms at his pleasure, will not the painter still satisfy the more? Have we not seen pictures which bear so close a resemblance to the actual thing that they have deceived both men and beasts?

If you know how to describe and write down the appearance of the forms, the painter can make them so that they appear enlivened with lights and shadows which create the very expression of the faces; herein you cannot attain with the pen where he attains with the brush.

How he who despises painting has no love for the philosophy in nature:

If you despise painting, which is the sole imitator of all the visible works of nature, it is certain that you will be despising a subtle invention which with philosophical and ingenious speculation takes as its theme all the various kinds of forms, airs and scenes, plants, animals, grasses and flowers, which are surrounded by light and shade. And this

37

truly is a science and the true-born daughter of nature, since painting is the offspring of nature. But in order to speak more correctly we may call it the grandchild of nature; for all visible things derive their existence from nature, and from these same things is born painting. So therefore we may justly speak of it as the grandchild of nature and as related to God himself.

That sculpture is less intellectual than painting, and lacks many of its natural parts:

As practicing myself the art of sculpture no less than that of painting, and doing both the one and the other in the same degree, it seems to me that without suspicion of unfairness I may venture to give an opinion as to which of the two is the more intellectual, and of the greater difficulty and perfection.

In the first place, sculpture is dependent on certain lights, namely, those from above, while a picture carries everywhere with it its own light and shade; light and shade therefore are essential to sculpture. In this respect, the sculptor is aided by the nature of the relief, which produces these of its own accord, but the painter artificially creates them by his art in places where nature would normally do the like. The sculptor cannot render the difference in the varying natures of the colors of objects; painting does not fail to do so in any particular. The lines of perspective of sculptors do not seem in any way true; those of painters may appear to extend a hundred miles beyond the work itself. The effects of aerial perspective are outside the scope of sculptors' work; they can neither represent transparent bodies nor luminous bodies nor angles of reflection nor shining bodies, such as mirrors and like things of glittering surface, nor mists, nor dull weather, nor an infinite number of things which I forbear to mention lest they should prove wearisome.

Painting

The one advantage which sculpture has is that of offering greater resistance to time; yet painting offers a like resistance if it is done upon thick copper covered with white enamel and then painted upon with enamel colors and placed in a fire and fused. In degree of permanence it then surpasses even sculpture.

It may be urged that if a mistake be made it is not easy to set it right, but it is a poor line of argument to attempt to prove that the fact of a mistake being irremediable makes the work more noble. I should say indeed that it is more difficult to correct the mind of the master who makes such mistakes than the work which he has spoiled.

We know very well that a good experienced painter will not make such mistakes; on the contrary, following sound rules he will proceed by removing so little at a time that his work will progress well. The sculptor also, if he is working in clay or wax, can either take away from it or add to it, and when the model is completed it is easy to cast it in bronze; and this is the last process and it is the most enduring form of sculpture, since that which is only in marble is liable to be destroyed, but not when done in bronze.

But painting done upon copper, which by the methods in use in painting may be either taken from or altered, is like the bronze, for when you have first made the model for this in wax it can still be either reduced or altered. While the sculpture in bronze is imperishable, this painting upon copper and enameling is absolutely eternal; and while bronze remains dark and rough, this is full of an infinite variety of varied and lovely colors, of which I have already made mention. But if you would have me speak only of panel painting, I am content to give an opinion between it and sculpture by saying that painting is more beautiful, more imaginative, and richer in resource, while sculpture is more enduring, but excels in nothing else.

Sculpture reveals what it is with little effort; painting seems a thing miraculous, making things intangible appear tangible, presenting in relief things which are flat, in distance things near at hand.

In fact, painting is adorned with infinite possibilities of which sculpture can make no use.

One of the chief proofs of skill of the painter is that his picture should seem in relief, and this is not the case with the sculptor, for in this respect he is aided by nature.

When the poet ceases to represent in words what exists in nature, he then ceases to be the equal of the painter; for if the poet, leaving such representation, were to describe the polished and persuasive words of one whom he wishes to represent as speaking, he would be becoming an orator and be no more a poet or a painter. And if he were to describe the heavens he makes himself an astrologer, and a philosopher or theologian when speaking of the things of nature or of God. But if he returns to the representation of some definite thing he would become the equal of the painter if he could satisfy the eye with words as the painter does with brush and color, [for with these he creates] a harmony to the eye, even as music does in an instant to the ear.

Why the picture seen with two eyes will not be an example of such relief as the relief seen with two eyes; this is because the picture seen with one eye will place itself in relief like the actual relief, having the same qualities of light and shade.

II · PRECEPTS OF THE PAINTER

WHICH is the more difficult: light and shade or good design?

I maintain that a thing which is confined by a boundary is more difficult than one which is free. Shadows have their boundaries at certain stages, and when one is ignorant of this his works will be lacking in that relief which is the importance and the soul of painting. Design is free, in so much as if you see an infinite number of faces they will be all different, one with a long nose and one with a short; the painter therefore must also assume this liberty, and where there is liberty there is no rule.

The mind of the painter should be like a mirror which always takes the color of the things that it reflects, and which is filled by as many images as there are things placed before it. Knowing therefore that you cannot be a good master unless you have a universal power of representing by your art all the varieties of the forms which nature produces—which indeed you will not know how to do unless you see them and retain them in your mind—look to it, O painter, that when you go into the fields you give your attention to the various objects, and look carefully in turn first at one thing and then at another, making a bundle of different things selected and chosen from among those of less value. And do not after the manner of some painters who, when tired by imaginative work, lay aside their work and take exercise by walking, in order to find relaxation, keeping, however, such weariness of mind as prevents them either seeing or being conscious of different objects; so that often when meeting friends or relatives, and being saluted by them, although they may see and hear them they know them no more than if they had met only so much air.

The various contrasts of the different degrees of shadows and lights often cause hesitation and confusion to the painter who aspires to imitate and reproduce the things that he sees. The reason is that if you see a white cloth side by side with a black one, it is certain that the part of this white cloth which is next to the black will seem whiter by far than the part that is next to something whiter than itself, and the reason of this is proved in my perspective.

[*Of the nature of the folds of draperies*]

That part of the fold which is farthest from the ends where it is confined will return most closely to its original form. Everything naturally desires to remain in its own state. Drapery, being of uniform density and thickness on the reverse and on the right side, desires to lie flat; consequently, whenever any folds or pleats force it to depart from this condition of flatness, it obeys the law of this force in that part of itself where it is most constrained, and the part farthest away from such constraint, you will find, returns most nearly to its original state, that is to say, lying extended and full.

The body of the atmosphere is full of an infinite number of the pyramids composed of radiating straight lines which are caused by the boundaries of the surfaces of the bodies in shadow that are found there, and the farther they are away from the object which produces them the more their angle becomes acute. And although they intersect and interlace in their passage, nevertheless they do not become confused with each other but proceed with divergent course, spreading themselves out and becoming diffused through all the surrounding air.

And they are of equal power among themselves, all equal to each, and each equal to all, and by means of them are transmitted the images of the objects, and these are transmitted in all, and all in each part; and each pyramid receives of itself in each of its smallest parts the whole form of the object which produces it.

Let the sketches for historical subjects be rapid, and the working of the limbs not too much finished. Content yourself with merely giving the positions of these limbs, which you will then be able at your leisure to finish as you please.

Among shadows of equal strength that which is nearest to the eye will seem of less density.

All colors in distant shadows are indistinguishable and undiscernible.

In the distance all colors are indistinguishable in shadows, because an object which is not touched by the principal light has no power to transmit its image, through the more luminous atmosphere, to the eye, because the lesser light is conquered by the greater.

For example, we see in a house that all the colors on the surface of the walls are visible instantly and clearly when the windows of the house are open; but, if we go out of the house and look through the windows at a little distance in order to see the paintings on the walls, we shall see instead of them a uniform darkness.

The painter ought first to exercise his hand by copying drawings by good masters; and having acquired facility in this under the advice of his instructor, he ought to set himself to copy good reliefs, following the rules given below.

He who draws from relief ought to take his position so that the eye of the figure he is drawing is on a level with his own. And this should be done whenever a head has to be drawn from nature, because generally figures or people whom you meet in the streets all have their eyes at the same level as yours, and if you make them higher or lower you will find that your portrait will not resemble them.

The painter ought always to consider, as regards the wall on which he intends to represent a story, the height of the position where he intends to place his characters, so that when he makes studies from nature for this purpose he should have his eye as much below the thing that he is drawing as the said thing appears in the picture above the eye of the spectator; otherwise the work will be deserving of censure.

Painters oftentimes despair of their power to imitate nature, on perceiving how their pictures are lacking in the power of relief and vividness which objects possess when seen in a mirror, though, as they allege, they have colors that for clearness and depth far surpass the quality of the lights and shadows of the object seen in the mirror, arraigning herein not reason but their own ignorance, in that they fail to recognize the impossibility of a painted object appearing in such relief as to be comparable to the objects in the mirror, although both are on a flat surface unless they are seen by a single eye. And the reason of this is that when two eyes see one thing after another, as in the case of *a b* seeing *n m, m* cannot entirely cover *n* because the base of the visual lines is so broad as to cause one to see the second object beyond the first. If however you close one eye as *s,* the object *f* will cover up *r,* because the visual line starts in a single point and makes its base in the first object, with the consequence that the second being of equal size is never seen.

Every bodily form as far as concerns the function of the eye is divided into three parts, namely, substance, shape and color. The image of its substance projects itself farther from its source than its color or its shape; the color also projects itself farther than the shape, but this law does not apply to luminous bodies.

The above proposition is clearly shown and confirmed by experience, for if you see a man near at hand you will be able to recognize the character of the substance, of the shape and even of the color, but, if he goes some distance away from you, you will no longer be able to recognize who he is because his shape will lack character, and if he goes still farther away you will not be able to distinguish his color but he will merely seem a dark body, and farther away still he will seem a very small round dark body. He will appear round because distance diminishes the various parts so much as to leave nothing visible except the greater mass. The reason of this is as follows: We know very well that all the images of objects penetrate to the imprensiva through a small aperture in the eye; therefore, if the whole horizon *a d* enters through a similar aperture and the object *b c* is a very small part of this horizon, what part must it occupy in the minute representation of so great a hemisphere? And since luminous bodies have more power in darkness than any others, it is necessary, since the aperture of the sight is considerably in shadow, as is the nature of all holes, that the images of distant objects intermingle within the great light of the sky, or if it should be that they remain visible they appear dark and black, as every small body must when seen in the limpidity of the air.

All bodies together, and each of itself, fill the surrounding air with an infinite number of their images which are all in all this air, and all in the parts of it, bearing with them the nature of the body, the color and the form of their cause.

Perspective is the bridle and rudder of painting.

Shadows which you see with difficulty, and whose boundaries you cannot define—but which you only apprehend and reproduce in your work with some hesitation of judgment—these you should not represent as finished or sharply defined, for the result would be that your work would seem wooden.

Reflections are caused by bodies of a bright nature and of a smooth and half-opaque surface, which when struck by the light, drive it back again to the first object like the rebound of a ball.

All solid bodies have their surfaces covered by various degrees of light and shadow. The lights are of two kinds: the one is called original, the other derived. Original I call that which proceeds from the flame of the fire, or from the light of the sun, or of the atmosphere. Derived light is the light reflected. But to return to the promised definition, I say that there is no luminous reflection on the side of the body which is turned towards objects in shadow, such as shaded scenes, meadows with grasses of varying height, green or bare woods—for these, although the part of each branch turned to the original light is imbued with the attributes of this light, have nevertheless so many shadows cast by each branch separately, and so many shadows cast by one branch on another, that in the whole mass there results such a depth of shadow that the light is as nothing; hence objects such as these cannot throw any reflected light upon bodies opposite to them.

[*Why the representing of groups of figures one above another is to be avoided*]

This custom, which is universally adopted by painters for the walls of chapels, is by right strongly to be censured, seeing that they represent one composition at one level with its landscape and buildings, and then mount to the stage above it and make another, and so vary the point of sight from that of the first painting, and then make a third, and a fourth, in such a way that the work on the one wall shows four points of sight, which is extreme folly on the part of such masters.

Now we know that the point of sight is opposite the eye

of the spectator of the composition, and if you were to ask me how I should represent the life of a saint when it is divided up in several compositions on the same wall, to this I reply that you ought to set the foreground with its point of sight on a level with the eye of the spectators of the composition, and at this same plane make the chief episode on a large scale, and then by diminishing gradually the figures and buildings upon the various hills and plains, you should represent all the incidents of the story. And on the rest of the wall up to the top you should make trees large as compared with the figures, or angels if these are appropriate to the story, or birds or clouds or similar things; but otherwise do not put yourself to the trouble, for the whole of your work will be wrong.

Figures in relief in the act of movement will in their standing position seem naturally to fall forward.

The youth ought first to learn perspective, then the proportions of everything, then he should learn from the hand of a good master in order to accustom himself to good limbs; then from nature in order to confirm for himself the reasons for what he has learnt; then for a time he should study the works of different masters; then make it a habit to practice and work at his art.

How the first picture was nothing but a line which surrounded the shadow of a man made by the sun upon a wall.

How historical pictures ought not to be crowded and confused by many figures.

How old men should be shown with slow listless movements, with the legs bent at the knees when they are standing up, with the feet parallel and separated one from another, the spine bent low, the head leaning forward, and the arms not too far apart.

How women should be represented in modest attitudes,

with legs close together, arms folded and with their heads low and bending sideways.

How old women should be represented as bold, with swift passionate movements like the infernal furies, and these movements should seem quicker in the arms and heads than in the legs.

Little children should be represented when sitting as twisting themselves about with quick movements, and in shy, timid attitudes when standing up.

How one ought not to give drapery a confusion of many folds, but only make them where it is held by the hands or arms, and the rest may be suffered to fall simply where its nature draws it: and do not let the contour of the figure be broken by too many lines or interrupted folds.

How draperies should be drawn from nature: that is, if you wish to represent woolen cloth, draw the folds from the same material, and if it is to be silk, or fine cloth, or homespun, or of linen or crepe, show the different nature of the folds in each; and do not make a costume, as many make it, upon models covered with pieces of paper or thin leather, for you will be deceiving yourself greatly.

Perspectives are of three kinds. The first has to do with the causes of the diminution or, as it is called, the diminishing perspective of objects as they recede from the eye. The second, the manner in which colors are changed as they recede from the eye. The third and last consists in defining in what way objects ought to be less carefully finished as they are farther away. And the names of these:

> Linear Perspective
> Perspective of Color
> Vanishing Perspective

How figures when dressed in a cloak ought not to show the shape to such an extent that the cloak seems to be next to the skin; for surely you would not wish that the cloak should be next to the skin, since you must realize that between the cloak and the skin are other garments which prevent the shape of the limbs from being visible and appearing through the cloak. And those limbs which you make visible, make thick of their kind so that there may seem to be other garments there under the cloak. And you should only allow the almost identical thickness of the limbs to be visible in a nymph or an angel, for these are represented clad in light draperies, which by the blowing of the wind are driven and pressed against the various limbs of the figures.

[*Of the way to present distant objects in painting*]

It is evident that the part of the atmosphere which lies nearest the level ground is denser than the rest, and that the higher it rises the lighter and more transparent it becomes.

In the case of large and lofty objects which are some distance away from you, their lower parts will not be much seen, because the line by which you should see them passes through the thickest and densest portion of the atmosphere. But the summits of these heights are seen along a line which, although when starting from your eye it is projected through the denser atmosphere, yet since it ends at the highest summit of the object seen, concludes its course in an atmosphere far more rarefied than that of its base. And consequently the farther away from you this line extends from point to point the greater is the change in the finer quality of the atmosphere.

Do you, therefore, O painter, when you represent mountains, see that from hill to hill the bases are always paler than the summits, and the farther away you make them one from another, let the bases be paler in proportion, and the loftier they are the more they should reveal their true shape and color.

How the atmosphere should be represented as paler in proportion as you show it extending lower:

Since the atmosphere is dense near the ground, and the higher it is the finer it becomes, therefore, when the sun is in the east and you look towards the west, taking in a part to the north and to the south, you will see that this dense air receives more light from the sun than the finer air, because the rays encounter more resistance. And if your view of the horizon is bounded by a low plain, that farthest region of the sky will be seen through that thicker whiter atmosphere, and this will destroy the truth of the color as seen through such a medium; and the sky will seem whiter there than it does overhead, where the line of vision traverses a lesser space of atmosphere charged with thick vapors. But if you look towards the east the atmosphere will appear darker in proportion as it is lower, for in this lower atmosphere the luminous rays pass less freely.

If the sun is in the east and you look towards the west, you will see that all the things which are illuminated are entirely deprived of shadow, because what you are looking at is what the sun sees.

And if you look to the south and the north, you will see that all the bodies are surrounded by light and shade, because you are looking both at the part that does not see and the part that sees the sun. And if you look towards the pathway of the sun, all the objects will present their shaded side to you, because this side cannot be seen by the sun.

[Of the way to represent a night scene]

Whatever is entirely deprived of light is all darkness. When such is the condition of night, if you wish to represent

a scene therein, you must arrange to introduce a great fire
there, and then the things which are nearest to the fire will
be more deeply tinged with its color, for whatever is nearest
to the object partakes most fully of its nature; and making
the fire of a reddish color you should represent all the things
illuminated by it as being also of a ruddy hue, while those
which are farther away from the fire should be dyed more
deeply with the black color of the night. The figures which
are between you and the fire will appear dark against the
brightness of the flame, for that part of the object which
you perceive is colored by the darkness of the night, and not
by the brightness of the fire; those which are at the sides
should be half in shadow and half in ruddy light; and those
visible beyond the edge of the flames will all be lit up with
ruddy light against a dark background. As for their actions,
show those who are near it making a screen with hands and
cloaks as a protection against the unbearable heat, with
faces turned away as though on the point of flight; while of
those farther away you should show a great number pressing
their hands upon their eyes, hurt by the intolerable glare.

Why of two objects of equal size the painted one will
look larger than that in relief:

This proposition is not so easy to expound as many others,
but I will nevertheless attempt to prove it, if not completely
then in part. Diminishing perspective demonstrates by reason
that objects diminish in proportion as they are farther away
from the eye, and this theory is entirely confirmed by experience. Now the lines of sight which are between the object
and the eye are all intersected at a uniform boundary when
they reach the surface of the painting; while the lines which
pass from the eye to the piece of sculpture have different
boundaries and are of varying lengths. The line which is the
longest extends to a limb which is farther away than the rest,

and consequently this limb appears smaller; and there are many lines longer than others, for the reason that there are many small parts, one farther away than another, and being farther away these of necessity appear smaller, and by appearing smaller they effect a corresponding decrease in the whole mass of the object. But this does not happen in the painting, because as the lines of sight end at the same distance, it follows that they do not undergo diminution, and as the parts are not themselves diminished they do not lessen the whole mass of the object, and consequently the diminution is not perceptible in the painting as it is in sculpture.

When you are representing a white body surrounded by ample space, since the white has no color in itself it is tinged and in part transformed by the color of what is set over against it. If you are looking at a woman dressed in white in the midst of a landscape, the side of her that is exposed to the sun will be so dazzling in color that parts of it, like the sun itself, will cause pain to the sight, and as for the side exposed to the atmosphere—which is luminous because of the rays of the sun being interwoven with it and penetrating it—since this atmosphere is itself blue, the side of the woman which is exposed to it will appear steeped in blue. If the surface of the ground near to her be meadows, and the woman be placed between a meadow lit by the sun and the sun itself, you will find that all the parts of the folds [of her dress] which are turned towards the meadow will be dyed by the reflected rays to the color of the meadow; and thus she becomes changed into the colors of the objects near, both those luminous and those nonluminous.

Make muscular such limbs as have to endure fatigue, and those which are not so used make without muscles and soft.

Make figures with such action as may be sufficient to show what the figure has in mind; otherwise your art will not be worthy of praise.

If you have a courtyard which, when you so please, you can cover over with a linen awning, the light will then be excellent. Or when you wish to paint a portrait, paint it in bad weather, at the fall of the evening, placing the sitter with his back to one of the walls of the courtyard. Notice in the streets at the fall of evening when it is bad weather the faces of the men and women—what grace and softness they display! Therefore, O painter, you should have a court-yard fitted up with the walls tinted in black and with the roof projecting forward a little beyond the wall; and the width of it should be ten braccia,[1] and the length twenty braccia, and the height ten braccia; and you should cover it over with the awning when the sun is on it, or else you should make your portrait at the hour of the fall of the evening when it is cloudy or misty, for the light then is perfect.

We see clearly that all the images of the visible things both large and small which serve us as objects enter to the sense through the tiny pupil of the eye. If, then, through so small an entrance there passes the image of the immensity of the sky and of the earth, the face of man—being almost nothing amid such vast images of things, because of the distance which diminishes it—occupies so little of the pupil as to remain indistinguishable; and having to pass from the outer surface to the seat of the sense through a dark medium, that is, through the hollow cells which appear dark, this

---

[1] A braccio is a little less than two feet.

image when not of a strong color is affected by the darkness through which it passes, and on reaching the seat of the sense it appears dark. No other reason can be advanced to account for the blackness of this point in the pupil; and since it is filled with a moisture transparent like the air, it acts like a hole made in a board; and when looked into it appears black, and the objects seen in the air, whether light or dark, become indistinct in the darkness.

Shadows become lost in the far distance, because the vast expanse of luminous atmosphere which lies between the eye and the object seen suffuses the shadows of the object with its own color.

Diminishing perspective shows us that in proportion as an object is farther away the smaller it becomes. And if you look at a man who is at the distance of a bowshot away from you and put the eye of a small needle close to your eye, you will be able through this to see the images of many men transmitted to the eye, and these will all be contained at one and the same time within the eye of the said needle. If then the image of a man who is distant from you the space of a bowshot is so transmitted to your eye as to occupy only a small part of the eye of a needle, how should you be able in so small a figure to distinguish or discern the nose or mouth or any detail of the body?

And not seeing these you cannot recognize the man, since he does not show you the features which cause men to differ in appearance.

The pit of the throat is above the foot. If an arm be thrown forward the pit of the throat moves from above the foot, and if the leg is thrown backwards the pit of the throat moves forwards, and so it changes with every change of attitude.

Painting

If you wish to represent a tempest properly, consider and set down exactly what are the results when the wind blowing over the face of the sea and of the land lifts and carries with it everything that is not immovable in the general mass. And in order properly to represent this tempest, you must first of all show the clouds, riven and torn, swept along in the path of the wind, together with storms of sand blown up from the seashores, and branches and leaves caught up by the irresistible fury of the gale and scattered through the air, and with them many other things of light weight. The trees and shrubs should be bent to the ground, as though showing their desire to follow the direction of the wind, with their branches twisted out of their natural growth and their leaves tossed and inverted. Of the men who are there, some should have fallen and be lying wrapped round by their garments and almost indistinguishable on account of the dust, and those who are left standing should be behind some tree with their arms thrown around it to prevent the wind from dragging them away; others should be shown crouching on the ground, their hands over their eyes because of the dust, their garments and hair streaming in the wind. Let the sea be wild and tempestuous, and between the crests of its waves it should be covered with eddying foam, and the wind should carry the finer spray through the stormy air after the manner of a thick and all-enveloping mist.

Of the ships that are there, some you should show with sail rent and the shreds of it flapping in the air in company with the broken halyards, and some of the masts broken and gone by the board, and the vessel itself lying disabled and broken by the fury of the waves, with some of the crew shrieking and clinging to the fragments of the wreck. You should show the clouds, driven by the impetuous winds, hurled against the high mountain tops, and there wreathing and eddying like waves that beat upon the rocks; the very air should strike terror through the murky darkness occasioned therein by the dust and mist and thick clouds.

When you desire to represent anyone speaking among a group of persons you ought to consider first the subject of which he has to treat, and how so to order his actions that they may be in keeping with this subject. That is, if the subject be persuasive, the actions should serve this intention; if it be one that needs to be expounded under various heads, the speaker should take a finger of his left hand between two fingers of his right, keeping the two smaller ones closed, and let his face be animated and turned towards the people, with mouth slightly opened, so as to give the effect of speaking. And if he is seated, let him seem to be in the act of raising himself more upright, with his head forward. And if you represent him standing, make him leaning forward a little with head and shoulders towards the populace, whom you should show silent and attentive, and all watching the face of the orator with gestures of admiration. Show the mouths of some of the old men with the corners pulled down in astonishment at what they hear, drawing back the cheeks in many furrows, with their eyebrows raised where they meet, making many wrinkles on their foreheads; and show some sitting with the fingers of their hands locked together and clasping their weary knees, and others—decrepit old men—with one knee crossed over the other, and one hand resting upon it which serves as a cup for the other elbow, while the other hand supports the bearded chin.

In order to increase the relief in a picture you should make it your practice to place, between the figure represented and that adjacent object which receives its shadow, a line of bright light in order to divide the figure from the object in shadow. And in this same object you will make two bright parts which shall have between them the shadow cast upon

the wall by the figure placed opposite; and do this frequently
with the limbs which you desire should stand out somewhat
from their body; and especially when the arms cross the
breast, show how between the line of incidence of the shadow
of the arm upon the breast and the real shadow of the arm,
there remains a streak of light which seems to pass through
the space that is between the breast and the arm. And the
more you wish the arm to seem detached from the breast,
the broader you must make this light. And always make it
your aim so to arrange bodies against their backgrounds that
the parts of the bodies that are in shadow end against a light
background, and the part of the body that is illuminated ends
against a dark background.

Take care that the shadows cast upon the surfaces of
bodies by different objects are always undulating with varying
curves produced by the variety of the limbs that create the
shadows and of the object that receives the shadow.

Shadow partakes of the nature of universal things which
are all more powerful at their beginning and grow weaker
towards the end. I refer to the beginning of all forms and
qualities visible or invisible, and not of things brought from
small beginnings to a mighty growth by time, as a great oak
would be which has its feeble beginning in a tiny acorn;
though I would rather say the oak is most powerful at the
spot where it is born in the ground, for there is the place of
its greatest growth. Darkness, therefore, is the first stage of
shadow, and light is the last. See, therefore, O painter, that
you make your shadow darkest near to its cause and make
the end of it become changed into light so that it seems to
have no end.

The shadows cast by the sun or other particular lights do
not impart grace to the body to which they belong, but rather

leave the parts separated in a state of confusion with a visible boundary of shadow and light. And the shadows have the same strength at the end that they had at the beginning.

Shadow is the absence of light; it is simply the obstruction caused by opaque bodies opposed to luminous rays. Shadow is of the nature of darkness, light is of the nature of brightness. The one hides and the other reveals. They are always in company attached to the bodies. And shadow is more powerful than light, for it impedes and altogether deprives objects of brightness, whereas brightness can never altogether drive away shadow from bodies, that is, from opaque bodies.

An inseparable shadow is one which is never parted from the illuminated bodies, as is the case with a ball, for when it is in the light it always has one of its sides covered by shadow, and this shadow never separates from it through any change in the position of the ball. A cast shadow may or may not be produced by the body itself. Let us suppose the ball to be at a distance of a braccio from the wall and the light to be coming from the opposite side: this light will throw just as broad a shadow upon the wall as upon the side of the ball that faces the wall. Part of a cast shadow will not be visible when the light is below the ball, for its shadow will then pass towards the sky, and finding there no obstruction in its course will become lost.

I will not refrain from setting among these precepts a new device for consideration which, although it may appear trivial and almost ludicrous, is nevertheless of great utility in arousing the mind to various inventions.

And this is that if you look at any walls spotted with various stains or with a mixture of different kinds of stones, if you are about to invent some scene, you will be able to see in it a resemblance to various different landscapes adorned with mountains, rivers, rocks, trees, plains, wide valleys and various groups of hills. You will also be able to see divers combats and figures in quick movement, and strange expressions of faces, and outlandish costumes, and an infinite number of things which you can then reduce into separate and well-conceived forms. With such walls and blends of different stones it comes about as it does with the sound of bells, in whose clanging you may discover every name and word that you can imagine.

Painting is concerned with all the ten attributes of sight, namely, darkness and brightness, substance and color, form and place, remoteness and nearness, movement and rest; and it is with these attributes that this my small book will be interwoven, recalling to the painter by what rules and in what way he ought by his art to imitate all things that are the work of nature and the adornment of the world.

As a means of practicing this perspective of the variation and loss or diminution of the proper essence of colors, take, at distances a hundred braccia apart, objects standing in the landscape, such as trees, houses, men and places, and in front of the first tree fix a piece of glass so that it is quite steady, and then let your eye rest upon it and trace out a tree upon the glass above the outline of the tree; and afterwards remove the glass so far to one side that the actual tree seems almost to touch the one that you have drawn. Then color your drawing in such a way that the two are alike in color and form, and that if you close one eye both seem painted on the glass and the same distance away. Then proceed in the same way with a second and a third tree at distances of a hundred braccia from each other. And these will always serve as your standards and teachers when you are at work on pictures where they can be applied, and they will cause the work to be successful in its distance.

But I find it is a rule that the second is reduced to four-fifths the size of the first when it is twenty braccia distant from it.

Whenever you make a figure of a man or of some graceful animal, remember to avoid making it seem wooden; that is, it should move with counterpoise and balance in such a way as not to seem a block of wood.

Those whom you wish to represent as strong should not be shown thus except in their manner of turning their heads upon their shoulders.

Linear perspective has to do with the function of the lines of sight, proving by measurement how much smaller is the second object than the first and the third than the second, and so on continually until the limit of things seen. I find by experience that if the second object is as far distant from the first as the first is from your eye, although as between themselves they may be equal size, the second will seem half as small again as the first; and if the third object is equal in size to the second, and it is as far beyond the second as the second is from the first, it will appear half the size of the second; and thus by successive degrees at equal distances the objects will be continually lessened by half, the second being half the first—provided that the intervening space does not amount to as much as twenty braccia; for at the distance of twenty braccia a figure resembling yours will lose four-fifths of its size, and at a distance of forty braccia it will lose nine-tenths, and nineteen-twentieths at sixty braccia, and so by degrees it will continue to diminish, when the plane of the picture is twice your own height away from you, for if the distance only equals your own height, there is a great difference between the first set of braccia and the second.

You should make the figure in the foreground in an historical composition proportionately less than life-size according to the number of braccia that you place it behind the front line, and then make the others in proportion to the first by the rule above.

I give the degrees of the things seen by the eye as the musician does of the sounds heard by the ear:

Although the things seen by the eye seem to touch as they recede, I will nevertheless found my rule on spaces of twenty braccia, as the musician has done with sounds, for although they are united and connected together he has nevertheless fixed the degrees from sound to sound, calling these first, second, third, fourth and fifth, and so from degree to degree he has given names to the varieties of the sound of the voice, as it becomes higher or lower.

When you make a figure and wish to see whether the shadow corresponds to the light, and is neither redder nor yellower than is the nature of the essence of the color which you wish to show in shadow, you should do as follows: with a finger make a shadow upon the illuminated part, and if the accidental shadow made by you is like the natural shadow made by your finger upon your work, it will be well then, by moving the finger nearer or farther off, to make the shadows darker or lighter, comparing them constantly with your own.

All those objects opposite to the eye which are too near to it will have their edges difficult to discern, as happens

when objects are near to the light and cast a large and indistinct shadow, even so this does when it has to judge of
objects outside it: in all cases of linear perspective its action
is similar to that of light. The reason of this is that the eye
has one principal line [of vision] which dilates as it acquires
distance, and embraces with exactness of perception large
things far away as it does small things close at hand. The
eye however sends out a multitude of lines on either side of
this principal center line, and these have less power to discern
correctly as they are farther from the center in this radiation.
It follows therefore when an object is placed close to the eye
that at that stage of nearness to the principal line of vision
this is not capable of distinguishing the edges of the object,
and so these edges must needs find themselves amid the lines
that have but a poor power of comprehension. Their part
in the functions of the eye is like that of setters at the chase,
who start the prey but cannot catch it. So while they cannot
themselves apprehend them they are a reason why the principal line of vision is diverted to the objects touched by these
lines.

It follows therefore that the objects which have their edges
judged by these lines are indistinct.

When you wish to know anything well by heart which you
have studied follow this method. When you have drawn the
same thing so many times that it seems that you know it
by heart try to do it without the model; but have a tracing
made of the model upon a thin piece of smooth glass and
lay this upon the drawing you have made without the model.
Note well where the tracing and your drawing do not tally,
and where you find that you have erred bear it in mind in
order not to make the mistake again. Even return to the
model in order to copy the part where you were wrong so
many times as to fix it in your mind; and if you cannot

procure smooth glass to make a tracing of the object take a piece of very fine parchment well oiled and then dried, and when you have used it for one drawing you can wipe this out with a sponge and do a second.

[*Of the way to represent a scene correctly*]

Take a piece of glass of the size of a half sheet of royal folio paper, and fix it well in front of your eyes, that is, between your eye and the object that you wish to portray. Then move away until your eye is two-thirds of a braccio away from the piece of glass, and fasten your head by means of an instrument in such a way as to prevent any movement of it whatsoever. Then close or cover up one eye, and with a brush or a piece of red chalk finely ground mark out on the glass what is visible beyond it; afterwards copy it by tracing on paper from the glass, then prick it out upon paper of a better quality and paint it if you so desire, paying careful attention to the aerial perspective.

If you wish thoroughly to accustom yourself to correct and good positions for your figures, fasten a frame or loom divided into squares by threads between your eye and the nude figure which you are representing, and then make the same squares upon the paper where you wish to draw the said nude, but very faintly. You should then place a pellet of wax on a part of the network to serve as a mark which as you look at your model should always cover the pit of the throat, or if he should have turned his back make it cover one of the vertebrae of the neck. And these threads will instruct you as to all the parts of the body, which in each attitude are found below the pit of the throat, below the angles of the shoulders, below the breasts, the hips and the other parts of the body; and the transverse lines of the network will show you how much higher the figure is above

the leg on which it is posed than above the other, and the
same with the hips, the knees and the feet. But always fix
the net by a perpendicular line and then see that all the
divisions that you see the nude take in the network, the nude
that you draw takes in the network of your sketch. The
squares you draw may be as much smaller than those of the
network in proportion as you wish your figure to be less than
life-size: then keep in mind in the figures that you make, the
rule of the corresponding proportions of the limbs as the
network has revealed it to you, and this should be three and
a half braccia in height and three wide, at a distance of
seven braccia from you and one from the nude figure.

[*How the mirror is the master of painters*]

When you wish to see whether the general effect of your
picture corresponds with that of the object represented after
nature, take a mirror and set it so that it reflects the actual
thing, and then compare the reflection with your picture, and
consider carefully whether the subject of the two images is
in conformity with both, studying especially the mirror. The
mirror ought to be taken as a guide—that is, the flat mirror
—for within its surface substances have many points of resemblance to a picture; namely, that you see the picture made
upon one plane showing things which appear in relief, and
the mirror upon one plane does the same. The picture is one
single surface, and the mirror is the same.

The picture is intangible, inasmuch as what appears round
and detached cannot be enclosed within the hands, and the
mirror is the same. The mirror and the picture present the
images of things surrounded by shadow and light, and each
alike seems to project considerably from the plane of its
surface. And since you know that the mirror presents detached things to you by means of outlines and shadows and
lights, and since you have moreover among your colors more

powerful shadows and lights than those of the mirror, it is certain that if you but know well how to compose your picture it will also seem a natural thing seen in a great mirror.

There is a certain class of painters who, though they have given but little attention to study, claim to live in all the beauty of gold and azure. These aver—such is their folly!—that they are not able to work up to their best standard because of the poor payment, but that they have the knowledge and could do as well as any other if they were well paid.

But see now the foolish folk! They have not the sense to keep by them some specimen of their good work so that they may say, "This is at a high price, and that is at a moderate price and that is quite cheap," and so show that they have work at all prices.

There is another kind of perspective which I call aerial, because by the difference in the atmosphere one is able to distinguish the various distances of different buildings when their bases appear to end on a single line, for this would be the appearance presented by a group of buildings on the far side of a wall, all of which as seen above the top of the wall look to be the same size; and if in painting you wish to make one seem farther away than another you must make the atmosphere somewhat heavy. You know that in an atmosphere of uniform density the most distant things seen through it, such as the mountains, in consequence of the great quantity of atmosphere which is between your eye and them, will appear blue, almost of the same color as the atmosphere when the sun is in the east. Therefore you should make the building which is nearest above the wall of its natural color, and that which is more distant make less defined and bluer; and one which you wish should seem as far away again make of double the depth of blue, and one you desire should seem five times as far away make five times as blue. And as a consequence of this rule it will come about that the buildings which above a given line appear to be of the same size will be plainly distinguished as to which are the more distant and which larger than the others.

We may frankly admit that certain people deceive themselves who apply the title "a good master" to a painter who can only do the head or the figure well. Surely it is no great achievement if by studying one thing only during his whole lifetime he attain to some degree of excellence therein! But since, as we know, painting embraces and contains within itself all the things which nature produces or which result from the fortuitous actions of men, and in short whatever can be comprehended by the eyes, it would seem to me that he is but a poor master who makes only a single figure well.

For do you not see how many and how varied are the actions which are performed by men alone? Do you not see how many different kinds of animals there are, and also of trees and plants and flowers? What variety of hilly and level places, of springs, rivers, cities, public and private buildings; of instruments fitted for man's use; of divers costumes, ornaments and arts? —Things which should be rendered with equal facility and grace by whomever you wish to call a good painter.

I have proved in my own case that it is of no small benefit on finding oneself in bed in the dark to go over again in the imagination the main outlines of the forms previously studied, or of other noteworthy things conceived by ingenious speculation; and this exercise is entirely to be commended, and it is useful in fixing things in the memory.

Surely when a man is painting a picture he ought not to refuse to hear any man's opinion, for we know very well that though a man may not be a painter he may have a true conception of the form of another man, and can judge aright whether he is humpbacked or has one shoulder high or low, or whether he has a large mouth or nose or other defects.

Since then we recognize that men are able to form a true judgment as to the works of nature, how much the more does it behoove us to admit that they are able to judge our faults. For you know how much a man is deceived in his own works, and if you do not recognize this in your own case observe it in others and then you will profit by their mistakes. Therefore you should be desirous of hearing patiently the opinions of others, and consider and reflect carefully whether or no he who censures you has reason for his censure; and correct your work if you find that he is right, but if not, then let it seem that you have not understood him, or, in case he is a man whom you esteem, show him by argument why it is that he is mistaken.

Any master who let it be understood that he could himself recall all the forms and effects of nature would certainly appear to me to be endowed with great ignorance, considering that these effects are infinite and that our memory is not of so great capacity as to suffice thereto.

Do you therefore, O painter, take care lest the greed for gain prove a stronger incentive than renown in art, for to gain this renown is a far greater thing than is the renown of riches.

For these, then, and other reasons which might be given, you should apply yourself first of all to drawing, in order to present to the eye in visible form the purpose and invention created originally in your imagination; then proceed to take from it or add to it until you satisfy yourself; then have men arranged as models draped or nude in the way in which you have disposed them in your work; and make the proportions and size in accordance with perspective, so that no part of the work remains that is not so counseled by reason and by the effects in nature.

And this will be the way to make yourself renowned in your art.

An object which is represented in white and black will appear in more pronounced relief than any other: and therefore I would remind you, O painter, that you should clothe your figures in as bright colors as you can, for if you make them dark in color they will be only in slight relief and be very little visible at a distance. This is because the shadows of all objects are dark, and if you make a garment dark there will be only a slight difference between its lights and shades, whereas with the bright colors there are many grades of difference.

If you desire to acquire facility in keeping in your mind the expression of a face, first learn by heart the various different kinds of heads, eyes, noses, mouths, chins, throats, and also necks and shoulders. Take as an instance noses— they are of ten types: straight, bulbous, hollow, prominent either above or below the center, aquiline, regular, simian, round and pointed. These divisions hold good as regards profile. Seen from in front, noses are of twelve types: thick in the middle, thin in the middle, with the tip broad, and narrow at the base, and narrow at the tip and broad at the base, with nostrils broad or narrow, or high or low, and with the openings either visible or hidden by the tip. And similarly you will find variety in the other features; of which things you ought to make studies from nature and so fix them in your mind. Or when you have to draw a face from memory, carry with you a small notebook in which you have noted down such features, and then when you have cast a glance at the face of the person whom you wish to draw you can look privately and see which nose or mouth has a resemblance to it, and make a tiny mark against it in order to recognize it again at home. Of abnormal faces I here say nothing, for they are kept in mind without difficulty.

When you, draftsmen, wish to find some profitable recreation in games you should always practice things which may be of use in your profession, that is, by giving your eye accuracy of judgment so that it may know how to estimate the truth as to the length and breadth of objects. So in order to accustom the mind to such things, let one of you draw a straight line anywhere on a wall; and then let each of you take a light rush or straw in his hand, and let each cut his own to the length which the first line appears to him when he is distant from it a space of ten braccia, and then let each go up to the copy in order to measure it against the length which he has judged it to be, and he whose measure comes nearest to the length of the copy has done best and is the winner, and he should receive from all the prize which was previously agreed upon by you. Furthermore, you should take measurements foreshortened, that is, you should take a spear or some other stick and look before you to a certain point of distance, and then let each set himself to reckon how many times this measure is contained in the said distance. Another thing is to see who can draw the best line one braccio in length, and this may be tested by tightly drawn thread.

Diversions such as these enable the eye to acquire accuracy of judgment, and this is the primary essential of painting.

I say and am prepared to prove that it is much better to be in the company of others when you draw rather than alone, for many reasons. The first is that you will be ashamed of being seen in the ranks of the draftsmen if you are outclassed by them, and this feeling of shame will cause you to make progress in study; secondly, a rather commendable envy will stimulate you to join the number of those who are more praised than you are, for the praises of the others will serve you as a spur; yet another is that you will acquire something of the manner of anyone whose work is better than yours, while if you are better than the others you will profit by seeing how to avoid their errors, and the praises of others will tend to increase your powers.

The winter evenings should be spent by youthful students in study of the things prepared during the summer; that is, all the drawings from the nude which you have made in the summer should be brought together, and you should make a choice from among them of the best limbs and bodies, and practice at these and learn them by heart.

Afterwards in the ensuing summer you should make choice of someone who has a good presence, and has not been brought up to wear doublets, and whose figure consequently has not lost its natural bearing, and make him go through various graceful and elegant movements. If he fails to show the muscles very clearly within the outlines of the limbs, this is of no consequence. It is enough for you merely to obtain good attitudes from the figure, and you can correct the limbs by those which you have studied during the winter.

The painter who has acquired a knowledge of the nature of the sinews, muscles and tendons will know exactly in the movement of any limb how many and which of the sinews are the cause of it, and which muscle by its swelling is the cause of this sinew's contracting, and which sinews having been changed into most delicate cartilage surround and contain the said muscle. So he will be able in divers ways and universally to indicate the various muscles by means of the different attitudes of his figures; and he will not do like many who in different actions always make the same things appear in the arm, the back, the breast and the legs; for such things as these ought not to rank in the category of minor faults.

Methinks it is no small grace in a painter to be able to give a pleasing air to his figures, and whoever is not naturally possessed of this grace may acquire it by study, as opportunity offers, in the following manner. Be on the watch to take the best parts of many beautiful faces of which the beauty is established rather by general repute than by your own judgment, for you may readily deceive yourself by selecting such faces as bear a resemblance to your own, since it would often seem that such similarities please us; and if you were ugly you would not select beautiful faces, but would be creating ugly faces like many painters whose types often resemble their master; so therefore choose the beautiful ones as I have said, and fix them in your mind.

The painter or draftsman ought to be solitary, in order that the well-being of the body may not sap the vigor of the mind; and more especially when he is occupied with the consideration and investigation of things which by being continually present before his eyes furnish food to be treasured up in the memory.

If you are alone you belong entirely to yourself; if you are accompanied even by one companion you belong only half to yourself, or even less in proportion to the thoughtlessness of his conduct; and if you have more than one companion you will fall more deeply into the same plight.

If you should say, "I will take my own course; I will retire apart, so that I may be the better able to investigate the forms of natural objects," then I say this must needs turn out badly, for you will not be able to prevent yourself from often lending an ear to their chatter; and not being able to serve two masters you will discharge badly the duty of companionship, and even worse that of endeavoring to realize your conceptions in art.

But suppose you say, "I will withdraw so far apart that their words shall not reach me nor in any way disturb me." I reply that in this case you will be looked upon as mad, and bear in mind that in so doing you will then be solitary.

If you must have companionship choose it from your studio; it may then help you to obtain the advantages which result from different methods of study. All other companionship may prove extremely harmful.

When you have thoroughly learned perspective, and have fixed in your memory all the various parts and forms of things, you should often amuse yourself when you take a walk for recreation, in watching and taking note of the attitudes and actions of men as they talk and dispute, or laugh or come to blows one with another, both their actions and those of the bystanders who either intervene or stand looking on at these things; noting these down with rapid strokes in this way,[2] in a little pocket book, which you ought always to carry with you. And let this be of tinted paper, so that it may not be rubbed out; but you should change the old for a new one, for these are not things to be rubbed out but preserved with the utmost diligence; for there is such an infinite number of forms and actions of things that the memory is incapable of preserving them, and therefore you should keep those [sketches] as your patterns and teachers.

If as draftsman you wish to study well and profitably, accustom yourself when you are drawing to work slowly, and to determine between the various lights which possess the highest degree and measure of brightness, and similarly

[2] Sketch of figure in text of MS.

as to the shadows which are those that are darker than the rest, and in what manner they mingle together, and to compare their dimensions one with another; and so with the contours to observe which way they are tending, and as to the lines what part of each is curved in one way or another, and where they are more or less conspicuous and consequently thick or fine; and lastly to see that your shadows and lights may blend without strokes or lines in the manner of smoke. And when you shall have trained your hand and judgment with this degree of care it will speedily come to pass that you will have no need to take thought thereto.

We know well that mistakes are more easily detected in the works of others than in one's own, and that oftentimes while censuring the small faults of others you will overlook your own great faults. In order to avoid such ignorance, make yourself first of all a master of perspective, then gain a complete knowledge of the proportions of man and other animals, and also make yourself a good architect, that is, in so far as concerns the form of the buildings and of the other things which are upon the earth, which are infinite in form; and the more knowledge you have of these the more will your work be worthy of praise; and for those things in which you have no practice do not disdain to draw from nature. But to return to what has been promised above, I say that when you are painting you should take a flat mirror and often look at your work within it, and it will then be seen in reverse, and will appear to be by the hand of some other master, and you will be better able to judge of its faults than in any other way.

It is also a good plan every now and then to go away and have a little relaxation; for then when you come back to the work your judgment will be surer, since to remain constantly at work will cause you to lose the power of judgment.

It is also advisable to go some distance away, because

then the work appears smaller, and more of it is taken in at a glance, and a lack of harmony or proportion in the various parts and in the colors of the objects is more readily seen.

We know clearly that the sight is one of the swiftest actions that can exist, for in the same instant it surveys an infinite number of forms; nevertheless it can only comprehend one thing at a time. To take an instance: you, O reader, might at a glance look at the whole of this written page, and you would instantly decide that it is full of various letters, but you will not recognize in this space of time either what letters they are or what they purport to say, and therefore it is necessary for you if you wish to gain a knowledge of these letters to take them word by word and line by line.

Again, if you wish to go up to the summit of a building it will be necessary for you to ascend step by step, otherwise it will be impossible to reach the top. So I say to you whom nature inclines to this art that if you would have a true knowledge of the forms of different objects you should commence with their details, and not pass on to the second until the first is well in your memory and you have practiced it. If you do otherwise you will be throwing away time, and to a certainty you will greatly prolong the period of study. And remember to acquire diligence rather than facility.

Further I remind you to pay great attention in giving limbs to your figures, so that they may appear to harmonize not merely with the size of the body but also with its age. So the limbs of youths should have few muscles and veins, and have a soft surface and be rounded and pleasing in color; in men they should be sinewy and full of muscles; in old men the surface should be wrinkled, and rough, and covered with veins, and with the sinews greatly protruding.

Little children have all the joints slender while the intervening parts are thick; and this is due to the fact that the
joints are only covered by skin and there is no flesh at all
over them, and this skin acts as a sinew to gird and bind
together the bones; and a flabby layer of flesh is found between one joint and the next, shut in between the skin and
the bone. But because the bones are thicker at the joints
than between them, the flesh as the man grows up loses that
superfluity which existed between the skin and the bone,
and so the skin is drawn nearer to the bone and causes the
limbs to seem more slender. But since there is nothing above
the joints except cartilaginous and sinewy skin, this cannot
dry up, and not being dried up it does not shrink. So for
these reasons the limbs of children are slender at the joints
and thick between the joints, as is seen in the joints of the
fingers, arms and shoulders which are slender and have great
dimples; and a man on the contrary has all the joints of
fingers, arms and legs thick, and where children have hollows
men have the joints protruding.

I find a great difference between men and small boys in
the length from one joint to another; for whereas the distance
from the joint of the shoulder to the elbow, and from the
elbow to the tip of the thumb, and from the humerus of one
of the shoulders to the other, in a man is twice the head,
in a child it is only once, because nature fashions the stature
of the seat of the intellect for us before that of its active
members.

Make first a general shadow over the whole of the extended part which does not see the light; then give to it the
half shadows and the strong shadows, contrasting these one
with another.
And similarly give the extended light in half-tone, adding

afterwards the half lights and the high lights and contrasting these in the same manner.

To make a head so that its features are in agreement with those of a head that turns and bends, use these means: you know that the eyes, eyebrows, nostrils, corners of the mouth and sides of the chin, jaw, cheeks, ears and all the parts of a face are placed at regular positions upon the face; therefore when you have made the face, make lines which pass from one corner of the eye to the other; and so also for the position of each feature. Then having continued the ends of these lines beyond the two sides of the face, observe whether on the right and the left the spaces in the same parallel are equal. But I would specially remind you that you must make these lines extend to the point of your vision.

You will treat first of the lights cast by windows to which you will give the name of restricted light; then treat of the lights of landscape to which you will give the name of free light; then treat of the light of luminous bodies.

You know that you cannot make any animal without its having its limbs such that each bears some resemblance to that of some one of the other animals. If therefore you wish to make one of your imaginary animals appear natural—let us suppose it to be a dragon—take for its head that of a mastiff or setter, for its eyes those of a cat, for its ears those of a porcupine, for its nose that of a greyhound, with the eyebrows of a lion, the temples of an old cock and the neck of a water tortoise.

See that when you are drawing and make a beginning of a line, that you look over all the object that you are drawing for any detail whatever which lies in the direction of the line that you have begun.

That figure is most worthy of praise which by its action best expresses the passion which animates it.

An angry figure should be represented seizing someone by the hair and twisting his head down to the ground, with one knee on his ribs, and with the right arm and fist raised high up; let him have his hair disheveled, his eyebrows low and knit together, his teeth clenched, the two corners of his mouth arched, and the neck, which is all swollen and extended as he bends over the foe, should be full of furrows.

A man who is in despair you should make turning his knife against himself, and rending his garments with his hands, and one of his hands should be in the act of tearing open his wound. Make him with his feet apart, his legs somewhat bent, and the whole body likewise bending to the ground, and with his hair torn and streaming.

The limbs should fit the body gracefully, in harmony with the effect you wish the figure to produce; and if you desire to create a figure which shall possess a charm of its own, you should make it with limbs graceful and extended, without showing too many of the muscles, and the few which your purpose requires you to show indicate briefly, that is, without giving them prominence, and with the shadows not sharply defined; and the limbs, and especially the arms, should be easy, that is, that no limb should be in a straight line with the part that adjoins it. And if the hips, which form as it were the poles of the man, are by his position placed so that the right is higher than the left, you should make the top shoulder joint so that a line drawn from it perpendicularly falls on the most prominent part of the hip, and let this right shoulder be lower than the left.

And let the hollow of the throat always be exactly over the middle of the joint of the foot which is resting on the ground. The leg which does not support the weight should have its knee below the other and near to the other leg.

The positions of the head and arms are numberless, and therefore I will not attempt to give any rule; it will suffice that they should be natural and pleasing and should bend and turn in various ways, with the joints moving freely so that they may not seem like pieces of wood.

As regards the arrangement of the limbs, you should bear in mind that when you wish to represent one who by some chance has either to turn backwards or on one side, you must not make him move his feet and all his limbs in the same direction as he turns his head; but you should show the process spreading itself and taking effect over the four sets of joints, namely those of the foot, the knee, the hip and the neck. And if you let his weight rest on the right leg, you should make the knee of the left bend inwards; and the foot of it should be slightly raised on the outside, and the left shoulder should be somewhat lower than the right; and the nape of the neck should be exactly above the outer curve of the ankle of the left foot, and the left shoulder should be above the toe of the right foot in a perpendicular line. And always so dispose your figures that the direction in which the head is turned is not that in which the breast faces, since nature has for our convenience so formed the neck that it can easily serve the different occasions on which the eye desires to turn in various directions; and to this same organ the other joints are in part responsive. And if ever you show a man sitting with his hands at work upon something by his side, make the chest turn upon the hip joints.

If, as experience shows, luminous rays come from a single point, and proceed in the form of a sphere from this point, radiating and spreading themselves through the air, the farther they go the more they are dispersed; and an object placed between the light and the wall is always reproduced larger in its shadow, because the rays that strike it have become larger by the time they have reached the wall.

A body which finds itself placed between two equal lights will put forth two shadows, which will take their direction equally according to the lines of the two lights. And if you move the body farther away or bring it nearer to one of the lights, the shadow which points to the nearer light will be less deep than that which points to the one more remote.

If an object placed in front of a particular light be very near to it you will see it cast a very large shadow on the opposite wall, and the farther you remove the object from the light the smaller will the shadow become.

The want of proportion of the shadow which is greater than its cause arises from the fact that as the light is less than its object it cannot be at an equal distance from the extremities of the object, and the part which is at a greater distance increases more than those which are nearer, and therefore the shadow increases.

Atmosphere which surrounds a light almost partakes of the nature of this light in brightness and in warmth; the farther away it recedes the more it loses this resemblance. An object which casts a large shadow is near to the light and finds itself lit up both by the light and by the luminous atmosphere, and consequently this atmosphere leaves the contours of the shadow indistinct.

I say that when objects appear of minute size, it is due to the said objects being at a distance from the eye; and when this is the case, there must of necessity be a considerable quantity of atmosphere between the eye and the object, and this atmosphere interferes with the distinctness of the form of the objects, and consequently the minute details of these bodies will become indistinguishable and unrecognizable.

Therefore, O painter, you should make your lesser figures only suggested, and not highly finished; for if you do otherwise, you will produce effects contrary to those of nature, your mistress.

The object is small because of the great space which exists between the eye and it. This great space contains within itself a great quantity of atmosphere; and this atmosphere forms of itself a dense body which interposes and shuts out from the eye the minute details of the objects.

Since one sees by experience that all bodies are surrounded by shadow and light, it is expedient, O painter, that you so dispose the part illuminated that it is outlined against a dark object, and that in the same way the part of the body in shadow is outlined against a bright object. And this rule will be a great help to you in giving relief to your figures.

When you have to draw from nature, stand three times as far away as the size of the object that you are drawing.

This benign nature so provides that over all the world you find something to imitate.

Where the shadow is bounded by light, note carefully where it is lighter or darker, and where it is more or less indistinct towards the light; and above all I would remind you that in youthful figures you should not make the shadows end like stone, for the flesh retains a slight transparency, as may be observed by looking at a hand held between the eye and the sun, when it is seen to flush red and to be of a luminous transparency.

And let the part which is brightest in color be between the lights and the shadows. And if you wish to see what depth of shadow is needed for the flesh, cast a shadow over it with your finger, and according as you wish it to be lighter or darker, hold your finger nearer or farther away from the picture, and then copy this shadow.

The disposition of the light should be in harmony with the natural conditions under which you represent your figure; that is, if you are representing it in sunlight, make the shadows dark with great spaces of light, and mark the shadows of all the surrounding bodies and their shadows upon the ground. If you represent it in dull weather, make only a slight difference between the lights and the shadows, and do not make any other shadow at the feet. If you represent it within doors, make a strong difference between the lights and shadows and show the shadow on the floor, and if you represent a window covered by a curtain and the wall white there should be little difference between the lights and shadows. If it is lit by a fire you should make the lights ruddy and powerful and the shadows dark; and the shadows should be sharply defined where they strike the walls or the floor, and the farther away they extend from the body the broader and larger should they become. And if it be lit in part by the fire and in part by the atmosphere, make the part lit by the atmosphere the stronger, and let that lit by the fire be almost as red as fire itself. And above all let the figures that you paint have sufficient light and from above, that is, all living persons whom you paint, for the people whom you see in the streets are all lighted from above; and I would have you know that you have no acquaintance so intimate but that if the light fell on him from below you would find it difficult to recognize him.

First of all copy drawings by a good master made by his art from nature and not as exercises; then from a relief, keeping by you a drawing done from the same relief; then from a good model; and of this you ought to make a practice.

When you are drawing from nature the light should be from the north, so that it may not vary; and if it is from the south keep the window covered with a curtain so that though the sun shine upon it all day long the light will undergo no change. The elevation of the light should be such that each body casts a shadow on the ground which is of the same length as its height.

Since we see that the quality of colors becomes known by means of light, it is to be inferred that where there is most light there the true quality of the color so illuminated will be most visible, and where there is most shadow there the color will be most affected by the color of the shadow. Therefore, O painter, be mindful to show the true quality of the colors in the parts which are in light.

Each part of the surface of a body is in part affected by the color of the thing opposite to it.

[*Example*]

If you set a spherical body in the midst of different objects, that is, so that on the one side it has the light of the sun and on the side opposite there is a wall illuminated by the sun, which may be green or some other color, the surface on which it is resting being red and the two transverse sides dark, you will see the natural color of this object take on the hues of those colors which are over against it. The strongest will be that proceeding from the light, the second that from the illuminated wall, the third that of the shadow. There yet remains, however, a portion which will take its hue from the color of the edges.

The supreme misfortune is when theory outstrips performance.

In the choice of figures aim at softness and delicacy rather than that they should be stiff and wooden.

That body will present the strongest contrast between its lights and shadows which is seen by the strongest light, such as the light of the sun or at night the light of a fire; but this should rarely be employed in painting, because the work will remain hard and devoid of grace.

A body which is in a moderate light will have but little difference between its lights and shadows; and this comes to pass at the fall of the evening, or when there are clouds: works painted then are soft in feeling and every kind of face acquires a charm.

Thus in every way extremes are injurious. Excess of light makes things seem hard; and too much darkness does not admit of our seeing them. The mean is excellent.

The lights cast from small windows also present a strong contrast of light and shadow, more especially if the chamber lit by them is large; and this is not good to use in painting.

The painter who draws by practice and judgment of the eye, without the use of reason, is like the mirror that reproduces within itself all the objects which are set opposite to it without knowledge of the same.

That countenance which in a picture is looking full in the face of the master who makes it will always be looking at all the spectators. And the figure painted when seen below from above will always appear as though seen below from above, although the eye of the beholder may be lower than the picture itself.

If nature had only one fixed standard for the proportions of the various parts, then the faces of all men would resemble each other to such a degree that it would be impossible to distinguish one from another; but she has varied the five parts of the face in such a way that although she has made an almost universal standard as to their size, she has not observed it in the various conditions to such a degree as to prevent one from being clearly distinguished from another.

As the body with great slowness produced by the length of its contrary movement turns in greater space and thereby gives a stouter blow, whereas movements which are continuous and short have little strength—so study upon the same subject made at long intervals of time causes the judgment to become more perfect and the better to recognize its own mistakes. And the same is true of the eye of the painter as it draws farther away from his picture.

A picture or any representation of figures ought to be done in such a way that those who see them may be able with ease to recognize from their attitudes what is passing through their minds. So if you have to represent a man of good repute in the act of speaking, make his gestures accord with the probity of his speech; and similarly if you have to represent a brutal man, make him with fierce movements flinging out his arms towards his hearer, and the head and chest, protruding forward beyond the feet, should seem to accompany the hands of the speaker.

Painting

Just so a deaf mute who sees two people talking, although being himself deprived of the power of hearing, is none the less able to divine from the movements and gestures of the speakers the subject of their discussion.

I once saw in Florence a man who had become deaf, who could not understand you if you spoke to him loudly, while if you spoke softly without letting the voice utter any sound, he understood you merely from the movement of the lips. Perhaps, however, you will say to me, "But does not a man who speaks loudly move his lips like one who speaks softly? And since the one moves his lips like the other, will not the one be understood like the other?" As to this I leave the decision to the test of experience. Set someone to speak softly and then [louder], and watch the lips.

The painter will produce pictures of little merit if he takes the works of others as his standard; but if he will apply himself to learn from the objects of nature he will produce good results. This we see was the case with the painters who came after the time of the Romans, for they continually imitated each other, and from age to age their art steadily declined.

After these came Giotto the Florentine, and he—reared in mountain solitudes inhabited only by goats and such like beasts—turning straight from nature to his art, began to draw on the rocks the movements of the goats which he was tending, and so began to draw the figures of all the animals which were to be found in the country, in such a way that after much study he not only surpassed the masters of his own time but all those of many preceding centuries. After him art again declined, because all were imitating paintings already done; and so for centuries it continued to decline until such time as Tommaso the Florentine, nicknamed Masaccio, showed by the perfection of his work how those who took as their standard anything other than nature, the supreme guide of all the masters, were wearying themselves in vain. Similarly I would say about these mathematical subjects, that those who study only the authorities and not the works of nature are in art the grandsons and not the sons of nature, which is the supreme guide of the good authorities.

Mark the supreme folly of those who censure such as learn from nature, leaving uncensured the authorities who were themselves the disciples of this same nature!

When you make figures one behind another, see that you draw them in their entirety, so that the limbs which are seen appearing beyond the surface of the first figure may retain their natural length and position.

The surface of each body takes part of the color of whatever is set against it. The colors of the objects in light are reproduced on each other's surface at different spots according to the varieties in the positions of these objects. [*Diagram*] Let *o* be a blue object in light, which alone by itself faces the space *b c* of the white sphere *a b c d e f,* and tinges it blue; and let *m* be a yellow object which is reflected on the space *a b* in company with the blue object *o,* and tinges it green, by the second of this which shows that blue and yellow together produce a most beautiful green, etc.— and the rest will be set forth in the Book of Painting. In that book it will be demonstrated, by transmitting the images of the bodies and colors of the things illuminated by the sun through a small round hole in a dark place onto a smooth surface which in itself is white. But everything will be upside down.

The painter requires such knowledge of mathematics as belongs to painting, and severance from companions who are not in sympathy with his studies, and his brain should have the power of adapting itself to the tenor of the objects which present themselves before it, and he should be freed from all other cares.

And if while considering and examining one subject a second should intervene, as happens when an object occupies the mind, he ought to decide which of these subjects presents greater difficulties in investigation, and follow that until it becomes entirely clear, and afterwards pursue the investigation of the other. And above all he should keep his mind as clear as the surface of a mirror, which becomes changed to as many different colors as are those of the objects within it, and his companions should resemble him in a taste for these studies, and if he fail to find any such he should accustom himself to be alone in his investigations, for in the end he will find no more profitable companionship.

I say that one ought first to learn about the limbs and how they are worked, and after having completed this knowledge one ought to study their actions in the different conditions in which men are placed, and thirdly to devise figure compositions, the studies for these being taken from natural actions made on occasion as opportunities offered; and one should be on the watch in the streets and squares and fields, and there make sketches with rapid strokes to represent features, that is for a head one may make an *o,* and for an arm a straight or curved line, and so in like manner for the legs and trunk, afterwards when back at home working up these notes in a completed form.

My opponent says that in order to gain experience and to learn how to work readily, it is better that the first period of study should be spent in copying various compositions made by different masters either on sheets of paper or on walls, since from these one acquires rapidity in execution and a good method. But to this it may be replied that the ensuing method would be good if it was founded upon works that were excellent in composition and by diligent masters; and since such masters are so rare that few are to be found, it is safer to go direct to the works of nature than to those which have been imitated from her originals with great deterioration and thereby to acquire a bad method, for he who has access to the fountain does not go to the water pot.

These rules are to be used solely in testing figures; for every man in his first compositions makes certain mistakes, and if he does not become conscious of them he does not correct them; therefore in order to discover mistakes you should test your work and where you find there mistakes correct them, and remember never to fall into them again. But if you were to attempt to apply all these rules in composition you would never make a beginning and would cause confusion in your work.

These rules are intended to help you to a free and good judgment; for good judgment proceeds from good understanding, and good understanding comes from reason trained by good rules, and good rules are the children of sound experience, which is the common mother of all the sciences and arts. If therefore you bear well in mind the precepts of my rules you will be able merely by the accuracy of your judgment to criticize and discern every error in proportion in any work, whether it is in the perspective or in the figures or other things.

All the limbs of every kind of animal should correspond with its age, that is, the young should not show their veins or nerves as most [painters] do in order to show their dexterity in art, spoiling the whole by mistakes in the limbs.

All the parts of an animal should correspond with the whole, that is, when a man is short and thick-set you must see that each of his limbs is short and thick-set.

Let the movements of men be such as are in keeping with their dignity or meanness.

Make your work to be in keeping with your purpose and design; that is, when you make your figure you should consider carefully who it is and what you wish it to be doing.

In order to produce an effect of similar action in a picture of an old man and a young, you must make the action of the young man appear more vigorous in proportion as he is more powerful than the old man, and you will make the same difference between a young man and an infant.

If you have to represent a man either as moving or lifting or pulling, or carrying a weight equal to his own weight, how ought you to fit the legs under his body?

Painters often deceive themselves by representing water in which they render visible what is seen by man; whereas the water sees the object from one side and the man sees it from the other; and it frequently happens that the painter will see a thing from above and the water sees it from beneath, and so the same body is seen in front and behind, and above and below, for the water reflects the image of the object in one way and the eye sees it in another.

We consider as a monstrosity one who has a very large head and short legs, and as a monstrosity also one who is in great poverty and has rich garments; we should therefore deem him well proportioned in whom the parts are in harmony with the whole.

The painter who has clumsy hands will reproduce the same in his works, and the same thing will happen with every limb unless long study prevents it. Do you then, O painter, take careful note of that part in yourself which is most misshapen, and apply yourself by study to remedy this entirely. For if you are brutal, your figures will be the same and devoid of grace, and in like manner every quality that there is within you of good or of evil will be in part revealed in your figures.

When you draw nudes be careful always to draw the whole figure, and then finish the limb which seems the best and at the same time study its relation to the other limbs, as otherwise you may form the habit of never properly joining the limbs together.

Take care never to make the head turn the same way as the chest nor the arm move with the leg; and if the head is turned towards the right shoulder make all the parts lower on the left side than on the right, but if you make the chest prominent and the head turning on the left side, then make the parts on the right side higher than those on the left.

Note in the movements and attitudes of the figures how the limbs and their expressions vary, because the shoulder blades in the movements of the arms and shoulders alter considerably the position of the backbone; and you will find all the causes of this in my Book of Anatomy.

You, who reproduce the works of nature, behold the dimensions, the degrees of intensity, and the forms of the lights and shadows of each muscle, and observe in the lengths of their figures towards which muscle they are directed by the axis of their central lines.

The background that surrounds the figures in any subject composition ought to be darker than the illuminated part of these figures, and lighter than their part in shadow.

That every part of a whole should be in proportion to its whole: thus if a man has a thick short figure he should be the same in every one of his limbs, that is, with short thick arms, big hands, fingers thick and short, with joints of the same character and so with the rest. And I would have the same understood to apply to all kinds of animals and plants; thus, in diminishing the parts, do so in proportion to their size, as also in enlarging.

In representing wind, in addition to showing the bending of the boughs and the inverting of their leaves at the approach of the wind, you should represent the clouds of fine dust mingled with the troubled air.

The first requisite of painting is that the bodies which it represents should appear in relief, and that the scenes which surround them with effects of distance should seem to enter into the plane in which the picture is produced by means of the three parts of perspective, namely the diminution in the distinctness of the form of bodies, the diminution in their size, and the diminution in their color. Of these three divisions of perspective, the first has its origin in the eye, the two others are derived from the atmosphere that is interposed between the eye and the objects which the eye beholds.

The second requisite of painting is that the actions should be appropriate and have a variety in the figures, so that the men may not all look as though they were brothers.

The painter ought to strive at being universal, for there is a great lack of dignity in doing one thing well and another badly, like many who study only the measurements and proportions of the nude figure and do not seek after its variety; for a man may be properly proportioned and yet be fat and short or long and thin, or medium. And whoever does not take count of these varieties will always make his figures in one mold, so that they will all appear sisters, and this practice deserves severe censure.

It is an easy matter for whoever knows how to represent man to afterwards acquire this universality, for all the animals which live upon the earth resemble each other in their limbs, that is, in muscles, sinews and bones, and they do not vary at all, except in length or thickness as will be shown in the Anatomy. There are also the aquatic animals, of which there are many different kinds; but with regard to these I do not advise the painter to make a fixed standard, for they are of almost infinite variety; and the same is also true of the insect world.

Those who are enamored of practice without science are like a pilot who goes into a ship without rudder or compass and never has any certainty where he is going.

Practice should always be based upon a sound knowledge of theory, of which perspective is the guide and gateway, and without it nothing can be done well in any kind of painting.

Of men and horses laboring in battle, the different parts should be darker in proportion as they are closer to the ground on which they are supported; and this is proved from the sides of wells, which become darker in proportion to their depth, this being due to the fact that the lowest part of the well sees and is seen by a lesser amount of the luminous atmosphere than any other part of it. And the pavements, when they are the same color as the legs of the men and horses, will always seem in higher light within equal angles than will these same legs.

[*How to pass judgment upon a painter's work*]

First you should consider the figures, whether they have the relief which their position requires, and the light that illuminates them, so that the shadows may not be the same at the extremities of the composition as in the center, because it is one thing for a figure to be surrounded by shadows, and another for it to have the shadows only on one side. Those figures are surrounded by shadows which are towards the center of the composition, because they are shaded by the dark figures interposed between them and the light; and those are shaded on one side only which are interposed between the light and the main group, for where they do not face the light they face the group, and there they reproduce the darkness cast by this group, and where they do not face the group they face the brightness of the light, and there they reproduce its radiance.

Secondly, you should consider whether the distribution or arrangement of the figures is devised in agreement with the conditions you desire the action to represent.

Thirdly, whether the figures are actively engaged on their purpose.

A very important part of painting consists in the backgrounds of the things painted. Against these backgrounds the contour lines of such natural bodies as possess convex curves will always reveal the shapes of these bodies, even though the colors of the bodies are of the same hue as the background.

This arises from the fact of the convex boundaries of the objects not being illuminated in the same manner as the background is by the same light, because frequently the contours are clearer or darker than the background.

Should, however, these contours be of the same color as the background, then undoubtedly this part of the picture will interfere with the perception of the figure formed by these contour lines. Such a predicament in painting ought to be avoided by the judgment of good painters, since the painter's intention is to make his bodies appear detached from the background; and in the above-mentioned instance the contrary occurs, not only in the painting but in the objects in relief.

There are many men who have a desire and love for drawing but no aptitude for it, and this can be discerned in children if they are not diligent and never finish their copies with shading.

The painter is not worthy of praise who does only one thing well, as the nude, or a head, or draperies, or animal life, or landscapes, or such other special subject; for there is no one so dull of understanding that after devoting himself to one subject only and continually practicing at this, he will fail to do it well.

[*The boundaries of bodies are the least of all things*]

The truth of this proposition is proved by the fact that the boundary of the substance is a surface, which is neither a part of the body enclosed by this surface nor a part of the atmosphere which surrounds this body, but is the medium interposed between the atmosphere and the body, as is proved in its place.

But the lateral boundaries of these bodies are the boundary

line of the surface, which line is of invisible thickness. Therefore, O painter, do not surround your bodies with lines, and
especially when making objects less than their natural size,
for these not only cannot show their lateral boundaries, but
their parts will be invisible, from distance.

The high lights or the luster of any particular object will
not be situated in the center of the illuminated part, but will
make as many changes of position as the eye that beholds it.

Painters have a good opportunity of observing actions in
players, especially at ball or tennis or with the mallet, when
they are contending together, better indeed than in any other
place or exercise.

It is the extremities of all things which impart to them
grace or lack of grace.

Men and words are actual, and you, painter, if you do not
know how to execute your figures, will be like an orator who
does not know how to use his words.

It is a necessary thing for the painter, in order to be able
to fashion the limbs correctly in the positions and actions
which they can represent in the nude, to know the anatomy
of the sinews, bones, muscles and tendons in order to know,
in the various different movements and impulses, which
sinew or muscle is the cause of each movement, and to make
only these prominent and thickened, and not the others all
over the limb, as do many who in order to appear great
draftsmen make their nudes wooden and without grace, so
that it seems rather as if you were looking at a sack of nuts
than a human form, or at a bundle of radishes rather than
the muscles of nudes.

In all things seen one has to consider three things, namely the position of the eye that sees, the position of the object seen and the position of the light that illumines this body.

The painter contends with and rivals nature.

[*On draperies*]

Variety in the subjects. The draperies thin, thick, new, old, with folds broken and pleated, *cride dolci* [?soft lights], shadows obscure and less obscure, either with or without reflections, definite or indistinct according to the distances and the various colors; and garments according to the rank of those who are wearing them, long and short, fluttering or stiff in conformity with the movements; so encircling the figures as to bend or flutter with ends streaming upwards or downwards according to the folds, clinging close about the feet or separated from them, according as the legs are shown at rest or bending or twisting or striking together within; either fitting closely or separating from the joints, according to the step or movement or whether the wind is represented.

And the folds should correspond to the quality of the draperies whether transparent or opaque.

When the subject of your picture is a history, make two points, one of the eye and the other of the light, and make the latter as far distant as possible.

Nature of movements in man. Do not repeat the same actions in the limbs of men unless the necessity of their action constrains you.

[*The way to represent a battle*]

Show first the smoke of the artillery mingled in the air with the dust stirred up by the movement of the horses and

of the combatants. This process you should express as follows: the dust, since it is made up of earth and has weight,
although by reason of its fineness it may easily rise and
mingle with the air, will nevertheless readily fall down again,
and the greatest height will be attained by such part of it as
is the finest, and this will in consequence be the least visible
and will seem also the color of the air itself.

The smoke which is mingled with the dust-laden air will
as it rises to a certain height have more and more the appearance of a dark cloud, at the summit of which the smoke will
be more distinctly visible than the dust. The smoke will
assume a bluish tinge, and the dust will keep its natural
color. From the side whence the light comes this mixture of
air and smoke and dust will seem far brighter than on the
opposite side.

As for the combatants the more they are in the midst of
this turmoil the less they will be visible, and the less will be
the contrast between their lights and shadows.

You should give a ruddy glow to the faces and the figures
and the air around them, and to the gunners and those near
to them, and this glow should grow fainter as it is farther
away from its cause. The figures which are between you and
the light, if far away, will appear dark against a light background, and the nearer their limbs are to the ground the less
will they be visible, for there the dust is greater and thicker.
And if you make horses galloping away from the throng,
make little clouds of dust as far distant one from another as
is the space between the strides made by the horse, and that
cloud which is farthest away from the horse should be the
least visible, for it should be high and spread out and thin,
while that which is nearest should be most conspicuous and
smallest and most compact.

Let the air be full of arrows going in various directions,
some mounting upwards, others falling, others flying hori-

zontally; and let the balls shot from the guns have a train of smoke following their course. Show the figures in the foreground covered with dust on their hair and eyebrows and such other level parts as afford the dust a space to lodge.

Make the conquerors running, with their hair and other light things streaming in the wind, and with brows bent down; and they should be thrusting forward opposite limbs, that is, if a man advances the right foot, the left arm should also come forward. If you represent anyone fallen you should show the mark where he has been dragged through the dust which has become changed to blood-stained mire, and round about in the half-liquid earth you should show the marks of the trampling of men and horses who have passed over it.

Make a horse dragging the dead body of his master, and leaving behind him in the dust and mud the track of where the body was dragged along.

Make the beaten and conquered pallid, with brows raised and knit together, and let the skin above the brows be all full of lines of pain; at the sides of the nose show the furrows going in an arch from the nostrils and ending where the eye begins, and show the dilatation of the nostrils which is the cause of these lines; and let the lips be arched displaying the upper row of teeth, and let the teeth be parted after the manner of such as cry in lamentation. Show someone using his hand as a shield for his terrified eyes, turning the palm of it towards the enemy, and having the other resting on the ground to support the weight of his body; let others be crying out with their mouths wide open, and fleeing away. Put all sorts of armor lying between the feet of the combatants, such as broken shields, lances, swords and other things like these. Make the dead, some half-buried in dust, others with the dust all mingled with the oozing blood and changing into crimson mud; and let the line of the blood be discerned by its color, flowing in a sinuous stream from the corpse to the dust. Show others in the death agony grinding their teeth and rolling their eyes, with clenched fists grinding against their bodies and with legs distorted. Then you might show one, disarmed and struck down by the enemy, turning on him with teeth and nails to take fierce and inhuman vengeance; and let a riderless horse be seen galloping with mane streaming in the wind, charging among the enemy and doing them great mischief with his hoofs.

You may see there one of the combatants, maimed and fallen on the ground, protecting himself with his shield, and the enemy bending down over him and striving to give him the fatal stroke; there might also be seen many men fallen in a heap on top of a dead horse; and you should show some of the victors leaving the combat and retiring apart from the crowd, and with both hands wiping away from eyes and cheeks the thick layer of mud caused by the smarting of their eyes from the dust.

And the squadrons of the reserves should be seen standing full of hope but cautious, with eyebrows raised, and shading their eyes with their hands, peering into the thick, heavy mist in readiness for the commands of their captain; and so too the captain with his staff raised, hurrying to the reserves and pointing out to them the quarter of the field where they are needed; and you should show a river, within which horses are galloping, stirring the water all around with a heaving mass of waves and foam, and broken water leaping high into the air and over the legs and bodies of the horses; but see that you make no level spot of ground that is not trampled over with blood.

[*Of a deluge and the representation of it in painting*]

Let the dark, gloomy air be seen beaten by the rush of opposing winds wreathed in perpetual rain mingled with hail, and bearing hither and thither a vast network of the torn branches of trees mixed together with an infinite number of leaves. All around let there be seen ancient trees uprooted and torn in pieces by the fury of the winds. You should show how fragments of mountains, which have already been stripped bare by the rushing torrents, fall headlong into these very torrents and choke up the valleys, until the pent-up rivers rise in flood and cover the wide plains and their inhabitants. Again there might be seen huddled together on the tops of many of the mountains many different sorts of animals, terrified and subdued at last to a state of tameness, in company with men and women who had fled there with their children. And the fields which were covered with water had their waves covered over in great part with tables, bedsteads, boats and various other kinds of rafts, improvised through necessity and fear of death, upon which were men and women with their children, massed together and uttering various cries and lamentations, dismayed by the fury of the winds which were causing the waters to roll over and over in mighty hurricane, bearing with them the bodies of the drowned; and there was no object that floated on the water but was covered with various different animals who had made truce and stood huddled together in terror, among them being wolves, foxes, snakes and creatures of every kind, fugitives from death. And all the waves that beat against their sides were striking them with repeated blows from the various bodies of the drowned, and the blows were killing those in whom life remained.

Some groups of men you might have seen with weapons in their hands defending the tiny footholds that remained to them from the lions and wolves and beasts of prey which sought safety there. Ah, what dreadful tumults one heard resounding through the gloomy air, smitten by the fury of the thunder and the lightning it flashed forth, which sped through it, bearing ruin, striking down whatever withstood its course! Ah, how many might you have seen stopping their ears with their hands in order to shut out the loud uproar caused through the darkened air by the fury of the winds mingled together with the rain, the thunder of the heavens and the raging of the thunderbolts! Others were not content to shut their eyes, but placing their hands over them, one above the other, would cover them more tightly in order not to see the pitiless slaughter made of the human race by the wrath of God.

Ah me, how many lamentations! How many in their terror flung themselves down from the rocks! You might have seen huge branches of the giant oaks laden with men borne along through the air by the fury of the impetuous winds. How many boats were capsized and lying, some whole, others broken in pieces, on top of men struggling to escape with acts and gestures of despair which foretold an awful death. Others with frenzied acts were taking their own lives, in despair of ever being able to endure such anguish; some of these were flinging themselves down from the lofty rocks, others strangled themselves with their own hands; some seized hold of their own children, and with mighty violence slew them at one blow; some turned their arms against themselves to wound and slay; others, falling upon their knees, were commending themselves to God.

Alas! How many mothers were bewailing their drowned sons, holding them upon their knees, lifting up open arms to heaven, and with divers cries and shrieks declaiming against the anger of the gods! Others with hands clenched and fingers locked together gnawed and devoured them with bites that ran blood, crouching down so that their breasts touched their knees in their intense and intolerable agony.

Herds of animals, such as horses, oxen, goats, sheep, were to be seen already hemmed in by the waters and left isolated upon the high peaks of the mountains, all huddling together, and those in the middle climbing to the top and treading on the others, and waging fierce battles with each other, and many of them dying from want of food.

And the birds had already begun to settle upon men and other animals, no longer finding any land left unsubmerged which was not covered with living creatures. Already had hunger, the minister of death, taken away their life from the greater number of the animals, when the dead bodies already becoming lighter began to rise from out the bottom of the deep waters, and emerged to the surface among the contending waves; and there lay beating one against another, and as balls puffed up with wind rebound back from the spot where they strike, these fell back and lay upon the other dead bodies.

And above these horrors the atmosphere was seen covered with murky clouds that were rent by the jagged course of the raging thunderbolts of heaven, which flashed light hither and thither amid the obscurity of the darkness.

The velocity of the air is seen by the movement of the dust stirred by the running of a horse; and it moves as swiftly to fill up the void left in the air which had enclosed the horse as is the speed of the horse in passing away from the aforesaid space of air.

But it will perhaps seem to you that you have cause to censure me for having represented the different courses taken in the air by the movement of the wind, whereas the wind is not of itself visible in the air; to this I reply that it is not the movement of the wind itself but the movement of the things carried by it which alone is visible in the air.

[*The divisions*]

Darkness, wind, tempest at sea, deluge of water, woods on fire, rain, thunderbolts from the sky, earthquakes and destruction of mountains, leveling of cities.

Whirlwinds which carry water and branches of trees and men through the air.

Branches torn away by the winds crashing together at the meeting of the winds, with people on the top of them.

Trees broken off laden with people.

Ships broken in pieces dashed upon the rocks.

Hail, thunderbolts, whirlwinds.

Herds of cattle.

People on trees which cannot bear them: trees and rocks, towers, hills crowded with people, boats, tables, troughs and other contrivances for floating—hills covered with men and women and animals, with lightnings from the clouds which illumine the whole scene.

[*Description of the deluge*]

First of all let there be represented the summit of a rugged mountain with certain of the valleys that surround its base, and on its sides let the surface of the soil be seen slipping down, together with the tiny roots of the small shrubs, and leaving bare a great part of the surrounding rocks. Sweeping down in devastation from these precipices, let it pursue its headlong course, striking and laying bare the twisted and gnarled roots of the great trees and overturning them in ruin. And the mountains, becoming bare, should reveal the deep fissures made in them by the ancient earthquakes; and let the bases of the mountains be in great part covered over and clad with the debris of the shrubs which have fallen headlong from the sides of the lofty peaks of the said mountains, and let these be mingled together with mud, roots, branches of trees, with various kinds of leaves thrust in among the mud and earth and stones. And let the fragments of some of the mountains have fallen down into the depth of one of the valleys, and there form a barrier to the swollen waters of its river, which having already burst the barrier rushes on with immense waves, the greatest of which are striking and laying in ruin the walls of the cities and farms of the valley. And from the ruins of the lofty buildings of the aforesaid cities let there rise a great quantity of dust, mounting up in the air with the appearance of smoke or of wreathed clouds that battle against the descending rain.

But the swollen waters should be coursing round the pool which confines them, and striking against various obstacles with whirling eddies, leaping up into the air in turbid foam, and then falling back and causing the water where they strike to be dashed up into the air; and the circling waves which recede from the point of contact are impelled by their impetus right across the course of the other circling waves which move in an opposite direction to them, and after striking against these they leap up into the air without becoming detached from their base.

And where the water issues forth from the said pool, the spent waves are seen spreading out towards the outlet; after which, falling or descending through the air, this water acquires weight and impetus; and then piercing the water where it strikes, it tears it apart and dives down in fury to reach its depth, and then recoiling, springs back again towards the surface of the lake accompanied by the air which has been submerged with it, and this remains in the slimy foam mingled with the driftwood and other things lighter than the water, and around these again are formed the beginnings of the waves, which increase the more in circumference as they acquire more movement; and this movement makes them lower in proportion as they acquire a wider base, and therefore they become almost imperceptible as they die away. But if the waves rebound against various obstacles then they leap back and oppose the approach of the other waves, following the same law of development in their curve as they have already shown in their original movement. The rain as it falls from the clouds is of the same color as these clouds, that is, on its shaded side; unless, however, the rays of the sun should penetrate there, for if this were so the rain would appear less dark than the cloud. And if the great masses of the debris of huge mountains or of large buildings strike in their fall the mighty lakes of the waters, then a vast quantity of water will rebound in the air, and its course will be in an opposite direction to that of the substance which struck the water, that is to say, the angle of reflection will be equal to the angle of incidence.

Of the objects borne along by the current of the waters, that will be at a greater distance from the two opposite banks which is heavier or of larger bulk. The eddies of the waters revolve most swiftly in those parts which are nearest to their center. The crests of the waves of the sea fall forward to their base, beating and rubbing themselves against the smooth particles which form their face; and by this friction the water as it falls is ground up in tiny particles, and becomes changed to thick mist, and is mingled in the currents of the winds in the manner of wreathing smoke or winding clouds, and at last rises up in the air and becomes changed into clouds. But the rain which falls through the air, being beaten upon and driven by the current of the winds, becomes rare or dense according to the rarity or density of these winds, and by this means there is produced throughout the air a flood of transparent clouds which is formed by the aforesaid rain, and becomes visible in it by means of the lines made by the fall of the rain which is near to the eye of the spectator. The waves of the sea that beats against the shelving base of the mountains which confine it, rush foaming in speed up to the ridge of these same hills, and in turning back meet the onset of the succeeding wave, and after loud roaring return in a mighty flood to the sea from whence they came. A great number of the inhabitants, men and different animals, may be seen driven by the rising of the deluge up towards the summits of the hills which border on the said waters.

III · COLOR

OF colors of equal whiteness, that will seem most dazzling which is on the darkest background, and black will seem most intense when it is against a background of greater whiteness.

Red also will seem most vivid when against a yellow background, and so in like manner with all the colors when set against those which present the sharpest contrasts.

The more white a thing is, the more it will be tinged with the color of the illuminated or luminous object.

But in the far distance that object will show itself most blue which is darkest in color.

Every object that has no color in itself is tinged either entirely or in part by the color [of the object] set opposite to it. This may be seen by experience, for every object which serves as a mirror is tinged with the color of the thing that is reflected in it. And if the object which is in part tinged is white, the portion of it that is illumined by red will appear red, and so with every other color whether it be light or dark.

Every opaque object that is devoid of color partakes of the color of that which is opposite to it: as happens with a white wall.

The variation in the colors of objects at a great distance can only be discerned in those portions which are smitten by the solar rays.

As regards the colors of bodies there is no difference at a great distance in the parts which are in shadow.

A dark object will appear more blue when it has a larger amount of luminous atmosphere interposed between it and the eye, as may be seen in the color of the sky.

[*A discussion on the colors of shadows*]

Colors seen in shadow will reveal more or less of their natural beauty in proportion as they are in fainter or deeper shadow.

But if the colors happen to be in a luminous space they will show themselves of greater beauty in proportion as the luminosity is more intense.

[*Adversary*]

The varieties in the colors of shadows are as numerous as the varieties in color of the objects which are in the shadows.

[*Reply*]

Colors seen in shadow will reveal less variety one with another according as the shadows wherein they lie are deeper. There is evidence of this from those who from a space without peer within the doorways of shadowy temples, for there the pictures clad as they are in divers colors all seem robed in darkness.

So therefore at a long distance all the shadows of different colors appear of the same darkness.

Of bodies clad in light and shade it is the illuminated part which reveals the true color.

No white or black is transparent.

Since white is not a color but is capable of becoming the recipient of every color, when a white object is seen in the open air all its shadows are blue; and this comes about in accordance with the fourth proposition, which says that the surface of every opaque body partakes of the color of surrounding objects. As therefore this white object is deprived of the light of the sun by the interposition of some object which comes between the sun and it, all that portion of it which is exposed to the sun and the atmosphere continues to partake of the color of the sun and the atmosphere, and that part which is not exposed to the sun remains in shadow, and partakes only of the color of the atmosphere.

And if this white object should neither reflect the green of the fields which stretch out to the horizon nor yet face the brightness of the horizon itself, it would undoubtedly appear of such simple color as the atmosphere showed itself to be.

The accidental colors of the leaves of trees are four, namely shadow, light, luster and transparency.

The accidental parts of the leaves of plants will at a great distance become a mixture, in which the accidental color of the largest will predominate.

The color of the object illuminated partakes of the color of that which illuminates it.

The surface of every body participates in the color of the body that illuminates it.

And in the color of the air that is interposed between the eye and this body, that is to say in the color of the transparent medium interposed between the object and the eye.

Among colors of the same quality, the second will never be of the same color as the first; and this proceeds from the multiplication of the color of the medium interposed between the object and the eye.

Painting

Of the various colors other than blue, that which at a great distance will resemble blue most closely will be that which is nearest to black, and so conversely the color which least resembles black will be the one which at a great distance will most retain its natural color.

Accordingly, the green in landscapes will become more changed into blue than will the yellow or the white, and so conversely the yellow and the white will undergo less change than the green, and the red still less.

The shadow of flesh should be of burnt *terra verde*.

The image imprinted in a mirror partakes of the color of the said mirror.

The surface of every dark body will participate in the color of the bodies placed against it.

The surface of every opaque body will be capable of participating and will be tinged with the color of the bodies placed against it.

The density of smoke from the horizon downwards is white and from the horizon upwards it is dark; and, although this smoke is in itself of the same color, this equality shows itself as different, on account of the difference of the space in which it is found.

As flame extends it becomes yellow in its upper part, then saffron in color, and this ends in smoke.

The surface of every opaque body participates in the color of its object.
The surface of the opaque body is the more completely steeped in the color of its object, in proportion as the rays

of the images of these objects strike the objects at more equal angles.

And the surface of opaque bodies is more steeped in the color of their object, in proportion as this surface is whiter, and the color of the object more luminous or illuminated.

The colors of the rainbow are not created by the sun, because in many ways these colors are produced without the sun, as happens when you hold up a glass of water close to the eye, for in the glass of it there are the tiny bubbles which are usually seen in glass that is imperfectly refined. And these bubbles, although they are not in sunlight, will produce on one side all the colors of the rainbow; and this you will see if you place the glass between the atmosphere and your eye in such a way as to be in contact with the eye, the glass having one side exposed to the light of the atmosphere, and on the other the shadow of the wall on the right or left side of the window—which side does not matter. So by turning this glass round you will see the aforesaid colors round about these bubbles in the glass. And we will speak of other methods in their place.

The eye in the experiment described above would seem to have some share in the creation of the colors of the rainbow, because the bubbles in the glass do not display these colors except through the medium of the eye. But if you place this glass full of water on the level of the window, so that the sun's rays strike it on the opposite side, you will then see the aforesaid colors producing themselves, in the impression made by the solar rays which have penetrated through this glass of water, and terminated upon the floor in a dark place at the foot of the window; and since here the eye is not employed we clearly can say with certainty that these colors do not derive in any way from the eye.

There are many birds in the various regions of the world in whose feathers most radiant colors are seen produced in their different movements, as is seen to happen among us with the feathers of peacocks, or on the necks of ducks or pigeons.

Moreover, on the surface of ancient glass found buried, and in the roots of radishes which have been kept a long time at the bottom of wells or other stagnant water, [we see] that each of these roots is surrounded by a sequence of colors like those of the rainbow. It is seen when some oily substance has spread on the top of water; as also in the solar rays reflected from the surface of a diamond or beryl. Also, in the facet of the beryl, every dark object which has as its background the atmosphere or other clear object is surrounded by this sequence of colors interposed between the atmosphere and the dark object; and so in many other ways, which I leave because these suffice for this present theme.

IV · LANDSCAPE

WITHIN the spaces between the rain one sees the redness of the sun, that is, of the clouds interposed between the sun and the rain.

The waves interposed between the rain and the eye never reveal to the eye the image of the darkness of this rain, and this is due to the fact that the side of the wave is not seen, nor does it see the rain.

And the clouds are of dark purple.

Of things seen through the mist, the part which is nearest to the extremities will be less visible, and so much less when they are more remote.

111

When rain is falling from broken clouds, one sees the shadows of these clouds upon the earth interrupted by the part of the earth that is illuminated by the sun.

When the sun is lower the arc of the rainbow has a larger circle, and when it is higher it will be the contrary.

When the sun is in the west, hidden behind some small and thick cloud, then this cloud will be surrounded by a ruddy splendor.

Why towers and campaniles at a great distance, although of uniform thickness, seem like inverted pyramids.

This arises from the fact that the lower tracts of air, being thick and misty, veil them more completely, and the more an object is veiled the more the perception of its extremities is lost, and consequently the perception of the object tends to concentrate about its central line.

At the first hour of the day, the atmosphere in the south near to the horizon has a dim haze of rose-flushed clouds; towards the west it grows darker; and towards the east the damp vapor of the horizon shows brighter than the actual horizon itself, and the white of the houses in the east is scarcely to be discerned; while in the south, the farther distant they are, the more they assume a dark rose-flushed hue, and even more so in the west; and with the shadows it is the contrary, for these disappear before the white.

[. . . .] in the east, and the tops of the trees are more visible than their bases, since the atmosphere is thicker lower down, and the structure becomes more indistinct at a height.

And in the south, the trees may scarcely be distinguished

by reason of the vapor which darkens in the west and grows clear in the east.

Buildings seen at a great distance in the evening or morning, through mist or heavy atmosphere, have only such portions in light as are illuminated by the sun, which is then near the horizon, and the parts of those buildings which are not exposed to the sun remain almost the same dim neutral color as the mist.

The landscapes which occur in representations of winter should not show the mountains blue as one sees them in summer, and this is proved by the fourth part of this [chapter], where it is stated that of the mountains seen at a great distance that will seem a deeper blue in color which is in itself darker; for when the trees are stripped of their leaves they look gray in color, and when they are with their leaves they are green, and in proportion as the green is darker than the gray, the green will appear a more intense blue than the gray; and by the fifth part of this [chapter], the shadows of trees which are clad with leaves are as much darker than the shadows of those trees which are stripped of leaves as the trees clad with leaves are denser than those without leaves; and thus we have established our proposition.

The definition of the blue color of the atmosphere supplies the reason why landscapes are a deeper shade of blue in summer than in winter.

The shadows of trees set in landscapes do not seem to occupy the same positions in the trees on the left as in those on the right, and this especially when the sun is on the right or the left. This is proved by the fourth, which states: opaque bodies placed between the light and the eye will show themselves entirely in shadow; and by the fifth: the eye that is interposed between the opaque body and the light sees the opaque body all illuminated; and by the sixth: when the eye and the opaque body are interposed between the darkness and the light, the body will be seen half in shadow and half in light.

When the smoke from dry wood comes between the eye of the observer and some dark space, it appears blue.

So the atmosphere appears blue because of the darkness which is beyond it; and if you look towards the horizon of the sky you will see that the atmosphere is not blue, and this is due to its density; and so, at every stage as you raise your eye up from this horizon to the sky which is above you, you will find that the atmosphere will seem darker, and this is because a lesser quantity of air interposes between your eye and the darkness.

And if you are on the top of a high mountain, the atmosphere will seem darker above you, just in proportion as it becomes rarer between you and the said darkness; and this will be intensified at every successive stage of its height, so that at the last it will remain blue.

That smoke will appear the bluest which proceeds from the driest wood, and is nearest to the place of its origin, and when it is seen against the darkest background with the light of the sun upon it.

The smoke that penetrates through the air if it is thick, and rises out of great flame which is fed by damp wood, does not mingle with it but makes itself seem denser above than in the center, and does this the more when the air is chilly; and the faint gleam that penetrates the air is always warm and always becoming fainter, and of the dust which passes through the air, the finest rises the highest.

Although leaves with a smooth surface are for the most part of the same color on the right side as on the reverse, it so happens that the side exposed to the atmosphere partakes of the color of the atmosphere, and seems to partake of its color more closely in proportion as the eye is nearer to it and sees it more foreshortened. And the shadows will invariably appear darker on the right side than on the reverse, through the contrast caused by the high lights appearing against the shadow.

The underside of the leaf, although its color in itself may be the same as that of the right side, appears more beautiful; and this color is a green verging upon yellow; and this occurs when the leaf is interposed between the eye and the light which illumines it from the opposite side. Its shadows also are in the same positions as those on the opposite side.

Therefore, O painter, when you make trees near at hand, remember that when your eye is somewhat below the level of the tree you will be able to see its leaves, some on the right side and some on the reverse; and the right sides will be a deeper blue as they are seen more foreshortened, and the same leaf will sometimes show part of the right side and part of the reverse, and consequently you must make it of two colors.

When there is one belt of green behind another, the high lights on the leaves and their transparent lights show more strongly than those which are against the brightness of the atmosphere.

And if the sun illumines the leaves without these coming between it and the eye, and without the eye facing the sun, then the high lights and the transparent lights of the leaves are extremely powerful.

It is very useful to make some of the lower branches, and these should be dark, and should serve as a background for the illuminated belts of green which are at some little distance from the first.

Of the darker greens seen from below, that part is darkest which is nearest to the eye, that is to say, which is farthest from the luminous atmosphere.

Never represent leaves as though transparent in the sun, because they are always indistinct; and this comes about because over the transparency of one leaf there will be imprinted the shadow of another leaf which is above it; and this shadow has definite outlines and a fixed density. And sometimes it is the half or third part of the leaf which is in the shadow, and consequently the structure of such a leaf is indistinct, and the imitation of it is to be avoided.

The upper branches of the spreading boughs of trees keep nearer to the parent bough than do those below.

That leaf is less transparent which takes the light at a more acute angle.

Of the plants which take their shadows from the trees which grow among them, those which are in front of the shadow have their stalks lighted up against a background of shadow, and the plants which are in shadow have their stalks dark against a light background, that is, against a background which is beyond the shadow.

Of the trees which are between the eye and the light, the part in front will be bright, and this brightness will be diversified by the ramification of the transparent leaves—as seen from the underside—with the shining leaves seen from the right side, and in the background, below and behind, the verdure will be dark, because it is cast in shadow by the front part of the said tree; and this occurs in trees which are higher than the eye.

When the leaves are interposed between the light and the eye, then that which is nearest to the eye will be the darkest, and that farthest away will be the lightest, if they are not seen against the atmosphere; and this happens with leaves which are beyond the center of the tree, that is, in the direction of the light.

The true method of practice in representing country scenes, or I should say landscapes with their trees, is to choose them when the sun in the sky is hidden, so that the fields receive a diffused light and not the direct light of the sun, for this makes the shadows sharply defined and very different from the lights.

The shadows of verdure always approximate to blue, and so it is with every shadow of every other thing, and they tend to this color more entirely when they are farther distant from the eye, and less in proportion as they are nearer.

The leaves which reflect the blue of the atmosphere always present themselves edgewise to the eye.

The part illuminated will show more of its natural color at a great distance when it is illuminated by the most powerful light.

When the sun is in the east and the eye is looking down upon a city from above, the eye will see the southern part of the city with its roofs half in shadow and half in light, and so also with the northern part; but the eastern part will be all in shadow and the western part all in light.

Landscapes ought to be represented so that the trees are half in light and half in shadow; but it is better to make them when the sun is covered by clouds, for then the trees are lighted up by the general light of the sky and the general shadow of the earth; and these are so much darker in their parts, in proportion as these parts are nearer to the middle of the tree and to the earth.

When the sun is in the east, the grasses in the meadows and the other small plants are of a most brilliant green, because they are transparent to the sun. This does not happen with the meadows in the west, and in those in the south and north the grasses are of a moderate brilliance in their green.

When the sun is in the east, all the parts of trees which are illuminated by it are of a most brilliant green; and this is due to the fact that the leaves illuminated by the sun within half our hemisphere, namely the eastern half, are transparent, while within the western semicircle the verdure has a somber hue and the air is damp and heavy, of the color of dark ashes, so that it is not transparent like that in the east, which is refulgent, and the more so as it is more full of moisture.

The shadows of the trees in the east cover a large part of the tree, and they are darker in proportion as the trees are thicker with leaves.

When the sun is in the east, the trees seen towards the east will have the light surrounding them all around their shadows, except towards the earth, unless the tree has been pruned in the previous year; and the trees in the south and in the north will be half in shadow and half in light, and more or less in shadow or in light according as they are more or less to the east or to the west.

The fact of the eye being high or low causes a variation in the shadows and lights of trees, for when the eye is above, it sees the trees with very little shadow, and when below with a great deal of shadow.

The different shades of green of plants are as varied as are their species.

When the sun is in the east, the trees towards the west will appear to the eye with very little relief and of almost imperceptible gradation, on account of the atmosphere which lies very thick between the eye and these trees, according to the seventh [part] of this [treatise]; and they are deprived of shadow, for although a shadow exists in each part of the ramification, it so happens that the images of shadow and light which come to the eye are confused and blended together, and cannot be discerned through the smallness of their size. And the highest lights are in the center of the trees, and the shadows are towards their extremities, and their separation is marked by the shadows in the spaces between these trees when the forests are dense with trees; and in those which are more scattered the contours are but little seen.

When the sun is in the east, the trees in that quarter are dark towards the center, and their edges are in light.

The smoke of cities is seen better and more distinctly in the eastern than in the western quarter when the sun is in the east. This is due to two causes: the first is that the sun shines with its rays through the particles of the smoke, and lightens these up and renders them visible; the second is that the roofs of the houses seen in the east at this hour are in shadow, because their slope prevents them from being lighted by the sun; the same happens with the dust, and both the one and the other are more charged with light in proportion as they are thicker; and they are thickest towards the middle.

When the sun is in the east, the smoke of cities will not be visible in the west, because it is neither seen penetrated by the solar rays nor against a dark background, since the roofs of the houses turn the same side to the eye that they show to the sun, and against this bright background the smoke will be scarcely visible. But dust when seen under the same conditions will appear darker than smoke, because it is thicker in substance than smoke, which is made up of vapor.

The intervening region of the air within the bodies of trees, and the spaces between the trees within the air at a great distance, do not reveal themselves to the eye, for where it requires an effort to discern the whole it would be difficult to distinguish the parts. But it forms a confused mixture, which derives most from that which forms the greatest mass. The open spaces of the tree being made up of particles of illuminated air, and being much less than the tree, one therefore loses sight of them much sooner than one does of the tree; but it does not therefore follow that they are not there. Hence of necessity there comes about a blending of air and of the darkness of the shaded tree, which float together to meet the eye of the beholder.

What outlines do trees show at a distance against the atmosphere which serves as their background? The outlines of the structure of trees against the luminous atmosphere, as they are more remote, approach the spherical more closely in their shape, and as they are nearer, so they display a greater divergence from the spherical form.

So the first tree a^1 as being near to the eye displays the true form of its ramification, but this is somewhat less visible in b, and disappears altogether in c, where not only can none of the branches of the tree be seen, but the whole tree can only be recognized with great difficulty.

---

[1] MS. contains a sketch of a row of trees seen in perspective.

Every object in shadow—be it of whatever shape you please—will at a great distance appear to be spherical; and this occurs because if an object be rectangular, then at a very short distance its angles become invisible, and a little farther off it loses more than it retains of the lesser sides, and so before losing the whole it loses the parts, since these are less than the whole.

In the representation of trees in leaf, be careful not to repeat the same color too often for a tree which has another tree of the same color as its background, but vary it by making the foliage lighter or darker, or of a more vivid green.

The lights on such leaves as are darkest in color will most closely resemble the color of the atmosphere reflected in them; and this is due to the fact that the brightness of the illuminated part mingling with the darkness forms of itself a blue color; and this brightness proceeds from the blue of the atmosphere, which is reflected in the smooth surface of these leaves, thereby adding to the blueness which this light usually produces when it falls upon dark objects.

But leaves of yellowish green do not when they reflect the atmosphere create a reflection which verges on blue; for every object when seen in a mirror takes in part the color of this mirror; therefore the blue of the atmosphere reflected in the yellow of the leaf appears green, because blue and yellow mixed together form a most brilliant green, and therefore the luster on light leaves which are yellowish in color will be a greenish yellow.

The trees, illuminated by the sun and by the atmosphere, which have leaves of a dark color, will be illuminated on one side by the atmosphere alone, and in consequence of being thus illuminated will share its blueness; and on the opposite side they will be illuminated both by the atmosphere and the sun, and the part which the eye sees illuminated by the sun will be resplendent.

The extremities of the branches of trees, if not dragged down by the weight of their fruit, turn towards the sky as much as possible.

The upper sides of their leaves are turned towards the sky in order to receive nourishment from the dew that falls by night.

The sun gives spirit and life to plants, and the earth nourishes them with moisture. In this connection I once made the experiment of leaving only one small root on a gourd and keeping this nourished with water; and the gourd brought to perfection all the fruits that it could produce, which were about sixty gourds of the long species; and I set myself diligently to consider the source of its life, and I perceived that it was the dew of the night which steeped it abundantly with its moisture through the joints of its great leaves, and thereby nourished the tree and its offspring, or rather the seeds which were to produce its offspring.

The rule as to the leaves produced on the last of the year's branches is that on twin branches they will grow in a contrary direction, that is, that the leaves in their earliest growth turn themselves round towards the branch, in such a way that the sixth leaf above grows over the sixth leaf below; and the manner of their turning is that if one turns towards its fellow on the right, the other turns to the left.

The leaf serves as a breast to nourish the branch or fruit which grows in the succeeding year.

The dark colors of the shadows of mountains at a great distance take a more beautiful and purer blue than those parts which are in light, and from this it follows that when the rock of the mountains is reddish the parts of it which are in light are fawn-colored, and the more brightly it is illuminated the more closely will it retain its natural color.

Smoke enters into the air in the form of a wave, like that which water makes when its force causes it to burst through other water.

Reeds in the light are scarcely visible, but between the light and the shade they stand out well.

To represent landscapes, choose when the sun is at the meridian and turn to the west or the east, and then begin your work.

If you turn to the north, every object placed on that side will be without shadow, and especially those nearest to the shadow cast by your head; and if you turn to the south, every object upon that side will be entirely in shadow.

All the trees which are towards the sun and which have the atmosphere for their background will be dark, and the other trees which have this darkness for their background will be black in the center and lighter towards the edges.

Landscapes are of a more beautiful azure when in fine weather the sun is at noon, than at any other hour of the day, because the atmosphere is free from moisture; and viewing them under such conditions you see the trees beautiful towards their extremities and the shadows dark towards the center; and in the farther distance the atmosphere which is interposed between you and them appears more beautiful when beyond it there is some darker substance, and consequently the azure is most beautiful.

Objects seen from the side on which the sun is shining will not show you their shadows. But if you are lower than the sun, you will see what was not seen by the sun, and that will be all in shadow.

The leaves of the trees which are between you and the sun are of five principal shades of color, namely a green most beautiful, shining and serving as a mirror for the atmosphere which lights up objects that cannot be seen by the sun, and the parts in shadow that only face the earth, and those darkest parts which are surrounded by something other than darkness.

Trees in the open country which are between you and the sun seem much more beautiful than those which have you between the sun and themselves; and this is the case because those which are in the same direction as the sun show their leaves transparent towards their extremities, and the parts that are not transparent—that is, at the tips—are shining; it is true that the shadows are dark, because they are not covered by anything.

The trees, when you place yourself between them and the sun, will only show themselves to you in their clear and natural color, which is not of itself very conspicuous, and besides this certain reflected lights, which, owing to their not being against a background that offers a strong contrast to their brightness, are but little in evidence; and if you are at a lower altitude than these, such parts of them may be visible as are not exposed to the sun, and these will be dark.
But if you are on the side from whence the wind is blowing, you will see the trees looking much lighter than you would see them from the other sides; and this is due to the fact that the wind turns up the reverse sides of the leaves, which are in all cases much paler than their right sides; and

especially will they be very light if the wind blows from the quarter where the sun happens to be, and if you have your back turned to it.

All trees seen against the sun are dark towards the center; this darkness will take the shape of the tree when it stands apart from others.

The shadows cast by trees on which the sun is shining are as dark as that of the center of the tree.

The shadow cast by trees is never less in mass than the mass of the tree; but it is larger in proportion as the place where it is thrown slopes more towards the center of the earth.

A shadow will be thickest towards the center of a tree when it has fewest branches.

Every branch gets the middle of the shadow of every other branch and as a consequence of all the tree.

The shape of every shadow of branch or tree is clothed with a bright part on the side from which the light comes; this brightness will be of the same shape as the shadow and may extend for a mile from the side where the sun is.

If it should happen anywhere that a cloud casts a shadow on some part of the hills, the trees there will undergo less change than in the distances or plains; for the trees upon the hills have their branches thicker because their growth each year is less than in the plains; therefore, as they are of the number of those naturally dark and full of shade, the shadows of the clouds cannot make them any darker, and the level spaces that come between the trees which have not lost any shadow vary much in tone, and especially those which are other than green, such as cultivated lands or the havoc of mountains or their barrenness or ruggedness.

Where trees are on the skyline they seem of the same color, unless they are very close together and with thick-set leaves, like the pine and similar trees.

When you see trees on the side on which the sun lights them you will see them of almost uniform brightness, and the shadows which are within them will be covered by the illuminated leaves which come between your eye and the shadows.

When trees come between the sun and the eye, beyond the shadows which spread out from their center you will see the green of the leaves in transparence; but this transparence will be broken in many places by the leaves and branches in shadow which come between you and them, and in the upper portions it will be accompanied by many reflections from the leaves.

When the sun is covered by clouds, objects have a low degree of visibility; because there is but little difference between the lights and shadows of the trees and buildings, through their being illuminated by the spaciousness of the atmosphere, which surrounds the objects in such a way that the shadows are few, and these few become fainter and fainter so that their extremities become lost in mist.

The trees in landscapes are of various different shades of green; for in some, such as firs, pines, cypresses, laurels, box and the like, it borders on black; others, such as walnuts and pears, vines and young foliage, approximate to yellow; others to darker shades of yellow, such as chestnuts, oaks and the like; others redden towards the autumn, these are sorbs, pomegranates, vines and cherry trees; others, such as willows, olives, bamboos and others like these, tend to become white.

All the leaves which hang down towards the ground as the twigs bend, owing to the branches being turned over, straighten themselves in the current of the winds; and here their perspective is inverted, for if the tree is between you and the quarter from which the wind is coming, the tips of the leaves which are towards you take their natural position, and those opposite, which should have their tips the contrary way, from the fact of their being upside down, will be turned with their tips towards you.

Trees in a landscape do not stand out distinctly one from another, because their illuminated parts border on the illuminated parts of those beyond them, and so there is little difference between the lights and the shadows.

When clouds come between the sun and the eye, all the edges of their rounded masses are clear, and they are dark towards the center, and this happens because towards the top these edges are seen by the sun from above while you are looking at them from below; and the same happens with the positions of the branches of the trees; and moreover the clouds, like the trees, through being somewhat transparent are partly bright, and at the edges show themselves thinner. But when the eye finds itself between the cloud and the sun, the appearance of the cloud is the contrary of what it was before, for the edges of its rounded masses are dark and they are bright towards the center. And this comes about because you are looking at that part which is also facing the sun, and because these edges have a degree of transparency and reveal to the eye the part that is hidden beyond them, and this, not being visible to the sun as are the parts which are turned towards it, is necessarily somewhat darker. It may also be that you see the details of these rounded masses from the underside while the sun sees it from above, and since they are not so situated as to give back the brightness of the sun, as in the former instance, therefore they remain dark.

The black clouds which are often visible above those that are bright and illuminated by the sun, are thrown into shadow by the other clouds, which are interposed between them and the sun.

Again, the rounded masses of the clouds that face the sun show their edges dark, because they are silhouetted against a bright background; and to see the truth of this you should observe the top of a cloud which is entirely light because it is silhouetted against the blue of the atmosphere, which is darker than the cloud.

I ask whether the true movement of the clouds can be recognized by the movement of their shadows, and similarly by the movement of the sun.

The sun will appear greater in moving water, or when the surface is broken into waves, than it does in still water. An example is of the light reflected on the strings of the monochord.

The clouds do not display their roundnesses except in those parts which are seen by the sun: other roundnesses are imperceptible because they are in the parts in shadow.

If the sun is in the east and the clouds are in the west, the position of the eye being between the sun and the cloud, it sees the edges of the roundnesses which are the component parts of these clouds as dark, and the portions which are surrounded by these darknesses become light. And this proceeds from the fact that the edges of the rounded forms of these clouds face the sky above and around them, so that it is mirrored in them.

The cloud and the tree display no roundness in those of their parts which are in shadow.

The shadows of clouds are lighter in proportion as they are nearer to the horizon.

That part of a tree which is against a background of shadow is all of one tone, and where the trees or branches are thickest, there it is darkest, because there is less perforation by the air. But where the branches are on a background of other branches, there the luminous parts show themselves brighter and the leaves more resplendent, because of the sun which illumines them.

The density of smoke below the horizon appears white and above the horizon dark, and even though the smoke is in itself of uniform color this uniformity will seem to vary, according to the difference of the space in which it is found.

V · LIGHT AND SHADE

LIGHT is the expeller of darkness. Shadow is the suppression of light.

Primary light is that which is the cause of the lighting of shaded bodies.

And the derived lights are those parts of bodies which are illumined by the primary light.

Primary shadow is that side of a body on which the light does not fall.

Derived shadow is simply the striking of shaded rays.

Each body which creates a concourse of rays fills the surrounding air with an infinite number of its images.

A shaded and luminous concourse is that mass of rays

which emanate from a shaded and luminous body running through the air without striking.

Shaded or luminous percussion is that which impedes and cuts above itself the concourse of shaded and luminous rays.

Every object seen is surrounded by second objects, and from this it is known: in proportion as the second object is farther away than the first, so much the more does the first cover it from the eye.

Among the things of equal obscurity which are situated at a considerable and equal distance, that will appear more obscure which has its station higher up from the earth.

The edges of a derived shadow will be most distinct where it is cast nearest to the original shadow.

A shaded body will appear of less size when it is surrounded by a very luminous background, and a luminous body will show itself greater when it is set against a darker background—as is shown in the heights of buildings at night when there are flashes of lightning behind them. For it instantly appears, as the lightning flashes, that the building loses a part of its height.

And from this it comes to pass that these buildings appear larger when there is mist, or by night, than when the air is clear and illumined.

The breadth and length of shadow and of light, although through foreshortening it may appear less in quantity, will not therefore appear diminished as to quality in respect of either brightness or darkness.

All the illuminated parts of a body which see the whole circle of the luminous body will be the more dissimilar in brightness, one from another, as they are nearer to the source of the light.

Every solid body is surrounded and clothed with light and darkness.

You will get only a poor perception of the detail of a body when the part visible is all the part in shadow, or only the part that is illumined.

The length of the space which exists between the eye and the solid bodies determines how much the part that is illumined increases, and that in shadow diminishes.

The shape of a body cannot be accurately perceived when its extremities are bounded by something of the same color as itself, and the eye is between the part in shadow and that in light.

No separated shadow can reproduce upon a wall the true form of the body of which it is the shadow, unless the center of the light is equidistant from the extremities of this body.

The boundaries of the images of any color which penetrate through a narrow hole into a dark place will be always of a more powerful color than its center.

Why black painted in juxtaposition with white never seems to show itself more black than where it borders upon black, and white does not show itself more white in juxtaposition with black than with white; as is seen with the images passed through a hole or at the edge of any dark obstacle.

This comes about because the images tinge with their color the spot on which they fall, and when the different images approach the same spot they make a blend of their colors, and this blend participates more in one color than in another is the one color is present in greater quantity than the other.

And the colors are more intense and more sharply defined at their edges than in any other part.

Those who have experience use in all intricate things, such as trees, meadows, hair, beards and fur, four stages of clearness in order to reproduce the same color; that is, first a dark foundation, second a blur which has something of the shape of the part, third a clearer and more defined part, fourth the lights more in high parts for movements of the figure [?]; it seems to me, however, that these varieties are infinite in the case of a continuous quantity, which is in itself divisible to infinity, and thus I prove it:

[*Two diagrams*]

Let *a g* be a continuous quantity and *d* the light that illumines it. I refer now to the fourth, which says that that part of the illuminated body will be more luminous which is nearer to the source of its illumination; *g* therefore is darker than *c* in proportion as the line *d g* is longer than the line *d c*. And from the conclusion that such grades of brightness, or if you so prefer of darkness, are not four only, but may be conceived of as infinite, because *c d* is a continuous quantity, and every continuous quantity is divisible to infinity, therefore the variety in the length of the lines that extend from the luminous to the illuminated body is infinite; and the proportion of the lights corresponds to the lengths of the lines between them, which extend from the center of the luminous body to the part of the object which is illuminated by it.

If you look at the sun or other luminous object and then shut your eyes, you will see it again in the same form within your eye for a long space of time; this is a sign that the images enter within it.

With reference to the light that penetrates the vent holes, it may be doubted whether it reconstitutes with the dilatation of its rays as much breadth of impression beyond the vent hole as the width of the body which is the cause of the rays. And in addition to this, whether this dilatation has a power equal to that of the luminous body. As regards the first doubt, the reply is that the dilatation made by the rays after their intersection re-creates as much breadth beyond the vent hole as in front of the vent hole, there being as much space from the luminous body to the vent hole as from the vent hole to the impress of its rays; this is proved by the straightness of the luminous rays, from which it follows that there is the same proportion between their breadth and between the distances at which they intersect.

But power does not proceed in the same proportion; as is proved where it is stated: just such proportion exists between the heat and the radiance in the different luminous rays as between their distances from their source. It is proved therefore that the luminous ray loses in heat and radiance in proportion as it is more remote from its luminous body. It is true, however, that the composite shadows, being derived and starting from the edges of these vent holes, break this rule by means of their intersections; and this is treated of fully in the second book concerning shadow.

Having, as I think, sufficiently treated of the natures and different characteristics of primary and derived shadows, and the manner of their incidence, it seems to me that the time has now come to explain the different results upon the various surfaces which are touched by these shadows.

It seems to me that the shadows are of supreme importance in perspective, seeing that without them opaque and solid bodies will be indistinct, both as to what lies within their boundaries and also as to their boundaries themselves, unless these are seen against a background differing in color from that of the substance. And consequently, in the first proposition I treat of shadows, and say in this connection that every opaque body is surrounded and has its surface clothed with shadows and lights; and to this I devote the first book. Moreover, these shadows are in themselves of varying degrees of darkness, because they have been abandoned by a varying quantity of luminous rays; and these I call primary shadows, because they are the first shadows and so form a covering to the bodies to which they attach themselves; and to this I shall devote the second book. From these primary shadows there issue certain dark rays, which are diffused throughout the air and vary in intensity according to the varieties of the primary shadows from which they are derived; and consequently I call these shadows derived shadows, because they have their origin in other shadows; and of this I will make the third book. Moreover, these derived shadows in striking upon anything create as many different effects as are the different places where they strike; and of this I will make the fourth book. And since where the derived shadow strikes, it is always surrounded by the striking of the luminous rays, it leaps back with these in a reflex stream towards its source and meets the primary shadow, and mingles with and becomes changed into it, altering thereby somewhat of its nature; and to this I will devote the fifth book. In addition to this I will make the sixth book to contain an investigation of the many different varieties of the rebound of the reflected rays, which will modify the primary shadow by as many different colors as there are different points from whence these luminous reflected rays proceed. Further, I will make the seventh division treat of the various distances that may exist between the point of striking of each reflected ray and the point from whence it proceeds, and of the various different shades of color which it acquires in striking against opaque bodies.

How natural figures when they have intense light on one side seem to be in the deepest shadow on the opposite side.

How men show a small variation from light to shadow when the atmosphere is overcast or the sun is on the point of setting.

For what reason objects as they recede from the eye are perceived poorly and seem to lose clearness of outline, and in the far distance appear blue.

Why things when painted seem greater than they are.

That light is brightest which has the greatest angle.

That shadow is darkest which is produced at a most acute angle.

Primary and derived shadow are deeper when they are caused by the light of the candle than by that of the atmosphere.

If you wish to measure a height by the shadow of the sun, take a stick which may be one braccio, set it up and wait until the sun makes it cast a shadow of two braccia. Then measure immediately the shadow of the tower, and if this is one hundred braccia the tower will be fifty; and this is a good rule.

Among bodies equal in size and distance, that which shines the more brightly seems to the eye nearer and larger.

If you cause the rays of the sun to pass through a small hole in the shape of a star, you will see beautiful effects of perspective in the percussion caused by the passage of the sun.

The forms of shadows are three: for if the substance which casts the shadow is equal in size to the light, the shadow is like a column which has no end; if the substance is greater than the light, its shadow is like a pyramid which grows larger as it recedes and of which the length has no end; but if the substance is smaller than the light, the shadow resembles a pyramid and comes to an end, as is seen in the eclipses of the moon.

If many luminous bodies are seen in a distant landscape, although they may be separated one from another, they will appear united and joined together.

Of things equal in respect of size, brightness, background and length, that which has the smoothest surface will seem largest.

If many shaded bodies, so near to each other as to be almost touching, are seen against a luminous background at a great distance, they will seem separated by a great space.

Among shadows of equal quality, that nearest the eye will appear least dark.

The surface of every opaque body shares in the color of surrounding objects.

Shadow is the diminution of light. Darkness is the exclusion of light.

Shadow is divided into two parts, of which the first is called primary shadow and the second derived shadow.

Primary shadow always serves as a basis for derived shadow.

The boundaries of derived shadows are straight lines.

The darkness of the derived shadow diminishes in proportion as it is farther removed from primary shadow.

That shadow will show itself darker which is surrounded by more dazzling brightness, and it will be less evident when it is produced on a darker ground.

Particular light has as a result that it gives better relief to shaded bodies than does universal light; as may be shown by the comparison of the part of a landscape lit by the sun and that shaded by a cloud which is lit merely by the universal light of the air.

The ray of the sun, after having passed through the bubbles of the surface of the water, sends to the bottom of the water an image of this bubble which bears the form of a cross. I have not yet investigated the cause, but I judge it to be a result of other small bubbles which are clustered together round the larger bubble.

The shadows of plants are never black, for where the atmosphere penetrates there cannot be utter darkness.

When drawing any object, remember in comparing the potency of the lights of its illuminated portions, that the eye is often deceived into thinking one brighter than it really is. The reason springs from our comparing them with the parts which border on them, for if there are two parts of unequal degrees of brightness, and the less bright borders on a dark part while the brighter is set against a light background, such as the sky or some similar bright surface, then that which is less bright, or I should say less radiant, will appear more radiant, and what was more radiant will seem darker.

When the sun is in the east and the eye is above the center of a city, the eye will see the southern part of this city with its roofs half in shadow and half in light, and the same towards the north; but those in the east will be entirely in shadow, and those in the west entirely in light.

Take careful note of the situation of your figures, for you will have the light and shade different if the object is in a dark place with a particular light, and if it is in a bright place with the direct light of the sun and different also if it is in a dark place with the diffused light of evening or in dull weather, and if it is in the diffused light of the atmosphere lit by the sun.

The image of the sun will show itself brighter in the small waves than in the large ones. This happens because the reflections or images of the sun occur more frequently in the small waves than in the large ones, and the more numerous brightnesses give a greater light than the lesser number.

The waves which intersect after the manner of the scales of a fir cone reflect the image of the sun with the greatest splendor; and this occurs because there are as many images as there are ridges of the waves seen by the sun, and the shadows which intervene between these waves are small and not very dark; and the radiance of so many reflections is blended together in the image which proceeds from them to the eye, in such a way that these shadows are imperceptible.

VI · PERSPECTIVE

SANDRO! you do not say why these second things seem lower than the third.[1]

The eye between two parallel lines will never see them at so great a distance that they meet in a point.

[1] Fragment probably of a discussion with Botticelli concerning the law of diminishing perspective.

All the cases of perspective are expressed by means of the five mathematical terms, to wit: point, line, angle, surface and body. Of these the point is unique of its kind, and this point has neither height nor breadth, nor length nor depth, wherefore we conclude that it is indivisible and does not occupy space. A line is of three kinds, namely straight, curved and bent, and it has neither breadth, height nor depth, consequently it is indivisible except in its length; its ends are two points.

An angle is the ending of two lines in a point, and they are of three kinds, namely right angles, acute angles and obtuse angles.

Surface is the name given to that which is the boundary of bodies, and it is without depth, and in such depth as it has it is indivisible as is the line or point, being divided only in respect of length or breadth. There are as many different kinds of surfaces as there are bodies that create them.

Body is that which has height, breadth, length and depth, and in all these attributes it is divisible. These bodies are of infinite and varied forms. The visible bodies are of two kinds only, of which the first is without shape or any distinct or definite extremities, and these though present are imperceptible and consequently their color is difficult to determine. The second kind of visible bodies is that of which the surface defines and distinguishes the shape.

The first kind, which is without surface, is that of those bodies which are thin or rather liquid, and which readily melt into and mingle with other thin bodies, as mud with water, mist or smoke with air, or the element of air with fire, and other similar things, the extremities of which are mingled with the bodies near to them, whence by this intermingling their boundaries become confused and imperceptible, for which reason they find themselves without surface, because they enter into each other's bodies, and consequently such bodies are said to be without surface.

The second kind is divided into two other kinds, namely transparent and opaque. The transparent is that which shows its whole self along the whole of its side, and nothing is hidden behind it, as is the case with glass, crystal, water and the like. The second division of bodies of which the surface reveals and defines the shape is called opaque.

Thus it behooves us to treat of at some length, seeing that out of it are derived an infinite number of cases.

The air is full of an infinite number of images of the things which are distributed through it, and all of these are represented in all, all in one, and all in each. Consequently it so happens that if two mirrors be placed so as to be exactly facing each other, the first will be reflected in the second and the second in the first. Now the first being reflected in the second carries to it its own image together with all the images which are represented in it, among these being the image of the second mirror; and so they continue from image to image on to infinity, in such a way that each mirror has an infinite number of mirrors within it, each smaller than the last, and one inside another.

By this example, therefore, it is clearly proved that each thing transmits the image of [itself] to all those places where the thing itself is visible, and so conversely this object is able to receive into itself all the images of the things which are in front of it.

Consequently the eye transmits its own image through the air to all the objects which are in front of it, and receives them into itself, that is, on its surface, whence the understanding takes them and considers them, and such as it finds pleasing, these it commits to the memory.

So I hold that the invisible powers of the images in the eyes may project themselves forth to the object as do the images of the object to the eye.

An instance of how the images of all things are spread

through the air may be seen in a number of mirrors placed in a circle, and they will then reflect each other for an infinite number of times, for as the image of one reaches another it rebounds back to its source, and then becoming less rebounds yet again to the object, and then returns, and so continues for an infinite number of times.

If at night you place a light between two flat mirrors which are a cubit's space apart, you will see in each of these mirrors an infinite number of lights, one smaller than another, in succession.

If at night you place a light between the walls of a [room], every part of these walls will become tinged by the images of this light, and all those parts which are exposed to the light will likewise be directly lit by it; that is, when there is no obstacle between them to interrupt the transmission of the images.

This same example is even more apparent in the transmission of solar rays, which all [pass] through all objects, and consequently into each minutest part of each object, and each ray of itself conveys to its object the image of its source.

That each body alone of itself fills the whole surrounding air with its images, and that this same air is [able] at the same time to receive into itself the images of the countless other bodies which are within it, is clearly shown by these instances; and each body is seen in its entirety throughout the whole of the said atmosphere, and each in each minutest part of the same, and all throughout the whole of it and all in each minutest part; each in all, and all in every part.

The true knowledge of the form of an object becomes gradually lost in proportion as distance decreases its size.

Among the various studies of natural processes, that of light gives most pleasure to those who contemplate it; and among the noteworthy characteristics of mathematical science, the certainty of its demonstrations is what operates most powerfully to elevate the minds of its investigators.

Perspective therefore is to be preferred to all the formularies and systems of the schoolmen, for in its province the complex beam of light is made to show the stages of its development, wherein is found the glory not only of mathematical but also of physical science, adorned as it is with the flowers of both. And whereas its propositions have been expanded with much circumlocution I will epitomize them with conclusive brevity, introducing, however, illustrations drawn either from nature or from mathematical science according to the nature of the subject, and sometimes deducing the results from the causes and at other times the causes from the results; adding also to my conclusions some which are not contained in these, but which nevertheless are to be inferred from them; even as the Lord who is the Light of all things shall vouchsafe to reveal to me, who seek to interpret this light—and consequently I will divide the present work into three parts.

If you wish to represent a figure in the corner of a dwelling which shall appear to have been made in a level place, get someone to strip naked, and with the light of a candle make their shadow fall as you wish in the said corner, and draw the outline of it with charcoal; but your sight will wish to be in the spot exactly through a hole placed where the light passed, and again the light of the window after its work will wish to come by the said line, so that the walls joined together in the corner will not be any darker on account of the shadow, the one than the other.

That the light has not any difference from the eye as regards losing the thing which is behind the first object is due to this reason: you know that in swiftness of movement and in concourse of straight lines the visual ray and the ray of light resemble each other. As an example: suppose you hold a coin near to the eye, that space which exists between the coin and the boundary of the position will be more capable of expansion, in proportion as the part of the boundary of the position which is not visible to the eye is the greater, and the nearer the coin is brought to the eye the more the boundary of the position will be filled up.

The same process may be seen with light, for as you bring the said coin nearer or remove it farther from this light you will see the shadow on the opposite wall growing larger or failing, and if you wish an example let it be in this form: have many bodies of different things placed in a large room, then take in your hand a long pole with a piece of charcoal at the point and mark with that on the ground and along the walls all the outlines of the things as they appear against the boundaries of the wall.

Then at the same distance and height place a light, and you will see the shadows of the said bodies covering as much of the wall as the part that found itself enclosed within the marks made by the charcoal placed at the point of the pole.

Of things of equal size situated at an equal distance from the eye, that will appear the larger which is whiter in color.

Equal things equally distant from the eye will be judged by the eye to be of equal size.

Equal things through being at different distances from the eye come to appear of unequal size.

Unequal things by reason of their different distances from the eye may appear equal.

Many things of great bulk lose their visibility in the far distance by reason of their color, and many small things in the far distance retain their visibility by reason of the said color.

An object of a color similar to that of the air retains its

visibility at a moderate distance, and an object that is paler than the air retains it in the far distance, and an object which is darker than the air ceases to be visible at a short distance.

But of these three kinds of objects, that will be visible at the greatest distance of which the color presents the strongest contrast to itself.

An object placed between the eye and an object of dazzling whiteness loses half its size.

If you place a candle between two tall mirrors shaped like curved roofing tiles in the manner here shown [*drawing*], you will see everything that offers resistance melted in this candle with the help of these mirrors.

Perspective is nothing else than the seeing of an object behind a sheet of glass, smooth and quite transparent, on the surface of which all the things may be marked that are behind this glass; these things approach the point of the eye in pyramids, and these pyramids are cut by the said glass.

Citation of the things that I ask to have admitted in the proofs of this my perspective: I ask that it may be permitted me to affirm that every ray which passes through air of uniform density proceeds in a direct line from its cause to its object or the place at which it strikes.

A second object as far removed from the first as the first is from the eye will appear half the size of the first, although they are of the same size.

A small object near at hand and a large one at a distance, when seen between equal angles will appear the same size.

I ask how far away the eye can see a nonluminous body, as for instance a mountain. It will see it to advantage if the sun is behind it, and it will seem at a greater or less distance away according to the sun's place in the sky.

Perspective is a rational demonstration whereby experience confirms how all things transmit their images to the eye by pyramidal lines. By pyramidal lines I mean those which start from the extremities of the surface of bodies, and by gradually converging from a distance arrive at the same point; the said point being, as I shall show, in this particular case located in the eye, which is the universal judge of all objects. I call a point that which cannot be divided up into any parts; and as this point which is situated in the eye is indivisible, no body can be seen by the eye which is not greater than this point, and this being the case it is necessary that the lines which extend from the object to the point should be pyramidal. And if anyone should wish to prove that the faculty of sight does not belong to this point, but rather to that black spot which is seen in the center of the pupil, one might reply to him that a small object never could diminish at any distance, as for example a grain of millet or panic seed or other similar thing, and that this thing which was greater than the said point could never be entirely seen.

As soon as the air is illuminated it is filled with an infinite number of images, caused by the various substances and colors collected together within it, and of these images the eye is the target and the magnet.

If you should ask how you can demonstrate these points to me from experience, I should tell you, as regards the vanishing point which moves with you, to notice as you go along by lands ploughed in straight furrows, the ends of

which start from the path where you are walking, you will
see that continually each pair of furrows seem to approach
each other and to join at their ends.

As regards the point that comes to the eye, it may be comprehended with greater ease; for if you look in the eye of
anyone you will see your own image there; consequently if
you suppose two lines to start from your ears and proceed
to the ears of the image which you see of yourself in the
eye of the other person, you will clearly recognize that these
lines contract so much that when they have continued only
a little way beyond your image as mirrored in the said eye
they will touch one another in a point.

If you wish to represent a thing near, which should
produce the effect of natural things, it is impossible for your
perspective not to appear false, by reason of all the illusory
appearances and errors in proportion of which the existence
may be assumed in a mediocre work, unless whoever is
looking at this perspective finds himself surveying it from
the exact distance, elevation, angle of vision or point at which
you were situated to make this perspective. Therefore it
would be necessary to make a window of the size of your
face or in truth a hole through which you would look at the
said work. And if you should do this, then without any doubt
your work will produce the effect of nature if the light and
shade are correctly rendered, and you will hardly be able to
convince yourself that these things are painted. Otherwise do
not trouble yourself about representing anything, unless you
take your viewpoint at a distance of at least twenty times the
maximum width and height of the thing that you represent;
and this will satisfy every beholder who places himself in
front of the work at any angle whatever.

If you wish to see a proof of this quickly, take a piece of
a staff like a small column eight times as high as its width

without plinth or capital, then measure off on a flat wall forty equal spaces which are in conformity with the spaces; they will make between them forty columns similar to your small column. Then let there be set up in front of the middle of these spaces, at a distance of four braccia from the wall, a thin band of iron, in the center of which there is a small round hole of the size of a large pearl; place a light beside this hole so as to touch it, then go and place your column above each mark of the wall and draw the outline of the shadow, then shade it and observe it through the hole in the iron.

There are three divisions of perspective as employed in painting. Of these the first relates to the diminution in the volume of opaque bodies; the second treats of the diminution and disappearance of the outlines of these opaque bodies; the third is their diminution and loss of color when at a great distance.

Among opaque bodies of equal magnitude, the diminution apparent in their size will vary according to their distance from the eye which sees them; but it will be in inverse proportion, for at the greater distance the opaque body appears less, and at a less distance this body will appear greater, and on this is founded linear perspective. And show secondly how every object at a great distance loses first that portion of itself which is the thinnest. Thus with a horse, it would lose the legs sooner than the head because the legs are thinner than the head, and it would lose the neck before the trunk for the same reason.

If two similar and equal things be placed one behind the other at a given distance, the difference in their size will appear greater in proportion as they are nearer to the eye

which sees them. And conversely there will appear less difference in size between them as they are farther removed from
the eye.

This is proved by means of the proportions that they have
between their distances, for if there are two bodies with as
great a distance from the eye to the first as from the first to
the second this proportion is called double; because if the
first is one braccio distant from the eye and the second is at
a distance of two braccia, the second space is double the first,
and for this reason the first body will show itself double the
second. And if you remove the first to a distance of a
hundred braccia and the second to a hundred and one
braccia, you will find that the first is greater than the second
by the extent to which a hundred is less than a hundred and
one, and this conversely.

The same thing also is proved by the fourth of this, which
says: in the case of equal things there is the same proportion
of size to size as that of distance to distance from the eye
that sees them.

Perspective as it concerns painting is divided into three
chief parts, of which the first treats of the diminution in the
size of bodies at different distances. The second is that which
treats of the diminution in the color of these bodies, the
third of the gradual loss of distinctness of the forms and
outlines of these bodies at various distances.

Perspective employs in distances two opposite pyramids,
one of which has its apex in the eye and its base as far away
as the horizon. The other has the base towards the eye and
the apex on the horizon. But the first is concerned with the
universe, embracing all the mass of the objects that pass
before the eye, as though a vast landscape were seen through
a small hole, the number of the objects seen through such
a hole being so much the greater in proportion as the objects

are more remote from the eye; and thus the base is formed on the horizon and the apex in the eye, as I have said above.

The second pyramid has to do with a peculiarity of landscape, in showing itself so much smaller in proportion as it recedes farther from the eye; and this second instance of perspective springs from the first.

The eye cannot comprehend a luminous angle when close to itself.

The shadows or reflections of things seen in moving water, that is to say with tiny waves, will always be greater than the object outside the water which causes them.

The eye cannot judge where an object high up ought to descend.

No surface will reveal itself exactly if the eye which sees it is not equally distant from its extremities.

An object of uniform thickness and color seen against a background of various colors will appear not to be of uniform thickness.

And if an object of uniform thickness and of various colors is seen against a background of uniform color, the object will seem of a varying thickness.

And in proportion as the colors of the background, or of the object seen against the background, have more variety, the more will their thickness seem to vary, although the objects seen against the background may be of equal thickness.

A dark object seen against a light background will seem smaller than it is.

A light object will appear greater in size when it is seen against a background that is darker in color.

If the eye be in the middle of a course with two horses running to their goal along parallel tracks, it will seem to it that they are running to meet one another.

This that has been stated occurs because the images of the horses which impress themselves upon the eye are moving towards the center of the surface of the pupil of the eye.

In the morning the mist is thicker up above than in the lower parts because the sun draws it upwards; so with high buildings the summit will be invisible although it is at the same distance as the base. And this is why the sky seems darker up above and towards the horizon, and does not approximate to blue but is all the color of smoke and dust.

The atmosphere when impregnated with mist is altogether devoid of blueness and merely seems to be the color of the clouds, which turn white when it is fine weather. And the more you turn to the west the darker you will find it to be, and the brighter and clearer towards the east. And the verdure of the countryside will assume a bluish hue in the half-mist but will turn black when the mist is thicker.

Buildings which face the west only show their illuminated side, the rest the mist hides.

When the sun rises and drives away the mists, and the hills begin to grow distinct on the side from which the mists are departing, they become blue and seem to put forth smoke in the direction of the mists that are flying away, and the buildings reveal their lights and shadows; and where the mist is less dense they show only their lights, and where it is more dense nothing at all. Then it is that the movement of the mist causes it to pass horizontally and so its edges are scarcely perceptible against the blue of the atmosphere, and against the ground it will seem almost like dust rising.

In proportion as the atmosphere is more dense the buildings in a city and the trees in landscapes will seem more infrequent, for only the most prominent and the largest will be visible.

And the mountains will seem few in number, for only those will be seen which are farthest apart from each other, since at such distances the increases in the density create a brightness so pervading that the darkness of the hills is divided, and quite disappears towards their summits. In the small adjacent hills it cannot find such foothold, and therefore they are less visible and least of all at their bases.

Darkness steeps everything with its hue, and the more an object is divided from darkness the more it shows its true and natural color.

VII · ARTISTS' MATERIALS

SINCE walnuts are covered with a certain thin skin which derives its nature from the husk, unless you peel this off when you are making the oil this husk will tinge the oil, and when you use it in your work the husk becomes separated from the oil and comes to the surface of the picture, and this is what causes it to change.

[*To make red on glass for flesh color*]

Take rubies of Rocca Nera or garnets and mix with *lattimo*[1]; also Armenian bole is good in part.

Sap of spurge and milk of the fig tree as a dissolvent.

You will make good ochre if you employ the same method that one uses to make white lead.

[*Varnish*]

Take cypress [oil] and distill it, and have a large jug and put the distilled essence in it with so much water as to make

---

[1] *Lattimo,* a substance which has the color of milk, used by glaziers.

it the color of amber, and cover it over well so that it does not evaporate; and when it has dissolved add in this jug of the said essence so that it shall be as liquid as you desire. And you must know that the amber is the latex of the cypress tree.

And since varnish is the gum of juniper, if you distill the juniper the said varnish can be dissolved in this essence in the manner spoken of above.

Tap a juniper tree and water its roots, and mix the latex that exudes with oil of walnut and you will have perfect varnish made with varnish, and this same you will make from the cypress, and you will then have varnish of the color of amber, beautiful and famous for its quality. Make it in May or April.

[*To make points for coloring in secco*]

Temper with a little wax and it will not flake. And this wax should be dissolved with water, so that after the white lead has been mixed this water having been distilled may pass away in steam and the wax only remain, and you will make good points. But know that it is necessary for you to grind the colors with a warm stone.

Make oil from seed of mustard, and if you wish to make it more easily mix the seed after grinding it with oil of linseed, and put it all under a press.

[*For stamping medals*]

Paste [is made] of emery mixed with spirits of wine, or iron filings with vinegar, or ashes of walnut leaves, or ashes of straw rubbed very fine.

The diamond is crushed [by being] wrapped up in lead and beaten with a hammer, the lead being several times spread out and folded up again, and it is kept wrapped up in paper so that the powder may not be scattered. Then melt the lead, and the powder rises to the surface of the lead when it has melted, and it is afterwards rubbed between two plates of steel so that it becomes a very fine powder; afterwards wash it with aqua fortis and the black coating of the iron will be dissolved and will leave the powder clean.

Lumps of emery can be broken up by placing them in a cloth folded many times and hitting it on the side with a hammer; and by this means it goes into flakes bit by bit and is then easily crushed; and if you place it on the anvil you will never break it on account of its size.

The grinder of enamels ought to practice in this way upon plates of tempered steel with a steel press, and then place it in aqua fortis which dissolves all the steel that is eaten away and mingled with this enamel and makes it black, with result that the enamel remains purified and clean.

If you grind it upon porphyry this porphyry is consumed and becomes mingled with the enamel and spoils it, and aqua fortis will never free it from the porphyry because it cannot dissolve it.

If you wish to make a beautiful blue, dissolve with tartar the enamel you have made and then take off the salt.

Brass vitrified makes a fine red.

VIII · NOTES FOR THE LAST SUPPER

[*Christ*]
Count Giovanni, of the household of the cardinal of Mortaro.

Giovannina, face of fantasy; lives at Santa Caterina at the hospital.

Alessandro Carissimo of Parmo for the hand of Christ.

Christofano da Castiglione lives at the Pietà, he has a fine head.

One who was drinking and left the cup in its place and turned his head towards the speaker.

Another twists the fingers of his hands together and turns with stern brows to his companion.

Another with hands opened showing their palms raises his shoulders towards his ears and gapes in astonishment.

Another speaks in the ear of his neighbor, and he who listens turns towards him and gives him his ear, holding a knife in one hand and in the other the bread half divided by this knife.

Another as he turns holding a knife in his hand overturns with this hand a glass over the table.

Another rests his hands upon the table and stares.

Another breathes heavily with open mouth.

Another leans forward to look at the speaker and shades his eyes with his hand.

Another draws himself back behind the one who is leaning forward and watches the speaker between the wall and the one who is leaning.

III

Sculpture, Architecture and Music

I · SCULPTURE

IT is better to copy the antique than modern work.

You cannot combine utility with beauty as it appears in fortresses and men.

The trot is almost of the nature of the free horse.

Where natural vivacity is lacking it is necessary to create it fortuitously.

The sculptor cannot represent transparent or luminous things.

How the eye cannot discern the shapes of bodies within their boundaries except by means of shadows and lights; and there are many sciences which would be nothing without the science of these shadows and lights: as painting, sculpture, astronomy, a great part of perspective and the like.

As may be shown, the sculptor cannot work without the help of shadows and lights, since without these the material carved would remain all of one color; and by the ninth of this [book] it is shown that a level surface illumined by uniform light does not vary in any part the clearness or obscurity of its natural color, and this uniformity of color goes to prove the uniformity of the smoothness of its surface.

It would follow therefore that if the material carved were not clothed by shadows and lights, which are necessitated by the prominences of certain muscles and the hollows interposed between them, the sculptor would not be able uninterruptedly to see the progress of his own work, and this the work that he is carving requires, and so what he fashioned during the day would be almost as though it had been made in the darkness of the night.

If you wish to make a figure of marble make first one of clay, and after you have finished it and let it dry, set it in a case, which should be sufficiently large that—after the figure has been taken out—it can hold the block of marble wherein you purpose to lay bare a figure resembling that in clay. Then after you have placed the clay figure inside this case make pegs so that they fit exactly into holes in the case, and drive them in at each hole until each white peg touches the figure at a different spot; stain black such parts of the pegs as project out of the case, and make a distinguishing mark for each peg and for its hole, so that you may fit them together at your ease. Then take the clay model out of the case and place the block of marble in it, and take away from the marble sufficient for all the pegs to be hidden in the holes up to their marks, and in order to be able to do this better, make the case so that the whole of it can be lifted up and the bottom may still remain under the marble; and by this means you will be able to use the cutting tools with great readiness.

[*Of the blow of sculptors—with diagram*]

Because the time of the blow is indivisible, like the contact caused by this blow, its operation is of such swiftness that time does not permit this blow to transfer itself to the foundations of the things struck with sufficient swiftness to prevent the blow being already dead in its upper parts, like the mason who breaks a stone in his hand with a hammer without violence or damage to the hand.

And this is why, after the iron *a b* has been struck by the blow of the hammer in its upper part *a,* this part has obeyed the nature of the blow rather than transferred it to its base *b,* so that the extremity is enlarged more than the base.

And from this it follows that sculptors work to better effect upon their marbles when they roughhew with a pointed hammer than with a chisel struck by the hammer.

[*How casts ought to be polished*]

You should make a bunch of iron wire as thick as fine string and scrub them with it with water, but keeping a tub beneath so that it may not cause mud below.

[*How to remove the rough edges of the bronze*]

You should make an iron rod which may be of the shape of a large chisel, and rub it along the edges which remain upon the casts of the guns and which are caused by the joins in the mould; but see that the rod is a good weight and let the strokes be long and sweeping.

[*To facilitate the melting*]

First alloy part of the metal in the crucible and then put it in the furnace: this being in a molten state will make a beginning in the melting of the copper.

When the copper begins to cool in the furnace proceed instantly as soon as you see this to slice it up with a stirring pole while it is in a paste, or if it has become entirely cold, cut it as you would lead with broad large chisels.

If you have to make a cast of a hundred thousand pounds, make it with five furnaces with two thousand pounds for each, or as much as three thousand pounds at most.

Cover with stucco the boss of the . . . [*ingnea?*] of plaster, and let this be made of Venus and Mercury[1] and smear this boss well over with a uniform thickness of the blade of a knife, doing it with a rule [*sagoma?*] and cover this with the body of a bell so that it may drip, and you will have again the moisture with which you formed the paste: dry the rest well and then fire it, and beat or burnish it with a good burnisher, and make it thick towards the side.

Powder the glass to a paste with borax and water, and make stucco; then drain it off so as to dry it, then varnish it with fire so that it shines well.

When you wish to cast in wax burn off the scum with a candle and the cast will come without holes.

[*To make a plaster cast for bronze*]

Take for every two cupfuls of plaster one of burnt ox-horn, and mix them together and make the cast.

Tartar burnt and powdered with plaster and used in casting causes such plaster to adhere together when it is annealed; then it is dissolved in water.

[*Mould of the horse—with sketch*]

Make the horse upon legs of iron, strong and firm in a good foundation. Then rub it with tallow and give it a good coating, letting it dry thoroughly layer by layer. And by this you will increase its thickness by the breadth of three fingers. Then fix and bind it with iron according to need. Besides this hollow out the mould, then get it to the required thickness, and then fill up the mould again by degrees and continue until it is entirely filled. Then bind it round with its irons and strap it up, and anneal it on the inner side where it has to touch the bronze.

[1] Ingnea, Venus and Mercury are written backwards in the text, i.e. they appear as aengni, erenev and oirucrem. Dr. Richter suggests that Venus and Mercury may mean 'marble' and 'lime' of which stucco is composed.

Mark upon the horse when finished all the pieces of the mould with which you wish to cover the horse, and after the clay has been laid on cut it to correspond in every piece, so that when the mould is finished you can take it off and then replace it in its first position with its catches by the countersigns.

The square block *a b* will go between the cover and the core, that is in the hollow space where the liquefied bronze is to be; and these square blocks of bronze will keep the spaces between the mould and the cover at an equal distance, and for this reason these blocks are of great importance.

The clay must be mixed with sand.

Take wax to give back and to pay for what has been used.

Dry one layer after another. Make the outer mould of plaster in order to save time in drying and the cost of wood; and with this plaster fasten the iron bands outside and inside for a thickness of two fingers; make terra cotta.

And this mould you will take a day to make; half a boat-load of plaster will serve you.

Good.

Stop it up again with paste and clay, or white of egg and brick and rubble.

Three irons which bind the mould.

If you wish to make casts rapidly and simply, make them with a box of river sand moistened with vinegar.

After having made the mould upon the horse you will make the thickness of the metal in clay.

Note in alloying how many hours are needed for each hundredweight. In casting each keep the furnace with its fire closed up. Let all the inside of the mould be saturated with linseed oil or turpentine. Then take a handful of powdered borax and hard rosin with aqua vitae and put a coat of pitch over the mould so that while underground the damp may not [injure it?].

In order to manage the large mould make a model of the small mould; make a small room in proportion.

Make the vents in the mould while it is upon the horse.

Hold the hoofs in tongs and cast them with fish glue.

Weigh the parts of the mould to find out what amount of metal it will take to fill them, and give so much to the furnace that it may supply each part with its quantity of metal; and this you will ascertain by weighing the clay of that part of the mould to which the quantity in the furnace has to correspond. And this is done so that the furnace that is for the legs fills them and does not have to supply metal for the head from the legs which would be impossible.

II · ARCHITECTURE

[*Ground-plan of castle with lake and boats on it*]
[*The palace of the prince ought to have a piazza in front*][1]

The rooms which you mean to use for dancing or to make different kinds of jumps or various movements with a crowd of people, should be on the ground floor, for I have seen them collapse and so cause the death of many. And above all see that every wall, however thin it may be, has its foundations on the ground or on well-planted arches.

Let the mezzanines of the dwellings be divided by walls made of narrow bricks, and without beams because of the risk of fire.

All the privies should have ventilation openings through the thickness of the walls, and in such a way that air may come in through the roofs.

Let the mezzanines be vaulted, and these will be so much the stronger as they are fewer in number.

---

[1] Words crossed out in MS.

Let the bands of oak be enclosed in the walls to prevent them from being damaged by fire.

Let the privies be numerous and be connected one with another, so that the smell may not spread through the rooms, and their doors should all close automatically.

[*Plans*] Kitchens. Stable. Eighty braccia wide and a hundred and twenty braccia long in ground plan. Combats by means of the boats, that is the combatants may be upon the boats. Ditch forty braccia. Road below.

At the angle *a* should be the keeper of the stable.

The largest division of the front of this palace is in two parts, that is the width of the court is half the length of the aforesaid front.

[*With plan*]

Stable for the Magnifico, for the lower part, one hundred and ten braccia long, and forty braccia wide, and it is divided into four rows for horses, and each of these rows is divided into thirty-two spaces, called intercolumnar, and each intercolumnar space has a capacity for two horses, between which is interposed a swing-bar.

This stable therefore has a capacity for a hundred and twenty-eight horses.

[*Architectural drawings: ground plans*]

He who is stationed in the buttery ought to have behind him the entrance to the kitchen, in order to be able to do his work expeditiously; and the window of the kitchen should be in the front of the buttery so that he may extract the wood.

The drawing that I have made has a larger façade behind than in front, whereas it should be the opposite.

The large room for the family away from the kitchen, so that the master of the house may not hear their clatter; and the kitchen may be convenient for washing the pewter so that it may not be seen being carried through the house.

Large room for the master. Room. Kitchen. Larder. Guard Room. Large room for the family.

Larder, logs, kitchen and hen coop [? *pollaro*] and hall, and the apartment will be or ought to be in contact for the convenience that ensues; and the garden and stable, manure and garden, in contact. The large room for the master and that for the family should have the kitchen between them, and in both the food may be served through wide and low windows, or by tables that turn on swivels.

The wife should have her own apartment and hall [*sala*] apart from that of the family, so that she may set her serving-maids to eat at another table in the same hall. She should have two other apartments as well as her own, one for the serving-maids the other for the wet nurses, and ample space for their utensils.

I wish to have one door to close the whole house.

[*A plan for laying out a water garden*]

The staircase is one braccio and three quarters wide and it is bent like a knee, and altogether it is sixteen braccia with thirty-two steps half a braccio wide and a quarter high; and the landing where the staircase turns is two braccia wide and four long, and the wall which divides one staircase from the other is half a braccio; but the breadth of the staircase will be two braccia and the passage half a braccio wider; so that this large room will come to be twenty-one braccia long and ten and half braccia wide, and so it will serve well; and let us make it eight braccia high, although it is usual to make the height tally with the width; such rooms however seem to me depressing for they are always somewhat in shadow because of their great height, and the staircases would then be too steep because they would be straight.

By means of the mill I shall be able at any time to produce a current of air; in the summer I shall make the water spring up fresh and bubbling, and flow along in the space between the tables, which will be arranged thus [*drawing*]. The channel may be half a braccio wide, and there should be vessels there with wines always of the freshest, and other water should flow through the garden, moistening the orange trees and citron trees according to their needs. These citron trees will be permanent, because their situation will be so arranged that they can easily be covered over, and the warmth which the winter season continually produces will be the means of preserving them far better than fire, for two reasons: one is that this warmth of the springs is natural and is the same as warms the roots of all the plants; the second is that the fire gives warmth to these plants in an accidental manner, because it is deprived of moisture and is neither uniform nor continuous, being warmer at the beginning than at the end, and very often it is overlooked through the carelessness of those in charge of it.

The herbage of the little brooks ought to be cut frequently so that the clearness of the water may be seen upon its shingly bed, and only those plants should be left which serve the fishes for food, such as watercress and other plants like these.

The fish should be such as will not make the water muddy, that is to say eels must not be put there nor tench, nor yet pike because they destroy the other fish.

By means of the mill you will make many water conduits through the house, and springs in various places, and a certain passage where, when anyone passes, from all sides below the water will leap up, and so it will be there ready in case anyone should wish to give a shower bath from below to the women or others who shall pass there.

Overhead we must construct a very fine net of copper

which will cover over the garden and shut in beneath it many different kinds of birds, and so you will have perpetual music together with the scents of the blossom of the citrons and the lemons.

With the help of the mill I will make unending sounds from all sorts of instruments, which will sound for so long as the mill shall continue to move.

[*The dimensions of a temple*]

You ascended by twelve flights of steps to the great temple, which is eight hundred feet in circumference and is built in the shape of an octagon. At the eight corners were eight large plinths, a braccio and a half in height and three in width and six in length at the base, with an angle in the center which served as the foundation for eight large pillars that rose to a height of twenty-four braccia above the base of the plinth, and on top of these stood eight capitals three braccia each [in length] and six wide. Above these followed architrave, frieze and cornice, four braccia and a half in height, carried on in a straight line from one pillar to another, and thus it surrounded the temple with a circuit of eight hundred braccia; between each of the pillars, as a support to this entablature, there stood ten large columns of the same height as the pillars, three braccia thick above their bases which were one braccio and a half in height.

You ascended to this temple by twelve flights of steps, the temple being upon the twelfth, built in the shape of an octagon, and above each angle rose a large pillar, and between the pillars were interposed ten columns of the same height as the pillars, which rose twenty-eight and a half braccia above the pavement. At this same height were placed architrave, frieze and cornice, which formed a circuit round the temple, eight hundred braccia in length and of uniform height. Within this circuit at the same level towards the center of the temple at a distance of twenty-four braccia rise pillars and columns, corresponding to the eight pillars of the angles and the columns placed in the façade. And they rise to the same height as those already mentioned, and above these pillars the continuous architrave goes back towards the pillars and columns first spoken of.

An inverted arch is better for making a support than an ordinary one, because the inverted arch finds a wall below it which resists its weakness, while the ordinary arch finds where it is weakest nothing but air.

An arch is nothing other than a strength caused by two weaknesses; for the arch in buildings is made up of two segments of a circle, and each of these segments being in itself very weak desires to fall, and as the one withstands the downfall of the other the two weaknesses are converted into a single strength.

When once the arch has been set up it remains in a state of equilibrium, for the one side pushes the other as much as the other pushes it; but if one of the segments of the circle weighs more than the other the stability is ended and destroyed, because the greater weight will subdue the less.

[*With architectural drawing*]

If you have your family in your house, make their habitations in such a way that at night neither they nor the strangers to whom you give lodging are in control of the egress of the house; in order that they may not be able to enter in the habitation where you live or sleep, close the exit *m,* and you will have closed the whole house.

[*With drawing of section of wall of a house*]

C is a stove which receives heat from the kitchen chimney by means of a copper flue two braccia high and one wide, and a stone is put over the place in summer in order that it may be possible to use the stove; *b* will be the place for keeping salt, and at the division *a* there will be an opening of a passage into the chimney for hanging up salted meats and such like things; and in the ceiling there will be many flues for the smoke, with different exits at the four sides of the chimney, so that if the north wind should begin to be trouble-some the smoke may find an outlet on the other side. And the smoke proceeds to spread itself through the numerous flues and to cure salted meats; tongues and sausages and things like these it brings to perfection. But see to it that when you push the small door *a* a window opposite opens, which gives light to the little room; and this will be done by means of a rod joined to the door and the window in this way.

[*Note with plan of section of town showing
    high- and low-level roads*]

The roads [marked] *m* are six braccia higher than the roads [marked] *p s,* and each road ought to be twenty braccia wide and have a fall of half a braccio from the edges to the center. And in this center at every braccio there should be an opening one braccio long and of the width of a finger, through which rain water may drain off into holes made at the level of the roads *p s.* And on each side of the extremity of the width of this road there should be an arcade six braccia broad resting on columns. And know that if anyone wishes to go through the whole place by the high-level roads, he will be able to use them for this purpose, and so also if anyone wishes to go by the low-level roads.

The high-level roads are not to be used by wagons or vehicles such as these but are solely for the convenience of the gentlefolk. All carts and loads for the service and con-venience of the common people should be confined to the low-level roads.

One house has to turn its back on another, leaving the low-level road between them. The doors *n* serve for the bringing in of provisions such as wood and wine and such-like things. The privies, the stables and such-like noisome places are emptied by underground passages, situated at a distance of three hundred braccia from one arch to the next, each passage receiving its light through the openings in the streets above. And at every arch there should be a spiral staircase; it should be round because in the corners of square ones nuisances are apt to be committed. At the first turn there should be a door of entry into the privies and public urinals, and this staircase should enable one to descend from the high-level to the low-level road.

The high-level roads begin outside the gates, and when they reach them they have attained a height of six braccia. The site should be chosen near to the sea or some large river, in order that the impurities of the city which are moved by water may be carried far away.

The earth which is dug out from the cellars ought to be raised at one side so as to construct a terrace garden at the same level as the hall; but see that between the earth of the terrace garden and the wall of the house there is an intervening space, so that damp may not spoil the principal walls.

Let the street be as wide as the universal height of the houses.

[*With diagrams*]

Let the houses be transported and arranged in order, and this can be done with ease because these houses are first made in parts upon the open places, and are then fitted together with their timbers on the spot where they are to remain.

Let fountains be made in each piazza.

Let the countryfolk dwell in parts of the new houses when the court is not there.

[With drawing]

The way in which one should construct a stable: you will first divide its width in three parts, its length does not matter; and these three divisions should be equal, each being six braccia wide and ten high. The center part should be for the use of the master of the stable, the two at the sides for the horses, each requiring for width three braccia and for length six braccia, and being half a braccio higher in front than behind.

The manger should be two braccia from the ground, the beginning of the rack three braccia, and the top of it four braccia.

To attempt however to keep my promise, namely to make the said place contrary to the usual custom clean and neat: as to the upper portion of the stable, that is, where the hay is, this part should have at its outer end a window six [? braccia] high and six wide, by which hay can easily be brought up to the loft as is shown in the machine *E;* and this should be erected in a place six braccia in breadth and as long as the stable, as is shown in *K p.* The other two parts, which have the first between them, are each divided into two parts. The two towards the hay are four braccia, and are entirely for the use and passage of the stable attendants; the other two which extend to the outside walls are two braccia, as is shown in *S R,* and these are for the purpose of giving the hay to the manger, by means of funnels narrow at the top, and broad above the mangers, so that the hay may not be stopped on the way. They should be well plastered and cleaned, as they are represented where it is marked 4 *f s.* In order that the horses may be given water, the troughs should be of stone, so made as to be able to be uncovered as are boxes by raising their lids.

When the crack in a wall is wider at the top than at the

bottom it is a clear sign that the source of the destruction of the wall lies outside the perpendicular of the crack.

Walls collapse as a result of cracks which are either vertical or slanting. Cracks which proceed vertically are caused by new walls being built in conjunction with old walls either vertically or with toothings fitted into the old walls; for as these toothings cannot offer any resistance to the insupportable weight of the wall joined on to them they must needs break and allow the new wall to settle down, in which process it will sink a braccio in every ten, or more or less according to the greater or smaller quantity of mortar used for the stones in the construction, and whether the mortar is very liquid or not. And remember always to build the walls first and then add the facing stones, because unless this is done, since the subsidence of the wall in settling will be greater than that of the outer shell, the toothings set in the sides of the wall will necessarily be broken, because the stones used for facing the walls being larger than the stones used in their construction will of necessity take a less quantity of mortar in their joints, and therefore the subsidence will be less. But this cannot happen if the facing of the wall is added after the wall has had time to dry.

A wall will always crack when it does not dry uniformly at the same time.

A wall of uniform thickness does not all become dry at the same time unless it is in contact with an equal medium; thus if a wall be so built that part of it touches a damp mound while the rest is exposed to the atmosphere, this latter part will become somewhat contracted while the damp portion will retain its original size.

For the part which becomes dried by the atmosphere draws itself together and shrinks, and the part in contact with the damp does not become dry, and the dry part readily breaks away from the damp part as this has not the coherence necessary for it to follow the movement of the part that is in process of becoming dry.

III · MUSIC

"MUSIC which is consumed in the very act of its birth."

Music has two ills, the one mortal, the other wasting; the mortal is ever allied with the instant which follows that of the music's utterance, the wasting lies in its repetition, making it seem contemptible and mean.

[*Drawing*]

Here you make a wheel with pipes that serve as clappers for a musical round called a Canon, which is sung in four parts, each singer singing the whole round. And therefore I make here a wheel with four cogs so that each cog may take the part of a singer.

With the help of the mill I will make unending sounds from all sorts of instruments, which will sound for so long as the mill shall continue to move.

IV

Anatomy

I · HUMAN ANATOMY

MAKE a discourse on the censure deserved by scholars who put obstacles in the way of those who practice anatomy and by the abbreviators of their researches.[1]

This work should commence with the conception of man, and should describe the nature of the womb, and how the child inhabits it, and in what stage it dwells there, and the manner of its quickening and feeding, and its growth, and what interval there is between one stage of growth and another, and what thing drives it forth from the body of the mother, and for what reason it sometimes emerges from the belly of its mother before the due time.

Then you should describe which are the limbs that grow more than the others after the child is born; and give the measurements of a child of one year.

Then describe the man fully grown, and the woman, and their measurements, and the nature of their complexions' color and physiognomy.

Afterwards describe how he is composed of veins, nerves, muscles and bones. This you should do at the end of the book.

Then represent in four histories four universal conditions of mankind, namely, joy, with various modes of laughing,

---

[1] There may be a veiled significance in the use of the word "abbreviatori," as the term was also applied to the secretaries at the Chancery of the Vatican. Leonardo in one of his letters complains of having been impeded in his anatomical researches as a result of information laid before the Pope.

and represent the cause of the laughter; weeping, the various ways with their cause; strife with various movements expressive of slaughterings, flights, fear, acts of ferocity, daring, homicide and all the things which connect with cases such as these.

Then make a figure to represent labor, in the act of dragging, pushing, carrying, restraining, supporting and conditions such as these.

Then describe the attitude and movement.

Then perspective through the office of the sight or the hearing. You should make mention of music and describe the other senses.

Afterwards describe the nature of the five senses.

We shall describe this mechanical structure of man by means of diagrams, of which the three first will treat of the ramification of the bones; that is, one from the front which shows the positions and shapes of the bones latitudinally; the second as seen in profile, showing the depth of the whole and of the parts and their position; the third diagram will show the bones from behind. Then we shall make three other diagrams from the same points of view with the bones sawn asunder so as to show their thickness and hollowness; three other diagrams we shall make for the bones entire, and for the nerves which spring from the nape of the neck and showing into what limbs they ramify; and three others for the bones and veins and where they ramify; then three for muscles and three for the skin and the measurements; and three for the woman to show the womb and the menstrual veins which go to the breasts.

[*Themes physiological and anatomical*]

Figure to show how catarrh is caused.

Tears.

Sneezing.

Yawning.

Trembling.

Epilepsy.

Madness.

Sleep.

Hunger.

Sensuality.

Anger when it works in the body.

Fear likewise.

Fever.

Disease.

Where poison injures.

Describe the nature of all the limbs.

Why the thunderbolt kills a man and does not wound him, and if the man blew his nose he would not die. Because it hurts the lungs.

Write what the soul is.

Of nature which of necessity makes the vital and actual instruments of suitable and necessary shapes and positions.

How necessity is the companion of nature.

Figure to show from whence comes the semen.

Whence the urine.

Whence the milk.

How nourishment proceeds to distribute itself through the veins.

Whence comes intoxication.

Whence vomiting.

Whence gravel and stone.

Whence colic.

Whence dreaming.

Whence frenzy by reason of sickness.

Why it is that by compressing the arteries a man falls asleep.

Why it is that a prick on the neck may cause a man to drop dead.

Whence come tears.

Whence the turning of the eyes when one draws the other after it.

Of sobbing.

[*How the five senses are the ministers of the soul*]

The soul apparently resides in the seat of the judgment, and the judgment apparently resides in the place where all the senses meet, which is called the common sense; and it is not all of it in the whole body as many have believed, but it is all in this part; for if it were all in the whole, and all in every part, it would not have been necessary for the instruments of the senses to come together in concourse to one particular spot; rather would it have sufficed for the eye to register its function of perception on its surface, and not to transmit the images of the things seen to the sense by way of the optic nerves, because the soul—for the reason already given—would comprehend them upon the surface of the eye.

Similarly, with the sense of hearing, it would be sufficient merely for the voice to resound in the arched recesses of the rock-like bone which is within the ear, without there being another passage from this bone to the common sense, whereby the said mouth might address itself to the common judgment.

The sense of smell also is seen to be forced of necessity to have recourse to this same judgment.

The touch passes through the perforated tendons and is transmitted to this sense; these tendons proceed to spread out with infinite ramifications into the skin which encloses the body's members and the bowels. The perforating tendons carry impulse and sensation to the subject limbs; these tendons passing between the muscles and the sinews dictate to these their movement, and these obey, and in the act of obeying they contract, for the reason that the swelling reduces their length and draws with it the nerves, which are inter-woven amid the particles of the limbs, and being spread throughout the extremities of the fingers, they transmit to the sense the impression of what they touch.

The nerves with their muscles serve the tendons even as soldiers serve their leaders, and the tendons serve the com-mon sense as the leaders their captain, and this common sense serves the soul as the captain serves his lord.

So therefore the articulation of the bones obeys the nerve, and the nerve the muscle, and the muscle the tendon, and the tendon the common sense, and the common sense is the seat of the soul, and the memory is its monitor, and its faculty of receiving impressions serves as its standard of reference.

How the sense waits on the soul, and not the soul on the sense, and how where the sense that should minister to the soul is lacking, the soul in such a life lacks conception of the function of this sense, as is seen in the case of a mute or one born blind.

How the nerves sometimes work of themselves, without the command of other agents or of the soul:

This appears clearly, for you will see how paralytics or those who are shivering or benumbed by cold move their trembling limbs, such as the head or the hands, without permission of the soul; which soul with all its powers cannot prevent these limbs from trembling. The same happens in the case of epilepsy or with severed limbs such as the tails of lizards.

[*Of spirits*]

We have just now stated that the definition of a spirit is a power united to a body, because of itself it can neither offer resistance nor take any kind of local movement; and if you say that it does in itself offer resistance, this cannot be so within the elements, because if the spirit is a quantity without a body, this quantity is what is called a vacuum, and the vacuum does not exist in nature, and granting that one were formed, it would be instantly filled up by the falling in of that element within which such a vacuum had been created. So by the definition of weight, which says that gravity is a fortuitous power created by one element being drawn or impelled towards another, it follows that any element, though without weight when in the same element, acquires weight in the element above it, which is lighter than itself; so one sees that one part of the water has neither gravity nor levity in the rest of the water, but if you draw it up into the air then it will acquire weight, and if you draw the air under the water, then the water on finding itself above this air acquires weight, which weight it cannot support of itself, and consequently its descent is inevitable, and therefore it falls into the water, at the very spot which had been left a vacuum by this water. The same thing would happen to a spirit if it were among the elements, for it would continually create a vacuum in whatsoever element it chanced to find itself; and for this reason it would be necessarily in perpetual flight towards the sky until it had passed out of these elements.

We have proved how the spirit cannot of itself exist among the elements without a body, nor yet move of itself by voluntary movement except to rise upwards. We now proceed to say that such a spirit in taking a body of air must of necessity spread itself through this air; for if it remained united, it would be separated from it and would fall, and so create a vacuum, as is said above; and therefore it is necessary, if it is to be able to remain suspended in the air, that it should spread itself over a certain quantity of air; and if it becomes mingled with the air two difficulties ensue, namely that it rarefies that quantity of air within which it is mingled, and consequently this air, becoming rarefied, flies upwards of its own accord, and will not remain among the air that is heavier than itself; and moreover, that as this ethereal essence is spread out, the parts of it become separated, and its nature becomes modified, and it thereby loses something of its former power. To these there is also added a third difficulty, and that is that this body of air assumed by the spirit is exposed to the penetrating force of the winds, which are incessantly severing and tearing in pieces the connected portions of the air, spinning them round and whirling them amid the other air; and therefore the spirit which was spread through this air would be dismembered or rent in pieces and broken, together with the rending in pieces of the air within which it was spread.

It is impossible that the spirit diffused within a quantity of air can have power to move this air; and this is shown by the former section in which it is stated that the spirit rarefies that quantity of air within which it has entered. This air consequently will rise up above the other air, and this will be a movement made by the air through its own levity, and not through the voluntary movement of the spirit; and if this air meets the wind, by the third part of this section this air will be moved by the wind and not by the spirit which is diffused within it.

Wishing to prove whether or no the spirit can speak, it is necessary first to define what voice is, and how it is produced, and we may define it as follows: the voice is movement of air in friction against a compact body, or of the compact body in friction against the air, which is the same thing; and this friction of compact with tenuous substance condenses the latter, and so makes it capable of resisting;

moreover, the tenuous substance, when in swift motion, and a similar substance moving slowly, condense each other at their contact, and make a noise or tremendous uproar; and the sound or murmur caused by one tenuous substance moving through another at a moderate pace [is] like a great flame which creates noises within the air; and the loudest uproar made by one tenuous substance with another is when the one swiftly moving penetrates the other which is unmovable, as for instance the flame of fire issuing from the cloud, which strikes the air and so produces thunderbolts.

We may say, therefore, that the spirit cannot produce a voice without movement of air, and there is no air within it, and it cannot expel air from itself if it has it not, and if it wishes to move that within which it is diffused it becomes necessary that the spirit should multiply itself, and this it cannot do unless it has quantity. And by the fourth part it is said that no tenuous body can move unless it has a fixed spot from whence to take its motion, and especially in the case of an element moving in its own element, which does not move of itself, except by uniform evaporation at the center of the thing evaporated, as happens with a sponge squeezed in the hand, which is held under water, since the water flows away from it in every direction with equal movement through the openings that come between the fingers of the hand within which it is squeezed.

Of whether the spirit has articulate voice—and whether the spirit can be heard—and what hearing is, and seeing; and how the wave of the voice passes through the air—and how the images of objects pass to the eye.

The common sense is that which judges the things given to it by the other senses.

And these senses are moved by the objects, and these objects send their images to the five senses by which they are transferred to the organ of perception [*imprensiva*] and

from this to the common sense; and from thence being judged
they are transmitted to the memory, in which according to
their potency they are retained more or less distinctly.

[*The five senses are these: seeing, hearing, touch, taste, smell*]
The ancient speculators have concluded that that faculty
of judgment which is given to man is caused by an instrument with which the other five are connected by means of
the organ of perception [*imprensiva*], and to this instrument
they have applied the name common sense, and they say
that this sense is in the center. And this name common
sense they use simply because it is the common judge of the
other five senses, namely seeing, hearing, touch, taste and
smell. The common sense is set in movement by means of
the organ of perception [*imprensiva*] which is situated in the
center between it and the senses. The organ of perception
acts by means of the images of the things presented to it by
the superficial instruments, that is the senses, which are
placed in the middle between the external things and the
organ of perception; and the senses act in the same way
through the medium of objects.

The images of the surrounding things are transmitted to
the senses, and the senses transmit them to the organ of
perception, and the organ of perception transmits them to
the common sense, and by it they are imprinted on the memory, and are retained there more or less distinctly according
to the importance or power of the thing given. That sense
functions most swiftly which is nearest to the organ of perception; this is the eye, the chief and leader of the others;
of this only we will treat and leave the others in order not
to lengthen out our material.

[*Description of the human body in process of dissection*]
This plan of mine of the human body will be unfolded to
you just as though you had the natural man before you. The

reason is that if you wish to know thoroughly the parts of a man after he has been dissected you must either turn him or your eye so that you are examining from different aspects, from below, from above and from the sides, turning him over and studying the origin of each limb; and in such a way the natural anatomy has satisfied your desire for knowledge. But you must understand that such knowledge as this will not continue to satisfy you, on account of the very great confusion which must arise from the mixture of membranes with veins, arteries, nerves, tendons, muscles, bones and the blood, which of itself tinges every part with the same color, the veins through which this blood is discharged not being perceptible by reason of their minuteness. The completeness of the membranes is broken during the process of investigation of the parts which they enclose, and the fact that their transparent substance is stained with blood prevents the proper identification of the parts which these cover on account of the similarity of the bloodstained color, for you cannot attain to any knowledge of the one without confusing and destroying the other.

Therefore it becomes necessary to have several dissections: you will need three in order to have a complete knowledge of the veins and arteries, destroying all the rest with very great care; and three others for a knowledge of the membranes [*panniculi*], three for the tendons, muscles and ligaments, three for the bones and cartilages, three for the anatomy of the bones, for these have to be sawn through in order to show which are hollow and which not, which are full of marrow, which spongy, which thick from the outside inwards, and which thin. And some have great thinness at one part and thickness at another, and at another part they are hollow or filled with bone or full of marrow, or spongy. Thus it may be that all these conditions will sometimes be found in the same bone and there may be another bone which has none of them. Three also must be devoted to the female body, and in this there is a great mystery by reason of the womb and its foetus.

Therefore by my plan you will become acquainted with every part and every whole by means of a demonstration of each part from three different aspects; for when you have seen any member from the front with the nerves, tendons and veins which have their origin on the opposite side, you will be shown the same member either from a side view or from behind, just as though you had the very member in your hand and went on turning it from side to side until you had a full understanding of all that you desire to know.

And so in like manner there will be placed before you three or four demonstrations of each member under different aspects, so that you will retain a true and complete knowledge of all that you wish to learn concerning the figure of man.

Therefore there shall be revealed to you here in fifteen entire figures the cosmography of the *minor mondo* [the microcosmos or lesser world] in the same order as was used by Ptolemy before me in his Cosmography. And therefore I shall divide the members as he divided the whole, into provinces, and then I shall define the functions of the parts in every direction, placing before your eyes the perception of the whole figure and capacity of man in so far as it has local movement by means of its parts.

And would that it might please our Creator that I were able to reveal the nature of man and his customs even as I describe his figure!

And I would remind you that the dissection of the nerves will not reveal to you the position of their ramification nor into which muscles they ramify by means of bodies dissected either in flowing water or in limewater; because, although the origin of their derivation may be discerned without the use of the water as well as with it, their ramifications tend to unite in flowing water all in one bunch, just as does flax or hemp carded for spinning, so that it becomes impossible to find out again into which muscles the nerves are distributed or with which or how many ramifications they enter the said muscles.

[*Dissection of the human hand*]

When you begin the hand from within, first separate all the bones a little from each other so that you may be able quickly to recognize the true shape of each bone from the palmar side of the hand, and also the real number and position of each, and have some sawn through down the center of their thickness, that is lengthwise, so as to show which is empty and which full. And having done this, place the bones together at their true contacts and represent the whole hand from within wide open. Then set down the complete figures of the first ligaments of the bones. The next demonstration should be of the muscles which bind together the wrist and the remainder of the hand. The fifth shall represent the tendons which move the first joints of the fingers. The sixth, the tendons which move the second joints of the fingers. The seventh, those which move the third joints of these fingers. The eighth shall represent the nerves which give them the sense of touch. The ninth, the veins and the arteries. The tenth shall show the whole hand complete with its skin and its measurements, and measurements should also be made of the bones. And whatever you do for this side of the hand, you should do the same for the other three sides, that is from the palmar or under side, from the dorsal side and from the sides of the extensor and the flexor muscles.

And thus in the chapter on the hand you will make forty demonstrations; and you should do the same with each member.

And in this way you will attain complete knowledge.

You should afterwards make a discourse concerning the hands of each of the animals, in order to show in what way they vary, as with the bear, in which the ligaments of the tendons of the toes are joined above the neck of the foot.

The body of anything whatsoever that receives nourishment continually dies and is continually renewed. For the nourishment cannot enter except in those places where the preceding nourishment is exhausted, and if it is exhausted it no longer has life. Unless therefore you supply nourishment equivalent to that which has departed, the life fails in its vigor; and if you deprive it of this nourishment, the life is completely destroyed. But if you supply it with just so much as is destroyed day by day, then it renews its life just as much as it is consumed; like the light of this candle formed by the nourishment given to it by the fat of this candle, which light is also continually renewed by swiftest succor from beneath, in proportion as the upper part is consumed and dies, and in dying becomes changed from radiant light to murky smoke. And this death extends for so long as the smoke continues; and the period of duration of the smoke is the same as that of what feeds it, and in an instant the whole light dies and is entirely regenerated by the movement of that which nourishes it; and its life receives from it also its ebb and flow, as the flicker of its point serves to show us. The same process also comes to pass in the bodies of the animals by means of the beating of the heart, whereby there is produced a wave of blood in all the veins, and these are continually either enlarging or contracting, because the expansion occurs when they receive the excessive quantity of blood, and the contraction is due to the departure of the excess of blood they have received; and this the beating of the pulse teaches us, when we touch the aforesaid veins with the fingers in any part whatsoever of the living body.

But to return to our purpose, I say that the flesh of the animals is made anew by the blood which is continually produced by that which nourishes them, and that this flesh is destroyed and returns by the mesaraic arteries and passes into the intestines, where it putrifies in a foul and fetid death, as they show us in their deposits and steam, like the smoke and fire which were given as a comparison.

[*Of the muscles which move the tongue*]

No member needs so great a number of muscles as the tongue—twenty-four of these being already known, apart from the others which I have discovered; and of all the members which are moved by voluntary action this exceeds all the rest in the number of its movements.

And if you shall say that this is rather the function of the eye, which receives all the infinite varieties of form and color of the objects set before it, and of the smell, with its infinite mixture of odors, and of the ear with its sounds, we may reply that the tongue also perceives an infinite number of flavors both simple and compounded; but this is not to our purpose, for our intention is to treat only of the particular movement of each member.

Consider carefully how by the movement of the tongue, with the help of the lips and teeth, the pronunciation of all the names of things is known to us; and how, by means of this instrument, the simple and compound words of a language arrive at our ears; and how these, if there were a name for all the effects of nature, would approach infinity in number, together with all the countless things which are in action and in the power of nature; and these would not be expressed in one language only, but in a great number of languages, and these also would tend to infinite variety, because they vary continually from century to century, and in one country and another, through the intermingling of the peoples, who by wars or other mischances are continually becoming mixed with each other; and these same languages are liable to pass into oblivion, and they are mortal like all the rest of created things; and if we grant that our world is everlasting we shall then say that these languages have been, and still must be, of infinite variety, through the infinite number of centuries which constitute infinite time.

Nor is this true in the case of any other sense; for these are concerned only with such things as nature is continually producing, and she does not change the ordinary kinds of things which she creates in the same way that from time to time the things which have been created by man are changed; and indeed, man is nature's chiefest instrument, because nature is concerned only with the production of elementary things, but man from these elementary things produces an infinite number of compounds, although he has no power to create any natural thing except another like himself, that is, his children. And of this the old alchemists will serve as my witnesses, who have never either by chance or deliberate experiment succeeded in creating the smallest thing which can be created by nature; and indeed, this generation deserves unmeasured praises for the serviceableness of the things which they have invented for the use of men, and would deserve them even more if they had not been the inventors of noxious things like poisons and other similar things which destroy the life or the intellect; but they are not exempt from blame in that by much study and experiment they are seeking to create, not, indeed, the meanest of nature's products, but the most excellent, namely gold, which is begotten of the sun—inasmuch as it has more resemblance to it than to anything else that is—and no created thing is more enduring than this gold. It is immune from destruction by fire, which has power over all the rest of created things, reducing them to ashes, glass or smoke. If, however, insensate avarice should drive you into such error, why do you not go to the mines where nature produces this gold, and there become her disciple? She will completely cure you of your folly by showing you that nothing which you employ in your furnace will be numbered among the things which she employs in order to produce this gold. For there is there no quicksilver, no sulphur of any kind, no fire nor other heat than that of nature giving life to our world; and she will show you the veins of the gold spreading through the stone—the blue lapis lazuli, whose color is unaffected by the power of the fire.

And consider carefully this ramification of the gold, and you will see that the extremities of it are continually expanding in slow movement, transmuting into gold whatever they come in contact with; and note that therein is a living organism which it is not within your power to produce.

The muscles which move the lips of the mouth are more numerous in man than in any other animal; and this order is a necessity for him on account of the many undertakings in which these lips are continually employing themselves, as in the four letters of the alphabet *b f m p,* in whistling, laughing, weeping and other actions like these. Also in the strange contortions used by clowns when they imitate faces.

The muscles which tighten the mouth, thus lessening its length, are in the lips themselves; or rather these lips are the actual muscles which close themselves. It is true that the muscle alters the position of the lip below the other muscles which are joined to it, of which one pair are those that distend it and move it to laughter; and that which contracts it is the same muscle of which the lower lip is formed, which restrains it by drawing in its extremities towards its center; and the same process goes on at the same time with the upper lip; and there are other muscles which bring the lips to a point and others that flatten them, others are those which cause them to curl back, others that straighten them, others which twist them all awry, and others that bring them back to their first position; and so always there are found as many muscles as correspond to the various attitudes of these lips and as many others as serve to reverse these attitudes; and these it is my purpose here to describe and represent in full, proving these movements by means of my mathematical principles.

[*Pronunciation of vowels*]

The membrane interposed between the passage that the air makes, in part through the nose and in part through the mouth, is the only one which man uses in order to pronounce the letter *a,* that is, the membrane *a n;* and though the tongue and lips may do what they can, this will never prevent the air which streams out from the trachea from forming the sound *a* while in this concavity *a n.* Moreover, *u* is formed at the same place, with the help of the lips, which tighten and thrust themselves out a little; and the more these lips thrust themselves out the better do they pronounce the letter *u.* True it is that the epiglottis *m* rises somewhat towards the palate.

And if it were not for its doing thus, the *u* would be changed into *o,* and this *o* . . .

And whether when *a o u* are pronounced distinctly and rapidly, it is necessary that in pronouncing them continuously without any interval of time, the opening of the lips should go on continually contracting, that is that in pronouncing *a* they should be wide apart, closer together in pronouncing *o* and much closer still in pronouncing *u.*

It is proved how all the vowels are pronounced with the back part of the movable palate which covers the epiglottis; and moreover, such pronunciation comes from the position of the lips, by means of which a passage is formed for the air as it streams out carrying with it the created sound of the voice, which even when the lips are closed streams out through the nostrils, but when issuing through such passage will never become a demonstrator of any of these letters.

From such an experiment one may conclude with certainty that the trachea does not create any sound of vowel, but that its office only extends to the creation of the aforesaid voice, and especially in *a o u*.

[*The muscles of the tongue*]

The tongue is found to have twenty-four muscles, which correspond to the six muscles of which the mass of the tongue which moves in the mouth is composed.

The present task is to discover in what way these twenty-four muscles are divided or apportioned in the service of the tongue in its necessary movements, which are many and varied; and in addition to this it has to be seen in what manner the nerves descend to it from the base of the brain, and in what manner they pass into this tongue, distributing themselves and breaking into ramifications. And it must further be noted how and in what manner the said twenty-four muscles convert themselves into six in the formation they make in the tongue. And furthermore you should show whence these muscles have their origin, that is in the vertebrae of the neck at the contact with the esophagus, and some in the maxilla on the inside, and some on the trachea on the outside and laterally. And similarly how the veins nourish them and how the arteries give them the spiritus (and how the nerves give them sensation).

Moreover, you shall describe and represent in what way the procedure of varying and modulating and articulating the voice in singing is a simple function of the rings of the trachea moved by the reversive nerves, and in this case no part of the tongue is used.

And this is proved by what I have proved before, that the pipes of the organ do not become deeper or sharper through the change of the fistula (that is that place in which the voice is produced), in making it wider or narrower; but only through the change of the pipe to be wide or narrow or long or short, as is seen in the expansion or compression of the winding trumpet; and also in the pipe which is of fixed width or length, the sound varies according as the wind is let into it with greater or less impetus. And this amount of variation is not found in the case of objects struck with a greater or less blow, as is perceived when bells are struck by very small or very large clappers; and the same thing occurs with pieces of artillery similar in width but differing in length, but in this case the shorter piece makes a louder and deeper noise than the longer one. And I do not go into this at greater length because it is fully treated in the book about harmonical instruments. And for this reason I will resume my discourse concerning the functions of the tongue where I left it.

The tongue works in the pronunciation and articulation of the syllables which are the constituent parts of all words. The tongue is also employed during the necessary revolutions of the food in the process of mastication and in the cleansing therefrom of the inside of the mouth together with the teeth. Its principal movements are seven—namely, stretching out, drawing together and drawing back, thickening, shortening, spreading out and pointing; and of these seven movements three are composite because one cannot be created without another also being created joined to it of necessity; and this is the case with the first and the second, that is, with stretching out and drawing together, for you cannot stretch out a substance which is capable of being expanded without its contracting and straightening itself on all its sides. And a similar result occurs in the third and fourth movements, which are contrary to the two first, that is, in the thickening and shortening.

After these come the fifth and sixth movements, which together form its third movement made up of three movements, namely, spreading out, pointing and shortening.

Although human subtlety makes a variety of inventions answering by different means to the same end, it will never devise an invention more beautiful, more simple or more direct than does nature, because in her inventions nothing is lacking, and nothing is superfluous; and she needs no countervailing weights when she creates limbs fitted for movement in the bodies of the animals, but puts within them the soul of the body which forms them, that is, the soul of the mother which first constructs within the womb the shape of the man, and in due time awakens the soul that is to be its inhabitant. For this at first remains asleep, in the guardianship of the soul of the mother, who nourishes and gives it life through the umbilical vein, with all its spiritual members; and so it will continue for such time as the said umbilical cord is joined to it by the secundines and the cotyledons by which the child is attached to the mother. And this is the reason why any wish or intense desire or fright experienced by the mother, or any other mental suffering, is felt more powerfully by the child than by the mother, for there are many cases in which the child loses its life from it.

This discourse does not properly belong here, but is necessary in treating of the structure of animated bodies; and the rest of the definition of the soul I leave to the wisdom of the friars, those fathers of the people who by inspiration know all mysteries. I speak not against the sacred books, for they are supreme truth.

[The human voice]

The extension and restriction of the trachea, together with its dilation and contraction, are the cause of the variation of the voice of the animals from high to deep and from deep to high; and as regards the second of these actions, as the shortening of the trachea is not sufficient when the voice is raised, it dilates itself somewhat towards the top part, which does not receive any degree of sound but produces a raising of the voice of this remnant of the shortened pipe. But of this we shall make an experiment in the anatomy of the animals, by pumping air into their lungs and compressing them, and so narrowing and dilating the fistula which produces their voice.

A man at three years will have reached the half of his height.

A woman of the same size as a man will weigh less than he does.

A dead woman lies face downwards in water, a man the opposite way.

The gait of man is always after the manner of the universal gait of four-footed animals. Seeing that as these move their feet crosswise, as a horse does when it trots, so a man moves his four limbs crosswise; that is, if he thrusts the right foot forward as he walks, he thrusts the left arm forward with it, and so it always continues.

The man who goes up stairs puts as much of his weight in front and at the side of the upper foot as he puts as counterpoise to the lower leg, and in consequence the work of the lower leg extends only to moving itself.

The first thing that the man does when he ascends by steps is to free the leg which he wishes to raise from the heaviness of the bust which is resting upon this leg, and in addition to this he loads the opposite leg with all the rest of the bulk of the man together with the other leg; then he raises the leg and places the foot upon the step where he wishes to raise it; having done this he gives back to the higher foot all the rest of the weight of the bust and of the leg, leans his hand upon his thigh, thrusts the head forward and makes a movement towards the point of the higher foot, raising swiftly the heel of the lower foot, and with the impetus thus acquired raises himself up, and at the same time extends the arm which he was resting upon the knee, and this extension of the arm pushes the bust and head upwards and thus straightens the curve of the back.

[*Action of muscles in breathing*]

These muscles have a voluntary and an involuntary movement, seeing that they are those which open and shut the lung. When they open they suspend their function, which is to contract, for the ribs which at first were drawn up and compressed by the contracting of these muscles then remain in liberty and resume their natural distance as the breast expands. And since there is no vacuum in nature, the lung which touches the ribs from within must necessarily follow their expansion; and the lung, therefore, opening like a pair of bellows, draws in the air in order to fill the space so formed.

[*Muscles of hand, leg and foot. Dated note*: 1510]

When you represent the hand, represent with it the arm as far as the elbow, and with this arm the sinews and muscles which come to move this arm away from the elbow. And do the same in the demonstration of the foot.

All the muscles that start at the shoulders, the shoulder blades and the chest serve for the movement of the arm from the shoulder to the elbow. And all the muscles that start between the shoulder and the elbow serve for the movement of the arm between the elbow and the hand. And all the muscles that start between the elbow and the hand serve for the movement of the hand. And all the muscles that start in the neck serve for the movement of the head and shoulders.

When you represent the muscles of the thigh, represent with these the bones of the leg, so that one may know where these muscles attach themselves to these bones of the legs.

You will then make the leg with its muscles attached to the bones of the leg, and make the bones bare. And you will follow the same plan for all the sinews.

The muscles of the feet serve for the movement of its toes, and in this movement they are aided by the tendons which spring from the muscles of the leg.

Which are the muscles of the leg which serve merely for the simple movement of the foot, and which are those of this leg that serve merely for the simple movement of the toes of this foot? And remember, in clothing the bones of the leg with its muscles, to represent first the muscles that move the feet, which you will join to the feet.

Represent here the foot of the bear, the monkey and other animals, in so far as they differ from the foot of man; and put also the feet of some of the birds.

The muscles of the leg from the knee to the joint of the foot are as many in number as the tendons attaching to the upper part of the toes of the feet; and it is the same below, adding to them those which move the feet upwards and downwards and to and fro, and of these those which raise the toes are five. And there are as many muscles of the feet above and below as the number of the fingers doubled. But as I have not yet finished this discourse I will leave it for the present, and this winter of the year 1510 I look to finish all this anatomy.

The tendons that lower the toes of the feet start from the muscles which have their beginning in the sole of this foot; but the tendons that raise these toes do not have their beginning in the outer part of the thigh as some have written, but they start in the upper part of the foot, called the instep. And if you desire to make certain of this, clasp the thigh with your hands a little above the knee and raise the toes of the feet, and you will perceive that the flesh of your thigh will not have any movement in it, in its tendons or muscles; so it is quite true.

[*Representation of the hand*]

The first demonstration of the hand will be made of the bones alone. The second, of the ligaments and various chains of nerves that bind them together. The third will be of the muscles which spring up upon these bones. The fourth will be of the first tendons which rest upon these muscles and go to supply movement to the tips of the fingers. The fifth will be that which shows the second set of tendons which move all the fingers and end at the last but one of the bones of the fingers. The sixth will be that which will show the nerves that impart sensation to the fingers of the hand. The seventh will be that which will show the veins and arteries that nourish and invigorate the fingers. The eighth and last will be the hand clothed with skin, and this will be shown for an old man, a young man and a child, and for each there should be given the measurement of the length, thickness and breadth of each of its parts.

[*Precepts for the topographical demonstration of the upper limb and especially the hand*]

Make first the bones, that is to say the arms, and show the motive power proceeding from the shoulder to the elbow in all its lines; then from the elbow to the arm; then from the arm to the hand; and from the hand to the fingers.

And in the arm you should show the movements of the fingers as they open; and these in their demonstration you will place alone.

In the second demonstration you will clothe these muscles with the second movements of the fingers; and you will do this stage by stage so as not to cause confusion; but first place upon the bones those muscles which join themselves with these bones without other confusion of other muscles, and with these you will place the nerves and veins which feed them, having first made the tree of the veins and nerves above the simple bones.

[*Representation of the limbs in action*]

After the demonstration of all the parts of the limbs of man and of the other animals, you will represent the proper method of action of these limbs, that is, in rising after lying down, in moving, running and jumping in various attitudes, in lifting and carrying heavy weights, in throwing things to a distance and in swimming; and in every act you will show which limbs and which muscles are the causes of the said actions, and especially in the play of the arms.

It often occurs that two muscles are joined together although they have to serve two limbs; and this has been done so that if one muscle were incapacitated by some injury the other muscle in part supplied the place of that which was lacking.

The substance of the spinal marrow enters for a certain distance within the origins of the nerves, and then follows the hollow nerve as far as its last ramifications; by which perforation it conveys sensation in each muscle, which muscle is composed of as many other very minute muscles as there are threads into which this muscle can be resolved; and each of the least of these muscles is wrapped up in almost imperceptible membranes into which the final ramifications of the before-mentioned nerves become changed, for these obey in order to contract the muscle as they retire, and to cause it to expand again with each demand of the sensation which passes through the vacuity of the nerve. But to return to the spinal marrow, this is wrapped in two membranes, of which only one clothes the pith-like substance of the spinal marrow, and in emerging from the hollow of vertebrae is transformed into nerve; the other clothes the nerve, together with its principal branches, and ramifies together with each branch of the nerve, and thus forms the second cover of the spinal marrow, interposing itself between the bone of the vertebrae and the first membrane of this spinal marrow.

The spinal marrow is the source of the nerves which give voluntary movement to the limbs.

The pia and the dura mater clothe all the nerves which start from the spinal marrow.

Before you open the heart, inflate the ventricles of the heart commencing from the artery of the aorta; and then tie them up and consider their size. Afterwards do the same with the right ventricle or the right *orecchio;* and by so doing you will see its shape and its purpose, for it was created in order to expand and contract and so cause the blood to revolve as it passes through its cells, which are full of tortuous passages divided by rounded walls without any angles, in order that the motion of the blood, not finding any angular obstructions, may have an easier revolution in its eddying course. And thus it comes to warm itself with so much more heat in proportion as the movement of the heart is the more rapid. So it sometimes attains to such great heat that the heart is suffocated; and I have already seen one case where it was burst as a man was fleeing before his enemies, and he poured out perspiration mingled with blood through all the pores of his skin; and this heat forms the spiritus vitales. And thus heat gives life to all things; as one sees the heat of the hen or of the turkey hen giving life and growth to the chickens, and as the sun in returning causes all the fruits to blossom and burgeon.

[*Division of surface of heart by vessels. Peeling the flesh
off to find certain vessels*]

The heart has its surface divided into three parts by three
veins which descend from its base, of which veins two termi-
nate the extremities of the right ventricle and have two
arteries in contact below them. As regards the third vein
I have not yet seen whether it has an artery with it, and
consequently I am about to remove some of the flesh of the
surface in order to satisfy myself. But the surface space of
the heart enclosed within its arteries occupies half the surface circle of the thickness of the heart and forms the outer
wall of the right ventricle.

[*Heating by churning, and by the action going on in
the heart*]

Observe whether when butter is being made the milk as it
revolves becomes heated; and by such means you will be
able to prove the efficacy of the ventricles of the heart, which
receive and expel the blood from their cavities and other
passages, as made only in order to heat and refine the blood
and make it more suitable for penetrating the wall through
which it passes from the right to the left ventricle, where by
means of the thickness of its wall, that is, of that of the left
ventricle, it conserves the heat which this blood brings to it.

Here is a doubt as to the pannicles which close up the
blood in the antechamber of the heart, that is, in the base of
the aorta, whether nature could have dispensed with them
or no, since one may clearly see how the three walls or hinges
where such pannicular valves of the heart are established, are
those which by their swelling shut this blood out from the
heart when the heart reopens on the side below these valves.

And this last closing nature carries out in order that the
great force which the heart employs in this left ventricle, as
it reopens in order to draw into itself the blood that perco-

lates through the narrow interstices of the wall that divides it from the left ventricle, should not for the restoring of the vacuum be obliged to draw with it the most delicate pannicles of the said valves of the heart.

The revolution of the blood in the antechamber of the heart, the base of the aorta, serves two effects, of which the first is that this revolution multiplied in many aspects causes great friction in itself, and this heats and lightens the blood and increases and vivifies the spiritus vitales, which always maintain themselves in warmth and moisture. The second effect of this revolution of the blood is to close up again the opened gates of the heart with a complete system of fastening with its first reflex movement.

As many as are the times which this gate expels the blood, so many are those which the heart beats, and for this reason those who are feverish become inflamed.

Between the cords [*cordae*] and threads of the muscles of the right ventricle, there are interwoven a quantity of minute threads of the nature and shape of the minute muscles which form the worm in the brain and of those which weave the rete mirabile; and these wind themselves round the most minute and imperceptible nerves and weave themselves with them. And these muscles are in themselves very capable of expansion and contraction, and they are situated within the fury of the rush of the blood, which passes in and out among the minute cords of the muscles before they are converted into the membranes [*panniculi*] of the valves.

[*Of the reason of the heat of the blood*]

The heat is produced by the movement of the heart, and this manifests itself because in proportion as the heart moves more swiftly the heat increases more, as is shown by the pulse of those suffering from fever, which is moved by the beating of the heart.

[*Drawing of heart—below*]

Marvelous instrument, invented by the supreme Master.

[*Mechanism of action of the heart*]

Heart open in the receptacle of the spirits, that is, in the artery; and in M it takes or rather gives the blood to the artery, and by the mouth, B, it refreshes itself with air from the lung, and by C it fills the auricles of the heart S.

N Firm muscle is drawn back, and it is the first cause of the movement of the heart, and as it draws back it thickens, and as it thickens it becomes shortened and draws back with it all the lower and upper muscles, and closes the door M, and shortens the space that intervenes between the base and the apex of the heart, and consequently comes to empty it and to draw to itself the fresh air.

Of the heart. This moves of itself and does not stop unless forever.

As many times as the pulse beats, so many times does the heart expand and contract.

Of the lung. This is moved by others, that is, by the first mover, which is the heart, which as it becomes constricted draws the veins after it, with which it restores the heated air to the lung, and opens it; and this lung can close either voluntarily or through oblivion, that is, forgetfulness through excess of thought. And by this means the heart draws back from it the heated air which it has given it; but this act cannot be repeated many times, for if it were not for its refreshing itself with new air it would come to suffocate.

Testicles, witnesses of coition. These contain in themselves ardor, that is, they are augmenters of the animosity and ferocity of the animals; and experience shows us this clearly in the castrated animals, of which one sees the bull, the boar, the ram and the cock, very fierce animals, which after having been deprived of these testicles become very cowardly; so one sees a ram drive before it a herd of wethers, and a cock put to flight a number of capons; and I have seen the same thing happen with a hen, and also with oxen.

Della verga. This confers with the human intelligence and sometimes has intelligence of itself, and although the will of the man desires to stimulate it, it remains obstinate and takes its own course, and moving sometimes of itself without license or thought by the man, whether he be sleeping or waking, it does what it desires; and often the man is asleep and it is awake, and many times the man is awake and it is asleep, many times the man wishes it to practice and it does not wish it; many times it wishes it and the man forbids it. It seems therefore that this creature has often a life and intelligence separate from the man, and it would appear that the man is in the wrong in being ashamed to give it a name or to exhibit it, seeking rather constantly to cover and conceal what he ought to adorn and display with ceremony as a ministrant.

[Organs which function independently of the will]

No inferior instrument in the human body is able to suspend its action voluntarily except the lung. You see the heart which carries on its function of itself, and the stomach also and the other intestines which are joined to it, and similarly the liver, the gall, the spleen, the testicles, the kidneys and the bladder.

[*Relation of nerves with muscles*]

There are as many ramifications of the nerves as there are muscles, and there cannot be either more or less, because these muscles can only be contracted or distended by reason of these nerves from which the muscles receive their sensation. And there are as many tendons that move the limbs as there are muscles.

[*Process for examination of the brain and the basilar nerves*]

You will take to pieces the substance of the brain as far as the confines of the dura mater which is interposed between this basilar bone and the substance of the brain; then note all the places where this dura mater penetrates the basilar bone, with the nerves clothed by it together with the pia mater; and this knowledge you will acquire with certainty whenever by diligence you raise this pia mater little by little, commencing with the extremities, and noting from one part to another the position of the before-mentioned perforations, commencing first at the right or left side, representing this in its entirety; and then you will follow the opposite part, which will give you knowledge as to whether the foregoing is well situated or no, and it will also bring you to an understanding of whether the right part is similar to the left part; and if you find that it varies you will look again in the other anatomies whether this variation is universal in all men and women.

Note where the exterior parts meet the interior parts.

I have found in the decrepit how the vein which proceeds from the door of the liver crosses behind the stomach and ramifies in the spleen. At this ramification, the veins in the young are straight and full of blood, and in the old they are twisted, flattened, wrinkled and emptied of blood.

And thus the liver, which in youth is usually of a deep color and of uniform consistency, in the old is pale, without any redness of blood, and the veins stay empty amidst the substance of this liver, which substance may be likened for its thin texture to bran steeped in a small quantity of water, and so readily disintegrating on being washed, leaving the veins that ramify within it freed from all the substance of the liver.

All the air that enters into the trachea is of equal quantity in all the degrees which are produced by its ramification; after the manner of the branches born during the seasonal growth of the plants, which every year, if the various thicknesses of all the branches that have been produced are reckoned together, equal the thickness of the stem of their plant.

But the trachea contracts itself in the larynx in order to condense the air, which seems a thing of life as it comes from the lung to create the various kinds of voices, and also to press and dilate the different passages and ventricles of the brain, because if the trachea were thus dilated at its upper end as it is in the throat, the air would not be able to condense itself and perform the duties and benefits which are necessary to life and to man, that is, in speaking, singing and the like. And the wind which is suddenly expelled from the lung as it produces the deep sighs proceeds by the help of the wall of the abdomen, which squeezes the intestines, and they raise the diaphragm that presses on the lung.

The function of the nerves is to convey sensation; they are the team of drivers of the soul, for they have their origin from its seat, and command the muscles so that they move the members at the consent of the will of this soul.

The muscles, the ministers of the nerves, draw to themselves the sinews, which are joined to these members in a similar manner.

The tendons are mechanical instruments which have no sensation of themselves but carry out as much work as is entrusted to them.

The membranes [*panniculi*] are joined to the flesh, being interposed between the flesh and the nerve, and most frequently they are joined to the cartilage.

The ligaments are joined to the tendons and are of the nature of membranes [*panniculi*] which bind together the joints of the bones and are converted into cartilage, and they are as many in number at every joint as are the tendons which move the joint and as are the tendons opposite to these which come to the same joint; and these ligaments join and mingle together, helping strengthening and connecting one with another.

The cartilage is a hard substance, like, let us say, hardened tendon or softened bone, and its position is always between the bone and the tendon because it partakes of both substances, and it is flexible and unbreakable, the flexibility acting in it like a spring.

Pellicles are certain muscular parts which are made up of flesh, tendons and nerves, the union of these forming a composition which is capable of being extended in any direction; flesh is a mixture made up of muscles, tendon, nerve, blood and artery.

Bone is a hardness, inflexible, adapted for resistance, and is without sensation and terminates in the cartilages which form its extremities; and its marrow is composed of sponge, blood and soft fat coated over with a very thin tissue. The sponge-like substance is a mixture of bone, fat 'and blood.

The membranes [*panniculi*] are of three kinds, that is,

made up of tendons, made up of nerves and made up of nerves and tendons; and the mixed membrane is woven of tendon, nerve, muscle, vein and artery.

The membranes that are between the tendons and the cartilages are so formed as to unite tendon with cartilage in a large and continuous joint, so that it may not break through excess of force; and when the muscle itself thickens, it does not draw to itself the tendon or any member, but the muscle is drawn by the tendon towards the membrane and the cartilage, as happens with the muscles inside the ventricles of the heart when they shut their openings. But the muscles of the other members are drawn towards the bone where they are joined, and draw their tendon behind them together with the member that is joined to this tendon.

The tears come from the heart and not from the brain.

The child does not draw breath in the body of its mother because it lies in water, and whoever breathes in water is immediately drowned.

Whether the child while within the body of its mother is able to weep or to produce any sort of voice or no.

The answer is no; because it does not breathe, neither is there any kind of respiration; and where there is no respiration there is no voice.

[*With drawing of child in womb*]

In the case of this child the heart does not beat and it does not breathe because it lies continually in water. And if it were to breathe it would be drowned, and breathing is not necessary to it because it receives life and is nourished from the life and food of the mother. And this food nourishes such a creature in just the same way as it does the other parts of the mother, namely the hands, feet and other members. And a single soul governs these two bodies, and the desires and fears and pains are common to this creature as to all the other animated members. And from this it proceeds that a thing desired by the mother is often found engraved upon those parts of the child which the mother keeps in herself at the time of such desire; and a sudden fear kills both mother and child.

We conclude therefore that a single soul governs the bodies and nourishes the two [bodies].

As one mind governs two bodies, inasmuch as the desires, the fears and the pains of the mother are one with the pains, that is the bodily pains and desires of the child which is in the body of the mother, in like manner the nourishment of the food serves for the child and it is nourished from the same cause as the other members of the mother, and its vital powers are derived from the air which is the common living principle of the human race and of other living things.

The black races in Ethiopia are not the product of the sun; for if black gets black with child in Scythia, the offspring is black; but if a black gets a white woman with child the offspring is gray. And this shows that the seed of the mother has power in the embryo equally with that of the father.

Make two air holes in the horns of the great ventricles and insert melted wax by means of a syringe, making a hole in the ventricle of the memoria, and through this hole fill the three ventricles of the brain; and afterwards, when the wax has set, take away the brain and you will see the shape of the three ventricles exactly. But first insert thin tubes in the air holes in order that the air which is in these ventricles may

escape and so make room for the wax which enters into the
ventricles.[2]

Which muscles are those which stand out as people grow
old or in the young when they become lean?

Which are the places in the human limbs in which the
flesh never increases on account of any degree of fatness or
diminishes on account of any degree of leanness?

What has to be sought for in this question will be found
in all the surface joints of the bones, as shoulder, elbow,
joints of the hands and fingers, hips, knees, ankles and toes
and similar things which shall be spoken of in their places.

The greatest thickness which the limbs acquire is in
the part of the muscle that is farthest away from their
attachments.

The flesh never increases upon the parts of the bones
which are near the surface of the limbs.

In the movement of man, nature has placed all those parts
in front which on being struck cause a man to feel pain;
so it is felt in the shins of the legs and in the forehead and
nose. And this is ordained for man's preservation, for if
such power of enduring suffering were not inherent in these
limbs the numerous blows received on them would be the
cause of their destruction.

Nature has provided man with functional muscles which
draw the sinews, and these are able to move the limbs
according to the will and desire of the common sense, after
the manner of officials stationed by their lord through various
provinces and cities to represent and carry out his will in
these places. And the official who on more than one occasion

[2] According to the editors of the Quaderni, Leonardo was the first to
make casts of the cerebral ventricles, and several hundred years elapsed
before the idea occurred to any other anatomist.

has carried out the commission given him by the mouth of his lord will then himself at the same time do something which does not proceed from the will of the lord. So one often sees with the fingers how after having with utmost docility learned things upon an instrument as they are commanded by the judgment, they will afterwards play them without the judgment accompanying. The muscles which move the legs do not, however, perform their functions without the man becoming conscious of it.

Saw a head in two between the eyebrows in order to find out by anatomy the cause of the equal movement of the eyes, and this practically confirms that the cause is the intersection of the optic nerves, that is of the equality of movement, if the eyes observe minutely the parts of a circle, and there are nerves which cause them to make a circular movement.

O speculator, concerning this machine of ours let it not distress you that you impart knowledge of it through another's death, but rejoice that our Creator has ordained the intellect to such excellence of perception.

And you who say that it is better to look at an anatomical demonstration than to see these drawings, you would be right, if it were possible to observe all the details shown in these drawings in a single figure, in which, with all your ability, you will not see nor acquire a knowledge of more than some few veins; while, in order to obtain an exact and complete knowledge of these, I have dissected more than ten human bodies, destroying all the various members, and removing even the very smallest particles of the flesh which surrounded these veins, without causing any effusion of blood other than the imperceptible bleeding of the capillary veins. And as one single body did not suffice for so long a time, it was necessary to proceed by stages with so many bodies as would render my knowledge complete; and this I repeated twice over in order to discover the differences.

But though possessed of an interest in the subject you may perhaps be deterred by natural repugnance, or if this does not restrain you, then perhaps by the fear of passing the night hours in the company of these corpses, quartered and flayed and horrible to behold; and if this does not deter you then perhaps you may lack the skill in drawing essential for such representation; and even if you possess this skill it may not be combined with a knowledge of perspective; while, if it is so combined, you may not be versed in the methods of geometrical demonstration or the method of estimating the forces and strength of muscles; or perhaps you may be found wanting in patience so that you will not be diligent.

Concerning which things, whether or no they have all been found in me, the hundred and twenty books which I have composed will give their verdict "yes" or "no." In these I have not been hindered either by avarice or negligence but only by want of time. Farewell.

[*Note at side of drawing of heart showing the arrangement of the veins and arteries*]

With what words, O writer, can you with a like perfection describe the whole arrangement of that of which the design is here?

II · COMPARATIVE ANATOMY

Ask the wife of Biagino Crivelli how the capon rears and hatches the eggs of the hen when he is in the mating season.

They hatch the chickens by making use of the ovens by the fireplace.

Those eggs which are of a round form will be cockerels and the long-shaped ones pullets.

Their chickens are given into the charge of a capon which has been plucked on the under part of its body, and then stung with a nettle and placed in a hamper. When the chickens nestle underneath it it feels itself soothed by the sensation of warmth and takes pleasure in it, and after this it leads them about and fights for them, jumping up into the air to meet the kite in fierce conflict.

[Organs of the senses in man as compared with those of other animals]

I have found in the constitution of the human body that, as among all the constitutions of the animals, it is of more obtuse and blunt sensibilities, so it is formed of an instrument less ingenious and of parts less capable of receiving the power of the senses. I have seen in the leonine species how the sense of smell forming part of the substance of the brain descends in a very large receptacle to meet the sense of smell which enters among a great number of cartilaginous cells with many passages that go to meet the above-mentioned brain.

The eyes of the leonine species have a great part of their head as their receptacle, so that the optic nerves may be in immediate conjunction with the brain. With man the contrary is seen to be the case, for the cavities of the eyes occupy but a small part of the head, and the optic nerves are thin and long and weak; consequently, as one sees, they work feebly by day and worse by night, whereas the aforesaid animals see better by night than by day; and the sign of this is seen in the fact that they hunt their prey by night and sleep by day, as do also the nocturnal birds.

The light or pupil of the human eye as it expands or contracts gains or loses the half of its size; and in the nocturnal animals its increase or decrease is more than a hundred times. This may be seen in the eye of the owl, a nocturnal bird, by bringing a lighted torch near to it, and still more by making it look at the sun, for then you will see the pupil which once occupied the whole of the eye diminished to the size of a grain of millet, and by this diminution it becomes equal to the pupil of the eye of man, and clear shining things seem the same color to it as they appear at this time to man, and as much more as the brain of this creature is less than the man's brain: from which it comes about that as the pupil increases in the nighttime a hundredfold more than that of the man, it sees a hundred times as much light as the man does, in such a way that this power of sight is not afterwards subdued by the darkness of night. And the pupil of man, which only doubles its quantity, sees only faint light, almost like the bat, which does not fly in times of too great darkness.

[*Pupil of cat*]

If the darkness of night is a hundred degrees more intense than that of evening, and the eye of man doubles the size of its pupil in darkness, this darkness is lessened by half in this eye because it has redoubled half its visible potency: there remain therefore fifty degrees of intensity of darkness. And if the eye of the owl has its pupil increased a hundred times in the aforesaid darkness, it increases its visual capacity one hundred times, so that one hundred degrees of visual capacity are acquired; and because things which are equal do not overcome one another, the bird sees in the darkness with the pupil increased a hundredfold, as in the day with the pupil diminished ninety-nine parts in the hundred.

And if you were to say that this animal does not see light by day and for this reason it remains shut up, to this I reply that the bird only shuts itself up in the day in order to free itself from the mobbing of birds which in a great multitude always surround it with a loud clamor, and frequently they would be put to death if they did not hide themselves in the grottos and caverns of the high rocks.

Of the nocturnal animals, only the lion species changes the shape of its pupil as that enlarges or lessens: for when it is at the utmost stage of diminution it is long in shape, when halfway it is oval, and when it has attained to its utmost expansion it is circular in shape.

When the eye of the bird closes with its two coverings it closes first the secondina, and this closes it from the lachrymal gland as far as the angle of the eye, and the first [covering] closes it from below upwards. And these two movements, having intersected, cover it first from the direction of the lachrymal gland, because they have already seen themselves safeguarded in front and below; and they only reserve the upper part because of the dangers from birds of prey which descend from above and behind, and they will first uncover the membrane in the direction of the angle, for if the enemy comes behind, the bird will have the opportunity of flying forward. It also has the membrane called the secondina, of such texture as to be transparent, for if it did not possess this shield it would not be able to keep its eyes open against the wind which strikes the eye in the fury of its swift flight. And its pupil expands and contracts as it beholds less or greater light, that is, radiance.

III · HUMAN PROPORTIONS

FROM the chin to the starting of the hair is a tenth part of the figure.

From the junction of the palm of the hand as far as the tip of the middle finger a tenth part.

From the chin to the top of the head an eighth part.

And from the pit of the stomach to the top of the chest is a sixth part.

And from the fork of the ribs as far as the top of the head a fourth part.

And from the chin to the nostrils is a third part of the face.

And the same from the nostrils to the eyebrows, and from the eyebrows to the starting of the hair.

And the foot is a sixth part, and the forearm to the elbow a fourth part. The breadth across the shoulders a fourth part.

There is as great a distance between the commencement of the one ear and that of the other as there is from the space between the eyebrows to the chin.

The size of the mouth in a well-proportioned face is equal to the distance between the parting of the lips and the bottom of the chin.

[*With sketches of heads*]

The cut or angle of the lower lip is midway between the bottom of the nose and the bottom of the chin.

The face in itself forms a square, of which the breadth is from one extremity of the eyes to the other, and the height is from the top of the nose to the bottom of the lower lip, and what is left over above and below this square has the height of a similar square.

The ear is precisely as long as the nose.

The slit of the mouth when seen in profile points to the angle of the jaw.

The length of the ear should equal the distance from the bottom of the nose to the top of the eyelid.

The space between the eyes is equal to the size of one eye.

In profile the ear is above the middle of the neck.

The foot from the toe to the heel goes twice into the space from the heel to the knee, that is to say where the bone of the leg is joined to that of the thigh.

The hand as far as where it unites with the bone of the arm goes four times into the space from the tip of the longest finger to the joint of the shoulder.

Every man at the third year is half his height.

The leg as far as its junction with the thigh is a quarter of the whole weight of the man.

The man draws more weight downwards than upwards, first because he gives more of his weight out of his central line, then because he passes all his foot from the central line, and thirdly because he does not slip with his feet.

The whole foot will go between the elbow and the wrist, and between the elbow and the inner angle of the arm towards the breast when the arm is folded. The foot is as long as the whole head of the man, that is, from beneath the chin to the very top of the head, as is here shown.

The foot goes three times from the tip of the long finger to the shoulder, that is, to its joint.

The nose will make two squares; that is, the breadth of the nose at the nostrils will be contained twice between the point of the nose and the beginning of the eyebrows; and similarly in profile the distance from the extreme edge of the nostril, where it unites with the cheek, to the tip of the nose, will be equal to the width of the nose in front from one nostril to the other.

If you divide into four equal parts the whole length of the nose, that is, from its tip to the insertion of the eyebrows, you will find that one of these parts extends from the top of the nostrils to the bottom of the point of the nose; and the upper part extends from the lachrymatory duct of the eye to the insertion of the eyebrows; and the two parts in the middle are equal to the length of the eye from the lachrymatory duct to its corner.

From the roots of the hair to the top of the breast *a b* is a sixth of a man's height; and this measure never varies.

It is as far from the outside part of one shoulder to another as it is from the top of the breast to the navel, and this goes four times into the distance from the sole of the foot to where the bottom of the nose begins.

The arm, from where it separates itself from the shoulder in front, goes six times into the space between the two extremities of the shoulders, and three times into a man's head, and four into the length of the foot, and three into the hand whether on the inside or the outside.

The foot from its beginning in the leg as far as the extremity of the big toe is equal to the space between the beginning of the top of the chin and the starting of the hair *a b,* and it is equal to five sixths of the face.

If anyone kneels down he will lessen his height by a fourth part.

If a man be kneeling with his hands across his breast, the navel will be at the half of his height, and so will be the points of the elbows.

The half of a man seated, that is from the seat to the crown of the head, will be from the arm below the breast and below the shoulder; this seated portion, that is from the seat to the crown of the head, will exceed the half the man's height by the breadth and length of the testicles.

A cubit is the fourth part of a man's height, and it is equal to the greatest width of the shoulders. From the one shoulder joint to the other is twice the head, and it is equal to the distance from the top of the breast to the navel. From this top to the commencement of the penis is the length of a head.

The foot is as much longer than the hand as the thickness of the arm to the wrist, that is where it is thinnest, seen in front.

Also you will find that the foot is as much longer than the hand as the space on the inner side from the joint of the little toe to the last projection of the big toe, taking the measure along the length of the foot.

The palm of the hand without the fingers goes twice into the foot without the toes.

If you hold your hand with its five fingers extended and close together, you will find that it is as wide as the maximum width of the foot, that is, where it is joined to the toes.

And if you measure from the point of the ankle on the inside to the end of the big toe, you will find that this measure is as long as the whole hand.

From the top of the joint of the foot to the top of the insertion of the toes is as far as from the commencement of the hand to the point of the thumb.

The smallest width of the hand is equal to the smallest width of the foot between its joining with the leg and the commencement of the toes.

The width of the heel at its under side is equal to the thickness of the arm where it joins the hand, and also to the leg where it is thinnest viewed in front.

The length of the longest toe from where it begins to be divided from the big toe to its extremity is the fourth part of the foot, that is, from the center of the ankle bone on the inner side to its tip; and it is equal to the width of the mouth. And the space that there is between the mouth and the chin is equal to that between the knuckles of the three middle fingers and their first joints, when the hand is extended, and equal to the [distance from] the joint of the thumb to the beginning of the nail when the hand is extended; and it is a fourth part of the hand and of the face.

The space between the inner and outer extremities of the poles of the feet, called the heels or ankles or bands of the feet, *a b,* is equal to the space between the mouth and the lachrymatory duct of the eye.

The big toe is the sixth part of the foot, measuring it in profile on the inside, where this toe springs, from the ball of the sole of the foot towards its extremity *a b;* and it is equal to the distance from the mouth to the bottom of the chin. If you are doing the foot in profile from the outside, make the little toe begin three quarters up the length of the foot, and you will find the distance that there is from the beginning of this toe to the farthest projection of the big toe.

Width across shoulders one quarter of the whole. From the joint of the shoulder to the hand, one third; from the line of the lip to below the shoulder blade is one foot.

From the top of the head to the bottom of the chin one eighth. From the commencement of the hair to the chin is one ninth of the distance there is from this commencement to the ground. The greatest width of the face is equal to the space between the mouth and the commencement of the hair, and it is one twelfth of the whole height. From the top of the ear to the top of the head is equal to the distance from the bottom of the chin to the lachrymatory duct of the eyes. And equal to the distance from the point of the chin to that of the jaw, and it is the sixteenth part of the whole. The bit of cartilage [*pincierolo*] which is within the hole of the ear towards the nose is halfway between the nape of the neck and the eyebrow.

The greatest thickness of a man from the breast to the spine goes eight times into the height and is equal to the space between the chin and the crown of the head.

The greatest width is at the shoulders and this goes four times.

The breadth of the neck in profile is equal to the space there is from the chin to the eyes, and equal to the space from the chin to the jaw, and it goes fifteen times into the whole man.

The arm bent is four heads.

The arm from the shoulder to the elbow in bending increases its length, that is, the length from the shoulder to the elbow; and this increase is similar to the thickness of the arm at the wrist when you see it in profile, and similar to the distance from the bottom of the chin to the line of the mouth. And the thickness of the two middle fingers of the hand, and the width of the mouth, and the distance from where the hair begins on the forehead to the crown of the head—these things that I have mentioned are similar to each other, but not similar to the above-named increase in the arm.

The arm from the elbow to the hand never increases when it is bent or straightened.

The arm when bent will measure twice the head from the top of the shoulder to the elbow, and two from this elbow to where the four fingers begin on the palm of the hand. The distance from where the four fingers begin to the elbow never changes through any change of the arm.

The lesser thickness of the leg as seen in front goes into the thigh three times.

The thickness of the arm at the wrist goes twelve times into the whole arm, that is, from the tips of the fingers to the shoulder joint; that is, three into the hand and nine into the arm.

The minimum thickness of the arm in profile, *m n*, goes

six times from the joint of the hand to the dimple of the elbow extended, fourteen times into the whole arm, and forty-two times into the whole man.

The maximum thickness of the arm in profile is the same as the maximum thickness of the arm in front. But the one is placed in the third of the arm from the joint to the breast, the other in the third from the joint to the hand.

A man is the same width below the arms as at the hips.

A man's width across his hips is the same as the distance from the top of the hips to the bottom of the buttocks when he is standing equally balanced on both his feet; and it is the same distance from the top of the hips to the joining of the shoulders. The waist or the part above the hips will be halfway between the joining of the shoulders and the bottom of the buttocks.

Flight

I · BIRDS

IN order to give the true science of the movement of the birds
in the air, it is necessary first to give the science of the winds,
and this we shall prove by means of the movements of the
water. This science is in itself capable of being received by
the senses: it will serve as a ladder to arrive at the perception
of flying things in the air and the wind.

Before you write about creatures which can fly, make a
book about the insensible things which descend in the air
without the wind, and another [on those] which descend with
the wind.

When two forces strike against each other, it is always
the swiftest which leaps backwards. So it is with the hand of
the swimmer when it strikes and presses upon the water and
makes his body glide away with a contrary movement; so it
is also with the wing of the bird in the air.

When the bird desires to turn to the right or left side by
beating its wings, it will beat lower with the wing on the side
on which it wishes to turn, and thus the bird will twist its
movement behind the impetus of the wing which moves most,
and make the reflex movement under the wind from the
opposite side.

When the bird desires to rise by beating its wings, it raises its shoulders and beats the tips of the wings towards itself, and comes to condense the air which is interposed between the points of the wings and the breast of the bird, and the pressure from this air raises up the bird.

The kite and the other birds which beat their wings only a little go in search of the current of the wind; and when the wind is blowing at a height, they may be seen at a great elevation, but if it is blowing low down, then they remain low.

When there is no wind stirring in the air, then the kite beats its wings more rapidly in its flight, in such a way that it rises to a height and acquires an impetus; with which impetus, dropping then very gradually, it can travel for a great distance without moving its wings.

And when it has descended it does the same over again, and so continues for many times in succession.

This method of descending without moving the wings serves it as a means of resting in the air after the fatigue of the above-mentioned beating of the wings.

All the birds which fly in spurts rise to a height by beating their wings; and during their descent they proceed to rest themselves, for while descending they do not beat their wings.

When the bird is moving to the east with the wind in the north and finds itself with its left wing above the said wind, it will be turned over, unless at the onset of this wind it puts its left wing under the wind and by some such movement throws itself towards the northeast and under the wind.

If the bird wishes to make headway against the wind, it beats its wings and moves them as oars backwards.

Unless the bird beats its wings downwards with more rapidity than there would be in its natural descent with its wings extended in the same position, its movement will be downwards. But if the movement of the wings is swifter than the aforesaid natural descent, then this movement will be upwards, with so much greater velocity in proportion as the downward stroke of the wings is more rapid.

The bird descends on that side on which the extremity of the wing is nearer to the center of its gravity.

The thrushes and other small birds are able to make headway against the course of the wind, because they fly in spurts; that is, they take a long course below the wind, by dropping in a slanting direction towards the ground, with their wings half closed, and they then open the wings and catch the wind in them with their reverse movement, and so rise to a height; and then they drop again in the same way.

When the slanting movement of the bird as it drops against the wind makes the weight of the bird more powerful than the wind that strikes it in front, the movement of this bird will become swift against this wind.

The bird which descends under the straight approach of the wind turns the wing somewhat over from the shoulder to the tip; and it does this in order to have as much leverage as possible in the more slanting movement against the wind.

The swallow has its wings quite different from those of the kite, for it is very narrow in the shoulder and long in the span of the wing. Its stroke when it flies is made up of two distinct actions, that is, the span of the wing is spread out like an oar in the direction of the tail, the shoulder towards the earth; and in this way, while the one movement impels it forward the other keeps it at its height, and the two combined carry it a stage onward wherever it pleases.

[*Of the flight of the bat and of the eagle*]

I say that if the bat weighs two ounces and measures half a braccio with wings expanded, the eagle ought according to this proportion to measure with wings expanded not less than sixty braccia, and we see by experience that its breadth is not more than three braccia. And it would seem to many who neither see nor have seen similar creatures that one of the two would not be able to fly, considering that if there exists the proper proportion between the bat's weight and the breadth of its wings, then in the case of the eagle they are not large enough; and if the eagle is properly equipped, the other has them too large and they will be inconvenient and unsuitable for its use. We see, however, both the one and the other borne with the utmost dexterity by their wings, and especially the bat, which by its swift turns and feints overcomes the rapid twists and retreats of the flies and gnats and other similar creatures.

The reason why the eagle supports itself with its small wings as the bat does with its large ones is contained in the comparison. . . .

When a single rush has the same proportion between its size and its length as a bundle of similar rushes has, it will in itself have the same strength and power of resistance as the said bundle. Therefore if the bundle has nine heads and supports nine ounces, a single one of these similar rushes of which there are nine heads will by chance support one ounce.

Place on the top of a rush a *danaro*[1] as a weight and you will see it bend down as far as the ground. Take a thousand of these rushes and tie them together stretched out, fix them at the foot and make the heads level and load them; you will perceive that whereas by the first reason it ought to support about three and a half pounds, it will in fact support more than forty.

[1] A small coin, about 20 grains Troy in weight.

So for this reason it follows that the expanse of air that supports the bat which weighs the two hundred and twentieth part of the weight of an eagle, if it had to be trodden down and pressed by the beating of the wings of the eagle, would need to be sixty times larger.

When a bird in beating its wings raises them higher above its center of gravity than it lowers them beneath it, it will have its head higher than its tail during its movement. This is proved by the fourteenth of this: the movable thing will bend its straight movement more towards the side where its movement is less impeded than to that where it is more impeded; and by the eighth, which says: it is as much to move the air against the immovable thing as to move the thing against the immovable air. Therefore, the wing when it moves farther downwards than upwards makes more percussion with the air that borders on it below than with that which touches it above; and for this reason its straight movement will slant upwards.

If the bird while moving its wings an equal distance below and above its center of gravity moves them more rapidly downwards than upwards, it will curve its level movement upwards. This is proved by the ninth of the foregoing, which said: of the equal movements made by the wings of birds, those which are the most rapid will have most power to compress the air which borders on them below; and by the seventeenth, which says: the percussion of a movable thing is more deflected which has struck against a spot that offers more resistance. Therefore, it is concluded that if the wing making equal movement downwards and upwards moves down more rapidly than up, it will curve its level movement upwards rather than downwards.

And by the converse of what has gone before, if the wings while making equal movement below and above the bird's center of gravity should rise more swiftly than they fall, the bird's movement will slant inclining towards the ground.

A complex slant is said to be that which birds make when they move in the air keeping their tail higher than their head and one wing lower than the other.

When a bird flies in a complex slant, the movement in the one slant will be so much swifter than in the other as the one is less oblique than the other.

The movement made by birds that fly with a complex slant is curved.

The curve created by the complex movement made by birds as they fly will be greater or less as the lateral slant is less or greater.

Before birds start on long journeys they wait for the winds favorable to their movements, and these favorable winds are of a different kind with different sorts of birds, because those which fly in jerks or bounds are obliged to fly against the wind, others receive the wind on one of their sides at different angles, and others receive it on both sides. But the birds that fly by jerks, such as fieldfares and other birds like these which fly in companies, have the feathers of their wings weak and poorly protected by the lesser feathers which form a covering for the larger ones. And this is why it is necessary that their flight should be against the course of the wind, for the wind closes up and presses one feather upon another and so renders their surface smooth and slippery when the air tries to penetrate it. It would be the contrary if the wind were to strike these birds towards the tail, because then it would penetrate under each feather and turn it over towards the head, and thus their flight would have a confused movement, like that of a leaf blown about in the course of the winds which goes perpetually whirling through the air, continually revolving; and in addition to this their flesh would be without protection against the buffeting of the cold winds. And in order to avoid such accidents they fly against the course of the wind with a curving movement, and their bounds acquire great impetus in their descent, which is made with wings closed under the wind. And the reflex movement proceeds with wings open above the wind, which brings the bird back to the same height in the air as that from which it first descended, and so it continues time after time until it arrives at the desired spot.

The reflex movement and the falling movement vary in birds in two ways, of which one variation occurs when the reflex movement is in the same direction as the falling movement, and the second when the reflex movement is in one direction and the falling movement in another.

The bird in the falling movement closes its wings and in the reflex movement it opens them: it does this because a bird becomes heavier in proportion as it folds its wings and so much lighter as it opens its wings more.

The reflex movement is always made against the wind and the falling movement is made in the direction in which the wind is moving.

If the flight of the bird turns to the south without beating its wings when the wind is in the east, it will make the falling movement rectilinear, with its wings somewhat contracted and underneath the wind. But the reflex movement which succeeds this falling movement will be with the wings and tail open and it will have been directed towards the east.

At the end of this movement it will turn its front back again to the south, and with its wings folded it will create again the succeeding falling movement which will be of the same nature at the first, desiring to make a long course with the help of this wind; and the junction of the falling movement with the reflex movement will always be of the nature of a rectangle, and so will be that of the reflex movement with the falling movement.

There are two ways in which the wind causes birds to become stationary in the air without beating their wings.

The first is when the wind strikes against the sides of steep mountains or other rocks by the sea, as the bird then sets itself at such an angle that it carries in front as much of its weight against the reflex wind as this wind in front has power in its resistance. And since equal powers cannot prevail over each other, it follows that in such a position a bird through its imperceptible vibration remains motionless. The second way is when the bird sets itself at such a slant above the course of the wind that it has as much power to descend as the wind has to resist its descent.

When by the help of the wind the bird rises without beating its wings and makes a circular movement, and when it spreads its tail at the uprising of the wind, it is being driven by two powers, one of which is that of the wind, which strikes the wings in the hollow beneath them, and the other is the weight of the bird, which is descending by a complex slant. And from the fact of its acquiring such velocity, it comes to pass that as it turns its breast to meet the onset of the wind, this wind acts under the bird after the manner of a wedge which lifts up a weight; thus the bird makes its reflex movement much higher than the commencement of its falling movement; and this is the true cause why birds rise some distance without beating their wings.

[*How the tail of the bird is used as a rudder*]

When the bird lowers its tail equally it descends by a straight slanting movement. But if it is more lowered on the right side, then the straight line of the descent will become curved and will bend towards the right side with a greater or less curve of movement in proportion as the right point of the tail is higher or lower, and if the left point of the tail is lowered it will do the same on the left side.

But if the tail is raised equally a little above the level of the back of the bird it will move along a straight line slanting upwards; but if it raises the right point of the tail more than the left, this movement will be curved towards the right side, and if it raises the left point of the tail, this straight movement will curve on the left side.

Birds raise their wings when open with greater ease than they lower them. And this is proved by the third of this, which says: parts of bodies which are convex are more suitable for penetrating the air than those which are concave.

It follows that as birds have their wings convex on the side that is uppermost and concave on the side below, they will raise their wings with greater ease than they lower them.

The feathers spread out one from another in the wings of birds when these wings are raised up, and this happens because the wing rises and penetrates the thickness of the air with greater ease when it is perforated than when it is united.

The spaces between the feathers in the wings of birds contract as the wings are lowered, in order that these wings by becoming united may prevent the air from penetrating between these feathers, and that with their percussion they may have a more powerful stroke to press and condense the air that is struck by these wings.

Bats when they fly have of necessity their wings covered completely with a membrane, because the creatures of the night on which they feed seek to escape by means of confused revolutions, and this confusion is enhanced by their various twists and turns. As to the bats, it is necessary sometimes that they follow their prey upside down, sometimes in a slanting position, and so in various different ways, which they could not do without causing their own destruction if their wings were of feathers that let the air pass through them.

When birds wish to commence their flight it is necessary for them to do so in one of two ways, one of which commences by lowering themselves with their body to the ground and then making a leap in the air by extending very rapidly their folded legs.

At the close of this leap the wings have completed their extension and the bird immediately lowers them swiftly towards the ground and reascends the second stage, which is slanting like the first; and thus continuing in succession it rises to whatsoever height it pleases. Some others first raise their wings to slant forward and lower themselves as far as they can with their breasts on the ground, and in this position they extend their legs very rapidly, leaping up and slanting forward, and then at the end of the effort they drop their wings so that they are slanting downwards and backwards. Thus they find themselves considerably above and in front of the place from which they set out and at the end of the effort they are in another; and so their movement continues.

There are other birds which, after having lowered themselves to the ground and having their wings extended high and forward, lower the wings and extend the legs at the same time, and thus the power produced by the first beating of the wings allied to the power acquired by extending the legs becomes very great, and this power united is the greatest that it is possible to create for the beginnings of the flights of these birds.

The second method employed by birds at the commencement of their flight is when they are descending from a height: they merely throw themselves forward and at the same time spread their wings high and forward and then in the course of the leap lower their wings downwards and backwards, and so using them as oars continue their slanting descent.

Others have the habit of throwing themselves forward with wings closed and then opening the wings as they descend, and having opened them, are stopped by the resistance of the air, and then close them and fall again.

The butterflies with four equal and separated wings [ant lions] always fly with the tail high, using it as a rudder for any sort of movement. That is, if one of these insects wishes to descend, it lowers its tail; and if it wishes to ascend, it raises its tail; and if it wishes to turn to the right or left, it bends its tail to the right or left; and the same with all sorts of angles of movement which lie between the said four principal movements. And this is the largest butterfly of the aforesaid species, black and yellow in color.

It uses its four wings in short wheeling flights when it wishes to prey on the small winged ants, moving sometimes the right forward and the left backward and sometimes the left forward and the right backward, because the rudder formed by the tail is not sufficient to regulate the speed of its movement.

The fly when it hovers in the air upon its wings beats its wings with great speed and din, raising them from the horizontal position up as high as the wing is long. And as it raises them it brings them forward in a slanting position in such a way as almost to strike the air edgewise; and as it lowers them it strikes the air and so would rise somewhat if it were not that the creature threw its weight in the opposite direction by means of its slant. As though the slant of the fly when stationary in the air was along the line *e f,* and the slant of the movement of the wings between the straight up and the straight down position followed the lines *a b, c d* which intersect with the line of the descent $e\,f$ between right angles, in such movement that the power of the descent by the slant $e\,f$ is equal to the power that it has to raise itself by the slant of the movement of the wings by the slant $d\,b\,c\,a$.

And the back legs serve it as a rudder, and when it wishes to fly, it lowers its wings as much as possible.

When the bird lowers one of its wings, necessity constrains it instantly to extend it, for if it did not do so it would turn right over. The bird when it wishes to turn does not beat its wings with equal movement, but moves the one which makes the convex of the circle it describes more than that which makes the concave of the circle.

The bird beats its wings repeatedly on one side only when it wishes to turn round while one wing is held stationary; and this it does by taking a stroke with the wing in the direction of the tail, like a man rowing in a boat with two oars, who takes many strokes on that side from which he wishes to escape, and keeps the other oar fixed.

The helms which are on the shoulders of the wings are necessary when the bird in its flight without beating its wings wishes to maintain itself in part of a tract of air, upon which it is either slipping down or rising, and when it wishes to bend either upwards or downwards or to right or left. It then uses these helms in this manner: if the bird wishes to rise, it spreads the helm in the opposite direction to the way the wind strikes it; and if to descend, it spreads the top part of the helm slanting to the course of the wind. If it turns to the right it spreads the right helm to the wind, and if it turns to the left it spreads the left helm to the wind.

A bird beats its wings frequently as it settles when it has descended from a height, in order to break the impetus of the descent, to settle itself on the ground and to diminish the force of the impact.

When the bird flies along a level line, it seems that the nearer it approaches the eye the more it rises.

The movement of things that fly is much swifter than that of the wind. For if it were not so, no bird would move against the wind. But its movement against the wind is as much less than its natural course within the still air as the degrees of movement of the wind are less than that of the bird.

Let us say the bird moves in the still air at a speed of six degrees and the wind of itself moves at a speed of two degrees, then this wind following its natural course takes away two degrees of speed from this bird and consequently of the six degrees there remain four.

But if such bird were to fly at six degrees of speed together with the course of the wind which imparts to it its two degrees, this bird would be flying at eight degrees of speed. Here, however, one should observe how the wing is supported in its percussion in the motionless air, the retreating air or the air that follows after it, and guide oneself according to these rules.

There are some birds which are in the habit of moving their wings more swiftly when they lower them than when they raise them, and this is seen to be the case with doves and such-like birds.

There are others which lower their wings more slowly than they raise them, and this is seen with rooks and other birds like these.

The birds which fly swiftly, keeping at the same distance above the ground, are in the habit of beating their wings downwards and behind them, downwards to the extent necessary to prevent the bird from descending, and behind when they wish to advance with greater speed.

The speed of birds is checked by the opening and spreading out of the tail.

The movement of a bird without beating of wings or help of wind is along a line that slants steeply downwards and then rises with a reflex movement. By this reflex movement it raises itself seven-eighths of the height of its falling movement, and it goes on doing this little by little until it reaches the ground.

II · OF MAN

You will make an anatomy of the wings of a bird together with the muscles of the breast which are the movers of these wings.

And you will do the same for a man, in order to show the possibility that there is in man [the desire] to sustain himself amid the air by the beating of wings.

The man in a flying machine [has] to be free from the waist upward in order to be able to balance himself as he does in a boat, so that his center of gravity and that of his machine may oscillate and change where necessity requires through a change in the center of its resistance.

Remember that your bird[1] should have no other model than the bat, because its membranes serve as an armor or rather as a means of binding together the pieces of its armor, that is, the framework of the wings.

And if you take as your pattern the wings of feathered birds, these are more powerful in structure of bone and sinew because they are penetrable, that is to say the feathers are

---

[1] Leonardo refers always to his projected flying machine as "the bird."

separated from one another and the air passes through them. But the bat is aided by its membrane, which binds the whole together and is not penetrated by the air.

Make a small one to go over the water, and try it in the wind without much depth of water over some part of the Arno, with the wind natural, and then as you please, and turn the sail and the helm.

See tomorrow to all these matters and the copies, and then efface the originals and leave them at Florence, so that if you lose those that you take with you the invention will not be lost . . . .

The man in the bird rests on an axis a little higher than his center of gravity.

A bird is an instrument working according to mathematical law, which instrument it is within the capacity of man to reproduce with all its movements, but not with a corresponding degree of strength, though it is deficient only in the power of maintaining equilibrium. We may therefore say that such an instrument constructed by man is lacking in nothing except the life of the bird, and this life must needs be supplied from that of man.

The life which resides in the bird's members will without doubt better conform to their needs than will that of man which is separated from them, and especially in the almost imperceptible movements which preserve equilibrium. But since we see that the bird is equipped for many obvious varieties of movements, we are able from this experience to declare that the most rudimentary of these movements will be capable of being comprehended by man's understanding; and that he will to a great extent be able to provide against the destruction of that instrument of which he has himself become the living principle and the propeller.

[*Diagrams of mechanism of flying machine*]

I conclude that the upright position is more useful than face downwards, because the instrument cannot get over-turned, and on the other hand the habit of long custom requires this.

And the raising and lowering movement will proceed from the lowering and raising of the two legs, and this is of great strength and the hands remain free; whereas if it were face downwards it would be very difficult for the legs to maintain themselves in the fastenings of the thighs.

And in resting, the first impact comes upon the feet, and in rising, they touch at *r S t;* and after these have been raised they support the machine, and the feet moving up and down lift these feet from the ground.

Q is fastened to the girdle; the feet rest in the stirrups *K h; m n* come beneath the arms behind the shoulders; *o* represents the position of the head; the wing in order to rise and fall revolves and folds . . . the same.

[*With drawings of parts of flying machine*]

Spring of horn or of steel fastened upon wood of willow encased in reed.

The impetus maintains the birds in their flying course during such time as the wings do not press the air, and they even rise upwards.

If the man weighs two hundred pounds and is at *n* and raises the wing with his block, which is a hundred and fifty pounds, when he was above the instrument, with power amounting to three hundred pounds, he would raise himself with two wings.

[*Drawing of wing of flying machine*]
1. Let *a* be the first movement.
2. Undo one and remove. . . .

3. Double canes . . . soaped. . . .

4. Of rag or [skin] of flying fish.

5. Spring with lock *n o* is a wire that holds the spring, and it is not straight. Spring of wing.

6. The spring *b* should be strong, and the spring *a* feeble and bendable, so that it may easily be made to meet the spring *b,* and between *a b* let there be a small piece of leather, so that it is strong, and these springs should be of oxhorn, and to make the model you will make it with quills.

7. Take instead of the spring filings of thin and tempered steel, and these filings will be of uniform thickness and length between the ties, and you will have the springs equal in strength and power of resistance if the filings in each are equal in number.

[*Drawing of wing of flying machine*]
  Net. Cane. Paper.
  Try first with sheets from the Chancery.
  Board of fir lashed in below.
  Fustian. Taffeta. Thread. Paper.

[*Drawing of wing of flying machine*]
  For Gianni Antonio di Ma[. . .]olo [Mariolo].
  Not to be made with shutters but united.[2]

The cord should be of oxhide well greased, and the joints also where the play is, or they should be soaped with fine soap.

The staff should be of stout cane or it may be of various

---

[2] Note referring probably to the construction of a machine for flight as a commission for a patron, Gian Antonio di Mariolo, who desired that the wings should be so made that they could not be penetrated by the wind.

different pieces of cane, and of any length you choose, since you make it in pieces. The springs should be made with bands of iron between the joints of each spring, uniform in thickness, number and length, so that they may all bend at the same time and not first one and then the other; and each spring should of itself have many of these bands of iron, of which it is made up. But if you prefer not to use bands of iron, take strips of cow's horn to make these springs.

[*With drawing of wing of flying machine*]

It requires less effort to raise the wing than to lower it, for as it is being raised the weight of the center which desires to drop assists it considerably.

Tomorrow morning on the second day of January, 1496, I will make the thong and the attempt.

[*Drawing—apparently of strip of leather stretched on frame*]

To make the paste, strong vinegar, in which dissolve fish glue, and with this glue make the paste, and attach your leather and it will be good.

[*Various diagrams in which figure of man is seen exerting force with arms and legs*]

Make it so that the man is held firm above, *a b,* so that he will not be able to go up or down, and will exert his natural force with his arms and the same with his legs.

Close up with boards the large room above, and make the model large and high, and you will have space upon the roof above, and it will be more suitable in all respects than the Piazza d'Italia.

And if you stand upon the roof at the side of the tower the men at work upon the cupola will not see you.

a b produces force estimated at three hundred, and the arms at two hundred, which makes five hundred, with great speed of . . .

The lever one braccio and the movement a half, the counter-lever eight braccia, and for the weight of the man I will say four, so that it comes to three hundred with the instrument.[3]

There is as much pressure exerted by a substance against the air as by the air against the substance.

Observe how the beating of its wings against the air suffices to bear up the weight of the eagle in the highly rarefied air which borders on the fiery element! Observe also how the air moving over the sea, beaten back by the bellying sails, causes the heavily laden ship to glide onwards!

So that by adducing and expounding the reasons of these things you may be able to realize that man when he has great wings attached to him, by exerting his strength against the resistance of the air and conquering it, is enabled to subdue it and to raise himself upon it.

[Sketch—man with parachute]

If a man have a tent made of linen of which the apertures have all been stopped up, and it be twelve braccia across

---

[3] On the same page of the manuscript Leonardo has drawn a rough map of Europe with names of provinces inserted. Below this the Iberian peninsula is repeated with lists of provinces arranged under the three heads—Spain, France and Germany. It is not perhaps entirely fantastic to suppose that these maps and lists of provinces, occurring on the same sheet as the foregoing memoranda of the construction of an instrument for flight, may have been connected in his mind with possibilities of travel that the invention of flying would open up, and that the sketches were in intention aviators' maps. The reference to the roof at the side of the tower as being out of sight of the men working upon the cupola shows that the model was being made in a house not far from the Cathedral.

and twelve in depth, he will be able to throw himself down from any great height without sustaining any injury.

[*With drawing of pair of balances in one of which the figure of a man is seen raising a wing*]

And if you wish to ascertain what weight will support this wing, place yourself upon one side of a pair of balances and on the other place a corresponding weight so that the two scales are level in the air; then if you fasten yourself to the lever where the wing is and cut the rope which keeps it up you will see it suddenly fall; and if it required two units of time to fall of itself you will cause it to fall in one by taking hold of the lever with your hands; and you lend so much weight to the opposite arm of the balance that the two become equal in respect of that force; and whatever is the weight of the other balance, so much will support the wing as it flies, and so much the more as it presses the air more vigorously.

[*With drawings*]

a b c causes the part *m n* to raise itself up quickly in the rising movement; *d e f* causes *m n* to descend rapidly in the falling movement, and so the wing performs its function.

r t lowers the wing by means of the foot, that is, by stretching out the legs; *v s* raises the wing by the hand and turns it.

The way to cause the wing to turn just as it rises or descends.

Device which causes the wing as it rises to be all pierced through and as it falls to be united. And this is due to the fact that as it rises, *b* separates from *a* and *d* from *c,* and so the air gives place to the rising of the wing, and as it falls, *b* returns to *a* and similarly *c* to *d*; and the net bound to the canes above makes a good protection, but take care that your direction be from *a* to *f* so that the landing does not find any obstacle.

Flight

[With drawings: section of wing]

Device so that when the wing rises up it remains pierced through, and when it falls it is all united. And in order to see this it must be looked at from below.

[Sketch of wing]

Make the meshes of this net one-eighth wide.

A should be of immature fir wood, light and possessing its bark.

B should be fustian pasted there with a feather to prevent it from coming off easily.

C should be starched taffeta, and as a test use thin pasteboard.

[With drawing of flying machine]

a twists the wing, b turns it with a lever, c lowers it, d raises it up, and the man who controls the machine has his feet at f d; the foot f lowers the wings, and the foot d raises them.

The pivot M should have its center of gravity out of the perpendicular so that the wings as they fall down also fall towards the man's feet; for it is this that causes the bird to move forward.

This machine should be tried over a lake, and you should carry a long wineskin as a girdle so that in case you fall you will not be drowned.

It is also necessary that the action of lowering the wings should be done by the force of the two feet at the same time, so that you can regulate the movement and preserve your equilibrium by lowering one wing more rapidly than the other according to need, as you may see done by the kite and other birds. Also the downward movement of both the feet produces twice as much power as that of one: it is true that the movement is proportionately slower.

The raising is by the force of a spring or if you wish by

the hand, or by drawing the feet towards you, and this is best, for then you will have the hands more free.

[*With drawing*]

The manner of the rods of the wings.

How one ought to have the canes strengthened and able to bend by means of joints.

[*With drawing—figure of man lying face downwards working machine*]

This can be made with one pair of wings and also with two.

If you should wish to make it with one, the arms will raise it by means of a windlass, and two vigorous kicks with the heels will lower it, and this will be useful.

And if you wish to make it with two pairs, when one leg is extended it will lower one pair of wings and at the same time the windlass worked by the hands will raise the others, helping also considerably those that fall, and by turning the hands first to the right and then to the left you will help first the one and then the other. This instrument resembles the large one . . . except that in this the traction is twisted on the wheel *M* and goes to the feet.

In place of the feet you should make a ladder in three parts of three poles of fir, light and slender, as is represented here in front, and it should be ten braccia in length.

[*With drawing—figure of man lying face downwards working machine*]

Under the body between the pit and the fork of the throat should be a chamois skin, and put it there with the head and the feet.

Hold a windlass with the hands, and with feet and hands together, you will exert a force equal to four hundred pounds, and it will be as rapid as the movement of the heels.

[*With drawing—figure of man, in vertical position, working machine*]

This man exerts with his head a force that is equal to two hundred pounds, and with his hands a force of two hundred pounds, and this is what the man weighs.

The movement of the wings will be crosswise after the manner of the gait of the horse.

So for this reason I maintain that this method is better than any other.

Ladder for ascending and descending; let it be twelve braccia high, and let the span of the wings be forty braccia, and their elevation eight braccia, and the body from stern to prow twenty braccia and its height five braccia and let the outside cover be all of cane and cloth.

[*With drawing of screw revolving round vertical axis*]

Let the outer extremity of the screw be of steel wire as thick as a cord, and from the circumference to the center let it be eight braccia.

I find that if this instrument made with a screw be well made—that is to say, made of linen of which the pores are stopped up with starch—and be turned swiftly, the said screw will make its spiral in the air and it will rise high.

Take the example of a wide and thin ruler whirled very rapidly in the air, you will see that your arm will be guided by the line of the edge of the said flat surface.

The framework of the above-mentioned linen should be of long stout cane. You may make a small model of pasteboard, of which the axis is formed of fine steel wire, bent by force, and as it is released it will turn the screw.

[*With drawing*]

If you wish to see a real test of the wings, make them of pasteboard covered by net, and make the rods of cane, the wing being at least twenty braccia in length and breadth, and fix it over a plank of a weight of two hundred pounds, and make in the manner represented above[4] a force that is rapid; and if the plank of two hundred pounds is raised up before the wing is lowered, the test is satisfactory, but see that the force works rapidly, and if the aforesaid result does not follow, do not lose any more time.

If by reason of its nature this wing ought to fall in four spaces of time and you by your mechanism cause it to fall in two, the result will be that the plank of two hundred pounds will be raised up.

You know that if you find yourself standing in deep water holding your arms stretched out and then let them fall naturally, the arms will proceed to fall as far as the thighs and the man will remain in the first position.

But if you make the arms which would naturally fall in four spaces of time fall in two, then know that the man will quit his position and moving violently will take up a fresh position on the surface of the water.

And know that if the above-named plank weighs two hundred pounds, a hundred of these will be borne by the man who holds the lever in his hand and a hundred will be carried upon the air by the medium of the wing.

Make the ladders curved to correspond with the body.

When the foot of the ladder _a_ touches the ground, it cannot give a blow to cause injury to the instrument because it is a cone which buries itself and does not find any obstacle at its point, and this is perfect.

Make trial of the actual machine over the water so that if you fall you do not do yourself any harm.

These hooks that are underneath the feet of the ladder act in the same way as when one jumps on the points of one's

[4] In the drawing the figure of a man is seen working a lever.

242

toes, for then one is not stunned as is the person who jumps upon his heels.

This is the procedure when you wish to rise from an open plain: these ladders serve the same purpose as the legs and you can beat the wings while it is rising. Observe the swift, how when it has settled itself upon the ground it cannot rise flying, because its legs are short. But when you have raised yourself, draw up the ladders as I show in the second figure above.

In constructing wings one should make one cord to bear the strain and a looser one in the same position, so that if the one breaks under the strain the other is in position to serve the same function.

The smaller these shutters the more useful are they.

And they will be protected by a framework of cane upon which is drawn a piece of gauze, and as it slants upward the movement of the whole is transversal, and such lines of shutters come to open by a slanting line and consequently the process of rising is not impeded.

Here the head n is the mover of this helm, that is, that when n goes towards b the helm becomes widened, and when it goes in the opposite direction the tail is contracted; and similarly when f is lowered, the tail is lowered on this side, and so lowering itself on the opposite side it will do the same.

Of necessity in flight at uniform altitude the lowering of the wings will be as great as their elevation.

When the mover of the flying body has power divisible in four through its four chief ministering members, it will then be able to employ them equally and also unequally and also all equally and all unequally, according to the dictates of the various movements of the flying body.

If they are all moved equally the flying body will be of regular movement.

If they are used unequally, as it would be in continuous proportion, the flying body will be in circling movement.

Suppose that here there is a body suspended, which resembles that of a bird, and that its tail is twisted to an angle of various different degrees; you will be able by means of this to deduce a general rule as to the various twists and turns in the movements of birds occasioned by the bending of their tails.

In all the varieties of movements the heaviest part of the thing which moves becomes the guide of the movement.

The movement of the bird ought always to be above the clouds so that the wing may not be wetted, and in order to survey more country and to escape the danger caused by the revolutions of the winds among the mountain defiles, which are always full of gusts and eddies of winds. And if moreover the bird should be overturned, you will have plenty of time to turn it back again, following the instructions I have given, before it falls down again to the ground.

If the point of the wing is struck by the wind and the wind enters underneath the point the bird will then find itself liable to be overturned unless it employs one of two remedies; that is either it suddenly enters with this point under the wind or lowers the opposite wing from the middle forward.

[*Figure*] *a b c d* are the four cords above for raising the wing, and they are as powerful in action as the cords below, *e f g h,* because of the bird being overturned so that they may offer as much resistance above as they do below, although a single strip of hide dressed with alum thick and large may chance to suffice: but finally, however, we must put it to the test.

The bird I have described ought to be able by the help of the wind to rise to a great height, and this will prove to be its safety, since even if all the above-mentioned revolutions were to befall it, it would still have time to regain a condition of equilibrium; provided that its various parts have a great power of resistance, so that they can safely withstand the fury and violence of the descent, by the aid of the defenses which I have mentioned; and its joints should be made of strong tanned hide, and sewn with cords of very strong raw silk. And let no one encumber himself with iron bands, for these are very soon broken at the joints or else they become worn out, and consequently it is well not to encumber oneself with them.

The cord *a* set for the purpose of extending the wing ought to be of thick dressed hide, so that if the bird should be turned upside down it may be able to subdue the fury of the wind which strikes it on the wing and seeks to close it, for this would be the cause of the destruction of the bird. But to make it more safe you should make exactly the same system of cords outside as within, and you will then avoid all suspicion of danger.

a b c are the terminating points of the cords from the three joints of the fingers of the wings; *d* marks the position of the mover of the lever *a d* which moves the wing.

If the wing and the tail are too far above the wind, lower half the opposite wing and so get the impact of the wind there within it, and this will cause it to right itself.

If the wing and the tail should be beneath the wind, raise

the opposite wing and it will right itself as you desire, provided that this wing which rises slants less than the one opposite to it.

And if the wing and the breast are above the wind it should lower the half of the opposite wing, and this will be struck by the wind and thrown back upwards, and this will cause the bird to right itself.

But if the wing and the spine are below the wind it ought then to raise the opposite wing and expand it in the wind, and the bird will immediately right itself.

And if the bird is situated with the hinder part above the wind the tail ought then to be placed beneath the wind, and thus there will be brought about an equilibrium of forces.

But if the bird should have its hinder parts below the wind [*raising its tail*][5] it should enter with its tail above the wind and it will right itself.

If the bird should wish to turn itself rapidly on one of its sides and to follow its circular movement, it will beat its wings twice on that side, moving the wing back like an oar and keeping the other wing steady or making only one beat with this as against two of the opposite wing.

Since the wings are swifter to press the air than the air is to escape from beneath the wings, the air becomes condensed and resists the movement of the wings; and the motive power of these wings by subduing the resistance of the air raises itself in a contrary movement to the movement of the wings.

That bird will descend with the swifter movement when its descent is at less of an angle.

The descent of a bird will be at less of an angle when the tips of the wings and their shoulders are nearer together.

The lines of the movements made by birds as they rise

[5] Words crossed out in MS.

are of two kinds, of which one is always spiral in the manner of a screw, and the other is rectilinear and curved.

That bird will rise up to a height which by means of a circular movement in the shape of a screw makes its reflex movement against the coming of the wind and against the flight of this wind, turning always upon its right or left side.

Thus if the north wind should be blowing, and you, coming above in reflex movement, should glide against the said wind, until, in this straight process of rising, the wind was in such a condition that it might turn you over, you are then at liberty to bend with the right or left wing, and holding the inner wing low you will pursue a curving movement, with the help of the tail, curving in the direction of the lower wing, and continually descending and pivoting round the wing that is held low, until you again make the reflex movement anew above the wind, behind the course of the wind; and when you are on the point of being turned over, this same lower wing will curve your line of movement, and you will return against the wind, underneath it, until you have acquired the impetus, and then raise yourself above the wind, facing its approach, and by means of the already acquired impetus, you will make the reflex movement greater than the falling movement.

A bird as it rises always sets its wings above the wind and without beating them, and it always moves in a circular movement.

And if you wish to go to the west without beating your wings, when the north wind is blowing, make the falling movement straight and beneath the wind to the west, and the reflex movement above the wind to the north.

A bird makes the same use of wings and tail in the air as a swimmer does of his arms and legs in the water.

If a man is swimming with his arms equally towards the

east, and his body exactly faces the east, the swimmer's movement will be towards the east. But if the northern arm is making a longer stroke than the southern arm, then the movement of his body will be to the northeast. And if the right arm is making a longer movement than the left the man's movement will be to the southeast.

The impetus of one of the wings extended edgewise towards the tail will occasion the bird a sudden circling movement following on the impetus of the above-mentioned wing.

When the bird raises itself in circles to a height above the wind, without beating its wings, by the force of the wind, it will be transported by this wind out of the region where it desires to return, still without beating its wings; then it turns so that it faces the approach of the wind, entering slantwise underneath this wind, and comes to descend slightly until it finds itself above the spot where it desires to return.

The destruction of these machines may come about in two ways, the first of which is when the machine breaks, the second is when it turns edgewise or almost on its edge, because it ought always to descend with a long slant and almost in a level line.

As regards the preventing of the machine from being broken, one may guard against this by making it as strong as possible in whatever line it may turn, that is, either edgewise falling with head or tail in front, or with the point of the right or left wing, or along lines that bisect or are the quarterings of these lines as the sketch shows [*figure*]. One ought to guard against this at the outset by turning almost edgewise.

As regards constructing the machine in such a way that in descending whatever may be the direction that it takes, it finds the remedy prepared; and this you will do by causing its center of gravity to be above that of the weight which it carries, always in a vertical line, and the one always at a sufficient distance from the other, that is, that if the machine is thirty braccia in width the centers are four braccia apart, and as has been said, one is beneath the other, and the heavier is below, because as it descends the heavier part always constitutes itself in part the guide of the movement. In addition to this, if the bird wishes to fall with its head downwards with a fraction of the slant that would cause it to turn over, this will not be able to happen, because the lighter part would be beneath the heavier and the light would be descending before the heavy, which is impossible in a descent of any length, as is proved in the fourth of the Elements of Mechanics.

And if the bird should fall head downwards with the body partly slanting towards the ground, the underneath sides of the wings ought to turn flat against the earth, and the tail to rise towards the back, and the head or the underpart of the jaw is also turned towards the ground, and from this there will immediately originate in this bird its reflex movement which will cast it up again towards the sky; for which reason, the bird at the close of its reflex movement will come to fall back unless it should while rising lower one of its wings slightly, which would curve such movement and cause it to turn into a half-circle; then this bird will find itself at the close of this movement with its bill turned to the spot at which this reflex movement started. And if this is done against the course of the wind, the end of the reflex movement will be much higher than was the commencement of the falling movement. And this is the way in which the bird rises up to a height without beating its wings and circling. And the remainder of the circle of which I have spoken is completed by the help of the wind, by a falling movement, with one of the wings always kept low and similarly one side of the tail. And it subsequently makes a reflex movement towards the direction of the wind and is left at the end with its bill turned in the direction of the wind, and then makes again the falling and reflex movements against the wind, always going in circles.

When the bird wishes suddenly to turn on one of its sides, it pushes out swiftly, towards its tail, the point of the wing on that side, and since *every movement tends to maintain itself,* or rather *every body that is moved continues to move so long as the impression of the force of its mover is retained in it,* therefore the movement of this wing with violence, in the direction of the tail, keeping still at its termination a portion of the said impression, not being able of itself to follow the movement which has already been commenced, will come to move the whole bird with it until the impetus of the moved air has been consumed.

When the tail is thrust forward with its face and the wind strikes upon it, it makes the bird move suddenly in an opposite direction.

[*An argument to dispose of the objections to the attempt*]

You will perhaps say that the sinews and muscles of a bird are incomparably more powerful than those of man, because all the girth and of so many muscles and of the fleshy parts of the breast goes to aid and increase the movement of the wings, while the bone in the breast is all in one piece and consequently affords the bird very great power, the wings also being all covered with a network of thick sinews and other very strong ligaments of gristle, and the skin being very thick with various muscles.

But the reply to this is that such great strength gives it a reserve of power beyond what it ordinarily uses to support itself on its wings, since it is necessary for it whenever it may so desire either to double or treble its rate of speed in order to escape from its pursuer or to follow its prey. Consequently, in such a case it becomes necessary for it to put forth double or treble the amount of effort, and in addition to this to carry through the air in its talons a weight corresponding to its own weight. So one sees a falcon carrying a duck and an eagle carrying a hare; which circumstance shows clearly enough where the excess of strength is spent; for they need but little force in order to sustain themselves, and to balance themselves on their wings, and flap them in the pathway of the wind and so direct the course of their journeyings; and a slight movement of the wings is sufficient for this, and the movement will be slower in proportion as the bird is greater in size.

Man is also possessed of a greater amount of strength in his legs than is required by his weight. And in order to show the truth of this, place a man to stand upon the seashore, and observe how far the marks of his feet sink in; and then set another man on his back, and you will see how much deeper the marks of his feet will be. Then take away the man from his back, and set him to jump straight up as high as he can; you will then find that the marks of his feet make a deeper impression where he has jumped than where he has had the other man on his back. This affords us a double proof that man is possessed of more than twice the amount of strength that is required to enable him to support himself. [*With drawing*] Leather bags with which a man falling from a height of six braccia will not do himself any harm, whether he falls into water or on land; and these leather bags tied after the fashion of the beads of a rosary are wrapped round by others.

If you should fall with the double chain of leather bags which you have tied underneath you, so manage that these are what first strike the ground.

[With drawing of part of mechanism of flying machine]

Since the wings have to row downwards and backwards, in order to keep the machine up, and so that it may progress forward, it moves by the lever *c d* with a slanting track, guided by the strap *a b*.

I might so make it that the foot which presses the stirrup *g* was that which in addition to its ordinary function pulled down the lever *f*. But this would not serve our purpose, because it is necessary that the lever *f* should first rise or descend before the stirrup *g* moves from its place, in order that the wing—as it throws itself forward and raises itself up at the time at which the already acquired impetus of itself drives the bird forward without its beating its wings— can present itself edgewise to the air, because if it did not do this the surface of the wings would clash upon the air, would hinder its movement and would not allow the impetus to carry the bird forward.

The great bird will take its first flight upon the back of the great swan, filling the whole world with amazement and filling all records with its fame; and it will bring eternal glory to the nest where it was born.

From the mountain which takes its name from the great bird, the famous bird will take its flight, which will fill the world with its great renown.[6]

[6] This passage should be regarded as a key to the one before it. In the phrase "*sopra del dosso del suo magnio cecero*," "upon the back of the great swan," Leonardo was apparently referring to Monte Ceccri, the mountain above Fiesole immediately to the south. It was from the summit or from a ridge of this mountain that he intended to make a trial of his flying machine. The locality is also referred to in another page of the same manuscript where he speaks of "the cortone a bird of prey which I saw going to Fiesole above the place of the Barbiga in the year 1505 on the fourteenth day of March" (*Sul Volo, Foglio Mancanti* 18 [17] v.). This points to the probability that 1505 was the year in which the trial took place. It may have been this trial of which Cardan chronicled the ill success.

VI

Warfare

I · ON LAND

WHEN besieged by ambitious tyrants I find a means of offense and defense in order to preserve the chief gift of nature, which is liberty; and first I would speak of the position of the walls, and then of how the various peoples can maintain their good and just lords.

[With drawing of tank]

These take the place of the elephants. One may tilt with them. One may hold bellows in them to spread terror among the horses of the enemy, and one may put carabineers in them to break up every company.

[War machines: with drawing]

When this is going through its own ranks, it is necessary to raise the machinery that moves the scythes, in order to prevent their doing any harm to anyone.

How the armored car is arranged inside.

It will need eight men to work it and make it turn and pursue the enemy.

This is good to break through the ranks, but it must be followed up.

[With drawing]

To make an airgun which shoots with marvelous force you should proceed as follows: stretch a steel wire the width of a finger on a wire-drawing machine by means of a windlass; then temper it, and beat round about it two plates of fine copper which you stretch on the wire-drawing machine. Then half to half solder them together with silver; wind thick copper wire about it and then smooth it with a hammer, but first solder it. And do this three or four times in the same way. And make [the airgun] two braccia long and make it so that it can shoot a dart of a third of a braccio which is of steel.

[*With drawing of two cannon placed vertically with stand between them*]

Whoever wishes to make trial which is the better must raise them on end and two judges should be in the center, and after first firing the one, it must be noted how much time there is from the explosion to the return of the ball to the ground, and then the same is done with the other—and the one which takes longer will have the honor.

But see that the tubes are of equal length, that the touch-holes work freely, that the balls are of the same weight, and the powder is from the same keg.

[*Fire-ball. With drawing*]

This ball should be made of melted pitch, sulphur and tow of hemp rubbed together so that when it burns, the enemy may not carry off the invention.

This ball should be two and a half braccia in height and filled with tubes which can throw a pound of balls, and these should be coated with pitch within the tubes so that they do not fall.

The tubes should be a braccio in length, and made of pasteboard after the manner of spokes, and the space between them should be filled with plaster and wadding; and the ball should be thrown upon the bastions by means of a mangonel.

The center of it will be a cannon ball to which the tubes serve as good epaulets, or a hollow ball of bronze which may be partly filled with powder, with its circumference perforated so that the fire is able to penetrate to the tubes; and the ball should be all tied up on the outside except for a hole to serve as a passage for the fire.

[*Drawing of fire-ball*]

This ball as it is thrown becomes extinguished, and as it reaches the ground the canes which are bound at the top with linen cloth that has been set alight are driven into it, thus igniting the powder which is all round a piece of tow that has been soaked in turpentine, the rest of it being wrapped in hemp which also has been soaked in turpentine, oil of flax and pitch, and the wrappings should be thin in order that the flames may get the air, for otherwise you will do nothing.

[*Powder for a bomb-ketch*]

One pound of charcoal
eleven ounces of sulphur
five pounds of saltpeter.

And mix it well and moisten it with good brandy, and dry it in the sun or at the fire. Then pound it until one cannot see a speck of sulphur or saltpeter but it is all black and uniform and fine, and moisten it again with the brandy and keep it so. Dry it in the sun in grains and crush just so much as can be placed upon the hole, and this will be sufficient.

If you are attacked by night in your quarters, or if you fear to be, take care to have mangonels in readiness which can throw iron caltrops;[1] and, if you should be attacked,

---

[1] A device with sharp points thrown upon the ground to impede foot or horse.

hurl them in among the enemy and you will gain time to set
your men in order against their assailants, the outwitted
enemies, who because of the pain caused by the wounds in
their feet, will be able to effect little. And the plan of your
attack you will make thus: divide your men into two squadrons and so encircle the enemy; but see to it that you have
soles to your shoes and that the horses are shod with iron,
as I have said before, since the caltrops will make no distinction between your men and those of the enemy, and see
that each mangonel throws a cartload of the said caltrops.

[*How to protect oneself from caltrops*]

If you wear between the foot and the sole of the shoe a
sole of cloth woven of cords of cotton of the thickness of a
finger, you will be safe from caltrops, which will not thrust
themselves into your feet.

You should make caltrops of plaster with the arch of iron
and the molds in three parts, and then the points should be
filed.

These caltrops should be kept in a leather bag by the side
of each person, so that if the expected victory should be
changed to a defeat through the strength of the enemy, the
fact of these being scattered behind them would be the cause
of checking the speed of the horses and of bringing about
the unhoped-for victory.

But lest in retreating, this crop should be the cause of a
similar mistake for yourselves, you should first have made
ready the irons for the horses in the form represented below,
and have nailed between the iron and the horse's foot a plate
of steel as thick and wide as the above-mentioned horse's
iron.

And in the case of foot soldiers they should have iron
plates fastened to the soles of their shoes, not tied tightly,

so that they may be able easily to raise their heels and take steps and run when necessary without any restraining obstacle, and the knot that is left loose should be as it is represented here below.

Moreover if you have a small bag of them by the side of each naval combatant and they are then thrown by hand on the enemy's galleys or ships, they will be sowing the seed of the approaching victory; but you should have the shoes bound with iron, as was said above, and covered over below with tiny points, in order that if it should come about that soft soap be thrown upon your ship you will be able to keep your feet, even though the enemy should throw chalk in the form of powder in such a dense cloud as to devastate the air which is breathed into the lungs.

You should set up four stations at four positions in the length of the ship, and at each of the four stations let there be a small barrel with a certain quantity of water, and large syringes which serve to force the water out through many small holes, so that the water may become changed into spray and may thus accompany the dust of the chalk and draw it downwards.

If anyone had formed the design of capturing a tower situated on the sea, he would cause one of his followers to take service with the commander, and when the guard was withdrawn he would affix to the battlements the rope ladder given him by the enemy and would fill the walls with soldiers. In order to prevent this, you should divide the tower into eight sets of staircases, spiral in shape, and divide into eight parts the ramparts and the soldiers' dwellings below; then, if one of the mercenaries should be disposed to be a traitor, the others cannot hold communications with him, and the section of the rampart will be so small that there will not be able to be more than four there. The commander, whose quarters are above those of all the others, can drive them out by attacking them from the machicolations, or shut them up by means of the portcullis and then put smoke at the entrance to the spiral staircases. On no account is it necessary that any alien soldier should lodge with the commander, but only his own family.

The confederate of the scaler of the wall should carry with him a ball of strong thread when he takes service with the commander, and when the opportunity comes the guard will draw up with this thread a coil of strong twine which has been given him by the scaler, and then with the twine he may draw up the rope which will afterwards be useful for drawing up the rope ladder as shown above.

[*Drawing—soldier on horseback galloping*]

This is a mounted carabineer, which is an extremely useful invention. The said carabineers should be provided with pouches full of rolls of plain paper filled with powder, so that by frequently inserting them they subdue the excessive numbers of the enemy. And these carabineers should stand in squadrons as do crossbowmen, so that when one part fires, the other loads; but first make sure that you have accustomed the horses to such noises; or else stop up their ears.

Order of mounted crossbowmen on the open field: *m n* are crossbowmen who as they turn left draw back loading; *r t* are those who go forward with crossbows loaded, and these four files are for one route; *a b* are four files of crossbowmen who turn with bows unloaded in order to load them anew; *c d* are those who come upon the enemy with their bows loaded; and this arrangement of eight lines is employed in open field.

And have it so that those who have unloaded come through the center, so that if sometimes they have been routed by the enemy the crossbowmen who are loaded, holding themselves on the flanks, may cause greater fear to these same enemies.

Order of mounted carabineers:

See that they are well supplied with guns with a thin single fold of paper filled with powder with the ball within, so that they have only to put it in and set alight. Being thus ready they will have no need to turn as have the crossbowmen when they are preparing to load.

[With drawing]

Of the way in which when the battle is begun by scaling the walls one may draw beams up above the top of the battlements, and then by giving them a push cause them to fall upon the ladders and the assailants; and the method of drawing the said beams rapidly should be made use of in the manner shown here.

If the river is dangerous by reason of its current you should set two lines of horses across the river at a distance of six braccia one from the other, and the horses in the lines should be so near as almost to touch each other, and the line or company of horses should have their heads turned towards the current of the water, and this is done solely in order to check and break the fury and impetus of the water. And between the one company and the other pass the soldiers, both those with and those without arms. The company that is higher up the stream should be made up of the bigger horses in order to be better able to stem the rush of the river, that lower down serves to hold up the soldiers when they fall, and to act as a support for them as they make the passage.

[With drawing]

If you wish to submerge a battlefield or to break through walls without the use of cannon and have the use of a river, do as is represented above. That is, you set piles as high as the bank of the river and put them half a braccio apart or farther if you have wider planks; then set these planks between each of the piles and so fill up [the spaces]. When these are filled up, raise the connecting rod *M*, then *a* the upper part of the plank will go forward and *b* the lower part of the plank will go back. In this way the parts of the said plank will be edgewise and the water will be free to escape. And make the sluices all to open at the blow of a carbine or other signal so that they may all open at the same time, in order that the flow of the water upon the object which opposes it may be driven by a greater blow and a more impetuous force. And if the river have a steep descent, make one of these every half mile, and let each of the panels open by means of a rope, to insure them working together, and in order that he who unlocks them may be in safety.

[*How to attack a fortress by subterranean galleries. With drawings*]

Rod filled with rockets for encountering the enemy at the outlet of a subterranean gallery [that opens] from below upwards, which will clear the ground of the men within the entrance.

Rod with rockets for placing in a gallery that leads into a cellar which would be in a fortress and would be well guarded.

m a b. The way of a winding gallery that will deceive the enemy when besieged.

We can clearly understand that all those who find themselves besieged employ all those methods which are likely to lead to the discovery of the secret stratagems of the besieger. You, therefore, who seek by subterranean ways to accomplish your desire, reflect well how your enemy will be on the alert, and how if you should make a gallery on one side he will make a trench up to your [gallery], and this will be well guarded by day and by night, for it will be supposed that the secret way, as is natural, has its outlet in the said gallery.

When you have made your gallery almost to its end and it is near to a cellar, break through suddenly and then thrust this [rod] in front of you filled with rockets if you find defenders there, but if not do not set fire to them lest you make a noise.

[*With drawings*]

Stlocladle. Place in the center powder formed of dried fungi.

These balls filled with rockets are to be thrown within the bastions of the enemy.

The *stlocladle* is a ball a foot wide, made up of hemp and fish glue and covered with the tails of rockets, and these tails do not exceed in length the length of a finger, and each tail is of fine copper veined or of sized pasteboard, and all the sail tails have their extremities pierced by a tiny hole, and they are all attached to a copper ball, which is full of many paths after the manner of a labyrinth, filled with powder; and the said paths are full of holes that cross them which meet with the holes of the rockets.

Then one sets fire to it by means of a bellows and the fire hurls itself through eight holes so that no one can control it or . . . [*ariegi*?], and when the fire has penetrated to the center the rockets begin suddenly one after another with a dreadful din to spit forth their deadly missiles. If you wish to make use of it on a galley, make the rockets of pasteboard, and fill the space between each with pitch mixed with powdered sulphur; and this will serve three purposes: first, it will do harm with the rockets; second, it will kindle a fire there which cannot be put out, and will burn the wood;

and, third, no one will be able to approach it because of the great stench.

The mortar ought to carry a ball of six hundred pounds and more, and by this rule you will take the measure of the diameter of the ball and divide it in six parts, and one of these parts will be its thickness at the muzzle, and it will always be half at the breech. And if the ball is to be of seven hundred pounds, one-seventh of the diameter of the ball will be its thickness at the muzzle, and if the ball is to be eight hundred, it will be the eighth of its diameter at the muzzle, and if nine hundred one-eighth and one-half of it, and if one thousand one-ninth.

If you wish it to throw a ball of stone, make the length of the tube as six or up to seven times the diameter of the ball; and if the ball is to be of iron make this tube up to twelve times the ball, and if the ball is to be of lead make it up to eighteen times. I mean when the mortar is to have its mouth fitted to receive within it six hundred pounds of stone ball and over.

If with its maximum power a bombard throws a ball of a hundred pounds three miles, how far will it throw one of two hundred or three hundred or any other weight more or less than a hundred?

If a bombard with four pounds of powder throws a ball weighing four pounds two miles with its maximum power, by how much ought I to increase the powder for it to carry four miles?

The cannon ball from the mortar, if it be of uniform substance, and its surface be equidistant from its center, and the fire strikes it in the middle, as reason would suggest, must needs take its course without any revolution. Seeing that the fire that expels it is of uniform nature, it drives equally the air which withstands its course, and as this also is equal it offers equal resistance.

Thus, for example, one sees the moon, which is also a spherical body and meets with equal resistance, to be much swifter as compared with the cannon ball, but nevertheless the dark spots that are on it never change their position, and the fact of this change not appearing clearly confirms the fact that it does not revolve.

[*Of digging a trench*]

Width of trench and its depth. Diameter of wheel and thickness of beam and cord. And position of men who turn it and number of men who work this wheel. How many there are in position and what weight they draw at one time, and how much time is required to fill and move in order to empty and turn, and similarly how many shovelfuls one man digs out in an hour, and what a shovelful weighs, and how far he throws it away from himself either upwards, across or downwards, beyond the hillock.

Which will fire the farthest, powder double in quantity or in quality or in fineness?

If you wish to find out where a mine runs, set a drum over all the places where you suspect the mine is being made and on this drum set a pair of dice, and when you are near the place where the mining is, the dice will jump up a little on the drum, through the blow given underground in digging out the earth.

That part of the bronze is most compressed within its mold which is most liquid.

And that is most liquid which is hottest, and that is hottest which comes first out of the furnace. One ought therefore always to make first in the casting that part of the cannon which has to receive the powder before that which has to contain the muzzle.

A long breech is an embarrassment and fills up space uselessly and unserviceably and causes loss of speed.

These balls should be filled with small dust of sulphur which will cause people to become stupefied.

This is the most deadly machine that exists: when the ball in the center drops, it sets fire to the edges of the other balls, and the ball in the center bursts and scatters the others, which catch fire in such time as is needed to say an Ave Maria, and there is a shell outside which covers everything.

The rockets of these balls should be made of paper, and the space between each filled with plaster ready to be molded, mingled with the clippings of cloths. And they should be set alight with a pair of bellows which will cause the flame to extend to the center of the ball among the powder, which separates at a considerable interval from each other all the balls filled with rockets.

Of the movement of the cannon balls of bombards, and of the nature of the stock and breech of these bombards.

Whether the ball moved by force will have a greater movement than that which is moved with ease or no.

Whether if a bombard can throw a ball of a hundred pounds, it is better to put two balls of fifty pounds for one and make the stock narrow, or rather with the stock wide to throw one ball of a hundred pounds.

If the bombard can throw two or three balls with ease, I ask whether it is better to make the ball long or no.

If a bombard throws a weight of a hundred pounds a distance of a mile, how far will it throw a hundred balls of one pound at one discharge?

Whether it is better for the bombard to be narrow at the

mouth and wide at the foot, or narrow at the foot and wide at the mouth.

If the bombard rests on the ground or a stump, or straw or feathers, what difference will there be in the recoil?

If two bombards can be fired in opposite directions, if the breach of the one be placed against that of the other in a straight line.

If the bombard is fired at sea or on the land, what difference there will be in its power.

What difference there is between the movements made upwards or crosswise, or in damp or dry weather, or when it is windy or rainy or with snow falling, either against or across or in the direction of the course of the ball.

Where the ball makes most rebounds—upon stones, earth or water.

How the smooth ball is swifter than the rough one.

Whether the ball revolves in the air or no.

Of the nature of the places struck by these balls.

For a bastion to have spring in it, it should have a layer of fresh willow branches placed in the soil at intervals of half a braccio.

II · ON SEA

[Notes relating to a submarine attack]

Do not impart your knowledge and you will excel alone.

Choose a simple youth and have the dress stitched at home.

Stop the galleys of the captains and afterwards sink the others and fire with the cannon on the fort.

[*With drawings of parts of the apparatus*]
Everything under water, that is, all the fastenings.
Here stands the man. Doublet. Hose. Level frame.

[*With drawing of small boat under poop of large*]
When the watch has gone its round, bring a small skiff under the poop and set fire to the whole all of a sudden.

[*With drawing of boat and chain*]
To fasten a galley to the bottom *m* on the side opposite to the anchor.

[*With drawing of figure in diving dress (half length)*]
A breastplate of armor together with hood, doublet and hose, and a small wineskin for use in passing water, a dress for the armor, and the wineskin to contain the breath, with half a hoop of iron to keep it away from the chest. If you have a whole wineskin with a valve from the [?ball MS. *da pal . . . ?palla*], when you deflate it, you will go to the bottom, dragged down by the sacks of sand; when you inflate it, you will come back to the surface of the water.

A mask with the eyes protruding made of glass, but let its weight be such that you raise it as you swim.

Carry a knife which cuts well so that a net does not hold you prisoner.

Carry with you two or three small wineskins, deflated, and capable of being inflated like balls in case of need.

Take provisions as you need them, and having carefully wrapped them up hide them on the bank. But first have an understanding about the agreement, how the half of the ransom is to be yours without deduction; and the storeroom of the prisons is near to Manetti, and payment may be made into the hand of Manetti, that is, of the said ransom.

Carry a horn in order to give a signal whether or no the attempt has been successful.

Warfare

You need to take an impression of one of the three iron screws of the workshop of Santa Liberata, the figure in plaster and the cast in wax.

[*With drawing of figure of man in diving dress. His right arm extended holds a staff which touches a square of cork. Two bags suspended from shoulders*]

It separates from the dress if it should be necessary to break it.

Cork which is to be fixed midway between the surface and the bottom.

Bags of sand.

Carry forty braccia of rope fastened to a bag of sand.[1]

I will destroy the harbor.

Unless you surrender within four hours you will go to the bottom.

[*Notes with drawings of three heads showing diving apparatus fitted over the nostrils*]

Have the said bag for your mouth ready for use when you are in the sea—for was not this your secret?

Try it first for four hours.

Pack-thread.

Of bronze, which is fastened with a screw that has been oiled, it should have been made in a mold.

[1] Alvise Manetti was sent by the Venetian senate on a legation to the Turks, which lasted from October, 1499, to the end of March, 1500, to attempt some arrangement for the surrender of the Venetian prisoners who were removed from Constantinople to Lepanto after the capture of that fortress by the Turks in August, 1499. Already in February, 1500, a despatch from Manetti had arrived in Venice which showed that his endeavors were not likely to reach a successful issue. It was presumably at about this time that Leonardo, who was then in Venice, set himself to devise some method of securing the release of the prisoners through the agency of Manetti, and also to consider a plan for destroying the enemy's ships in the harbor by piercing them below the waterline.

[*Drawing of buoy, below which, connected by a long bar that moves freely on swivels, hangs what is apparently a very large awl or borer. At the side of the buoy a long tube is fastened so that one end projects just above it; it is bound by a number of rings, and its lower end terminates in a sort of bag, which is apparently fixed over the mouth of the diver. A dotted horizontal line shows that this is level with the top of the borer*]

Line to find the middle.

In case you have to make use of the sea, make an armor of copper by setting the plates one above another thus: [*drawing*]. That is, one inside the other, so that a hook may not grapple you.

Measure first the depth, and if you see that it will be sufficient merely to bore without sinking the ship, pursue that course; otherwise fasten it in the way indicated.

Hole by which the water makes its exit when the ring is lowered.

Oars. Twelve braccia the lever. Twelve braccia. For the final turn you need a bent lever. In order to turn this screw use a pair of slippers with heels, or hooks, so that the foot may stand firm.

These are the implements which belong to it; but construct it so that the wineskin which serves as a boat, and the implements and the man who is there, shall be midway between the surface and the bottom of the sea; and have a valve put in this wineskin, so that when it is deflated it will sink to the bottom where your station is, and the hands will serve as oars.

The way of wings.

The smoke of [. . .] for use as an opiate.

Take seed of darnel as remedy, and [. . .] spirits of wine in cotton. Some white henbane. Some teasel.

Seed and root of *mappello*[?],[2] and dry everything; mix this powder with camphor and it is made.

Deadly smoke (*fumo mortale*):

Take arsenic and mix with sulphur or realgar.

Remedy rose water.

Venom of toad, that is, a land toad.

Slaver of mad dog and decoction of dogwood berries.

Tarantula from Taranto.

Powder of verdigris or of chalk mixed with poison to throw on ships.

[*Greek fire*]

Take charcoal of willow, and saltpeter, and aqua vitæ, and sulphur, pitch, with incense and camphor and Ethiopian wool, and boil them all up together. This fire is so eager to burn that it will run along wood even when it is under water. You should add to the mixture liquid varnish, petroleum, turpentine and strong vinegar, and mix everything together and dry it in the sun or in an oven when the bread has been taken out, and then stick it round hempen or other tow, molding it to a round form and driving very sharp nails into every side of it. Leave, however, an opening in this ball to serve for a fuse, and then cover it with resin and sulphur.

This fire, moreover, when fixed to the top of a long lance, which has a braccio of its point covered with iron in order that it may not be burnt by it, is useful for avoiding and warding off the hostile ships in order not to be overwhelmed by their onset.

Throw also vessels of glass filled with pitch onto the ships of the enemy when their crews are engaged in the battle, and by then, throwing similar lighted balls after these, you will have it in your power to set every ship on fire.

[2] *Mappello*, an as yet unidentified tree or shrub.

[*With drawing*]

To throw poison in the form of powder upon galleys.

Chalk, fine sulphide of arsenic and powdered verdigris may be thrown among the enemy ships by means of small mangonels. And all those who, as they breathe, inhale the said powder with their breath will become asphyxiated.

But take care to have the wind so that it does not blow the powder back upon you, or to have your nose and mouth covered over with a fine cloth dipped in water so that the powder may not enter. It would also be well to throw baskets covered with paper and filled with this powder from the crow's nest or the deck of the ship.

[*How to stave in the bows of a ship. With drawing*]

It is necessary first that they be engaged, that is, fastened together in such a way that you for your part can unlock yourself at your pleasure, so that when the ship goes to the bottom it may not drag yours with it. Let this be done as follows: draw a weight up to a height and then release it; and as it falls it will give such a blow as a pile driver gives, and in falling it will draw back the head of a beam which is in equilibrium when upright, and as the head of the aforesaid beam comes back, the end that is below advances and staves in the bow of the ship. But see to it that the beam has a cutting edge, so that as it rushes to give the stroke the water does not offer resistance to it. And above all see that the chains which hold the ships fastened together are such as can at your pleasure be severed from your side, so that the enemy's ship when it sinks may not drag you down with it.

[*With drawing*]

If you wish to build a fleet for action you should make use of these ships in order to ram the enemy's ships, that is, make ships a hundred feet[3] in length and eight feet wide and arrange them so that the rowers of the left oars sit on the right side of the ship and the rowers of the right oars on the left side, as is shown at *M* [*figure*], in order that the leverage of the oars may be longer. And this ship should be a foot and a half in thickness, that is, made of beams fastened inside and outside by planks set crosswise.

And let the vessel have fastened to it a foot below the water's edge a spike shod with iron of the weight and size of an anvil. And by the might of the oars this vessel will be able to draw back after it has struck the first blow, and will then hurl itself forward again with fury and deal the second blow and then the third, and so many others as to destroy the ship.

[*With drawings*]

Of the means of defense in case the enemy should throw soft soap, or caltrops, or small boards studded with nails, or similar things upon the ships.

You should do this: keep, when you go into the combat, on your feet, underneath your shoes, iron soles, divided in the middle as is shown in the drawing above, so that it is possible to bend the feet; and the under side of these soles should have the form of a rasping file, or be filled with blunted points of nails, in order to prevent the soap from causing the foot to slip and so making the man fall down flat; and, as they are of iron, the small boards and caltrops will be thrown in vain.

[*Figure*] This ship is to serve as a defense against cannon, and it attacks the other ships with its cannon; it is covered with sheet metal as a protection against fire, and bristling

---

[3] Dimensions here given in feet, more usually in braccia. According to Fanfani's Dictionary, a foot was about 30 centimeters, and a braccio (fiorentino) was 58 centimeters.

with points of nails so that the enemy may not leap upon it with impunity.

How by an appliance many are able to remain for some time under water. How and why I do not describe my method of remaining under water for as long a time as I can remain without food; and this I do not publish or divulge on account of the evil nature of men who would practice assassinations at the bottom of the seas, by breaking the ships in their lowest parts and sinking them together with the crews who are in them; and although I will furnish particulars of others, they are such as are not dangerous, for above the surface of the water emerges the mouth of the tube by which they draw in breath, supported upon wineskins or pieces of cork.

VII

Experiments and Inventions

If you place your second finger under the tip of the third in such a way that the whole of the nail is visible on the far side, then anything that is touched by these two fingers will seem double, provided that the object touched is round.

Since every continuous quantity is divisible to infinity, if a quantity of wine be placed in a vessel through which water is continually passing, it will never come about that the water which is in the vessel will be without wine.

If you wish to find the part of the magnet that naturally turns towards the north, get a large tub and fill it with water; and in this water place a wooden cup and set in it the magnet without any more water. It will remain floating in the manner of a boat, and by virtue of its power of attraction it will immediately move in the direction of the north star; and it will move towards this, first turning itself with the cup in such a way that it is turned towards this star, and will then move through the water and touch the edge of the tub with its north side, as before mentioned.

A drop of dew with its perfect round affords us an opportunity of considering some of the varied functions of the watery sphere; how it contains within itself the body of the earth without the destruction of the sphericity of its surface.

For if first you take a cube of lead of the size of a grain of millet, and by means of a very fine thread attached to it you submerge it in this drop, you will perceive that the drop will not lose any of its first roundness, although it has been increased by an amount equal to the size of the cube which has been shut within it.

Whether the greater light with less heat causes concave mirrors to reflect rays of more powerful heat than a body of greater heat and less light.

For such an experiment a lump of copper should be heated and placed so that it may be seen through a round hole, which in size and distance from the mirror is equal to the heated copper.

You will thus have two bodies equal in distance but differing in heat and differing in radiance, and you will find that the greater heat will produce a reflection of greater heat in the mirror than the aforesaid flame.

We may say, therefore, that it is not the brightness of the sun which warms but its natural heat.

It is proved that the sun in its nature is warm and not cold as has already been stated.

The concave mirror although cold when it receives the rays of the fire reflects them hotter than the fire.

A ball of glass when filled with cold water sends out from itself rays caught from the fire which are even hotter than the fire.

From the two experiments referred to, it follows, as regards this warmth of the rays that issue from the mirror or from the ball of cold water, that they are warm of their own essence, and not because the mirror or ball are hot. And in this case the same thing happens when the sun has passed through the bodies which it warms by its own essence. And from this it has been concluded that the sun is not hot, whilst by the experiments referred to it has been proved that it is extremely hot—from the experiment which has been mentioned, of the mirror and of the ball which being cold and taking the rays of the heat of the fire convert them into warm rays because the primary cause is warm. And the same thing happens with the sun, which being itself warm, in passing through these cold mirrors reflects great heat.

You will discover the various degrees of thinness of the waters by suspending at a uniform depth of the opposite ends a strip of old linen cloth, which should be dry, and which should penetrate on each side as far as the bottom of two vases filled with the two different kinds of water with which you wish to make your experiment. Then these waters will rise a certain distance on the cloth and will proceed gradually to evaporate, and as much as has been the evaporation of that which has risen up, so much will it rise again from the rest until the vase is dried up. And if you refill the vase the water will all rise in the piece of cloth with imperceptible slowness, and so as has been said, it will gradually become dried up. And by this means the piece will remain full of the rest of the water which has evaporated, and in this way, by means of the weights that have been acquired, you will be able to tell which water holds more earth in solution than the other.

If you have some strong glue, half tepid and half cold, and only slightly liquid, and press paste of vermicelli on it, congealed and solidified, and of any color you like, this will make very beautiful twists, and the parts of them will be exactly like thin narrow ribbons.

To take away the smell from oil:
Take some crude oil and put ten pints of it in a vessel.

Make a mark on the vessel according to the height of the oil, and then proceed to add a pint of vinegar, and boil until the oil has gone down as low as the mark that was made. By this means you will be sure that the oil has come back to its first amount and that all the vinegar has evaporated, and has carried all the bad smell away with it.

I believe that it is possible to do the same with nut oil, and with every other oil which has a bad smell.

If a cask is filled four braccia high with wine and throws the wine a distance of four braccia away, when the wine has become so lowered that it has dropped to a height of two braccia in the cask, will it also throw the wine through the same pipe a distance of two braccia, that is, whether the fall, and the range that the pipe can throw, diminish in equal proportion or no.

If from the cask when full two jugs are filled through the pipe in an hour, when the cask is half full it ought for this reason to fill only one jug in an hour, if pouring from the same pipe.

This rule with all the other similar ones about waters which are poured through pipes ought to be put at the commencement of the instruments, in order to be able through various rules the better to proceed to the proofs of these instruments.

In order to make trial of anyone and see whether he has a true judgment as to the nature of weights, ask him at what point one ought to cut one of the two equal arms of the balance so as to cause the part cut off, attached to the extremity of its remainder, to form with precision a counterpoise to the opposite arm. The thing is never possible, and if he gives you the position it is clear that he is a poor mathematician.

Cause an hour to be divided into three thousand parts, and this you will do by means of a clock by making the pendulum lighter or heavier.

If you wish to make a fire which shall set a large room in a blaze without doing any harm you will proceed thus: first perfume the air with dense smoke of incense or other strongly smelling thing, then blow or cause to boil and reduce to steam ten pounds of brandy.

But see that the room is closed altogether, and throw powder of varnish among the fumes and this powder will be found floating upon the fumes; then seize a torch and enter suddenly into the room and instantly everything will become a sheet of flame.

Take away that yellow surface which covers the orange and distil it in a retort until the extract is pronounced perfect.

Close up a room thoroughly and have a brazier of copper or iron with a fire in it, and sprinkle over it two pints of brandy a little at a time in such a way that it may be changed into smoke. Then get someone to come in with a light and you will see the room suddenly wrapped in flame as though it was a flash of lightning, and it will not do any harm to anyone.

[*Diagrams*]

Here there is need of a clock to show the hours, minutes and seconds.

For measuring how great a distance one goes in an hour with the current of the wind.

For learning the quality and density of the air and when it will rain.

For reckoning the mileage of the sea.

[*With drawing*]

This is the way to dredge a harbor, and the plough *m n* will have in front of it spikes shaped like ploughshares and knives, and this plough will be used to load a large cart with mud. The cart will have its back perforated after the manner of a net in order that the water may not be shut within the box; and the said plough is to be moved along above the place where the mud is to be dug out, and along with it a barge; and when it has reached the bottom the windlass *b* will draw it underneath the windlass *a,* and the windlass *a* will raise it up when it is full as far as its beam, in such a way that there will be room for the barge to go underneath it and take the mud from the plough; and so this plough will be able to dislodge the mud from the bottom and unload it upon the barge which is placed underneath it.

[*With drawings*]

These scissors open and shut with a single movement of the hand.

Scissors used by the bonnet-makers for cutting cloth. Rapid in the action of opening and shutting like the others.

This [tool] has in itself so much more ease in its movement because the user does not have to adjust the spring or curve, as is the case with those scissors which are all in one piece. With these it is not necessary to wait in order to cut the threads of the cloth, or to bend by force the spring which is in the heel of the scissors.

This closes at the same rate of speed as the rest; but opens much more rapidly.

[*A way of saving oneself in a tempest or shipwreck at sea. With drawing*]

It is necessary to have a coat made of leather with a double hem over the breast of the width of a finger, and double also from the girdle to the knee, and let the leather of which it is made be quite airtight. And when you are obliged to jump into the sea, blow out the lappets of the coat through the hems of the breast, and then jump into the sea.

And let yourself be carried by the waves, if there is no shore near at hand and you do not know the sea.

And always keep in your mouth the end of the tube through which the air passes into the garment; and if once or twice it should become necessary for you to take a breath when the foam prevents you, draw it through the mouth of the tube from the air within the coat.

A clock to be used by those who grudge the wasting of time.

And this is how it works: when as much water has been poured through the funnel into the receiver as there is in the opposite balance, this balance rises and pours its water into the first receiver; and this being doubled in weight jerks violently upwards the feet of the sleeper, who is thus awakened and goes to his work.

In order to drill through a beam it is necessary to hold it suspended and drill from below upwards so that the hole may empty of itself, and you should make this canopy so that the sawdust may not fall upon the head of him who turns the screw; and see that the turners rise at the same time as the said screw. And make the hole first with a fine auger and then with a larger one.

[*Timepiece. With drawing*]

Four springs for a timepiece, so that when one has finished its course the other commences, and as the first turns, the second remains motionless. And the first is fixed above the second like a screw, and when it is fixed, the second spring takes the same movement completely, and so do all.

[Paddle-boat. With drawing]

Barge made of beams and covered over above. But make a large wheel of oars concealed within it, and make a furrow from one end of it to the other, as appears in *a,* where the wheel can touch the water.

[To make concrete. With drawings]

a is a box which can open and empty itself, and in it you can make a concrete formed of fine pebbles and chalk. Let these blocks dry on the ground and then place them one upon another under the water, in order to form a dam against the rush of the water.

Frames filled with gravel and twigs of birch, that is, a layer of twigs [*sketch*] placed vertically in this direction and a layer of gravel, then a layer in this contrary direction [*sketch*] and then a layer of gravel, and thus you will construct it bit by bit.

See if there are a number of small stones of different sizes whether the heaviest goes farthest when one throws it, then try alone with the same instrument and force, and see whether it travels a greater or less distance alone than when accompanied. And whether also if the stones are all of the same form and weight, like the balls of an air gun, and are thrown by the same force in the same time, they travel the same distance.

[With drawing]

Webbed glove for swimming in the sea.

[Water bellows. With drawings]

These are kinds of bellows without leather and they are of admirable utility and extremely durable. And their method of use is as follows: The bellows is always from the center downwards full of water, that is *M N,* and in the continual revolution of the bellows, *N* rises until it reaches the air hole *S T,* which is made in the outside of the second covering, as appears in the instrument below, and comes to meet with the said pipe *S T* the hole *o,* which is in the reservoir *N;* and as much as is the volume of water that goes from *N* to *M,* so much air enters through the hole *o* in the reservoir *N,* and as much air is driven out of the reservoir *M* as *N* gives it of water. And the air which is driven out from *M* by the water is that which blows the bellows. The said bellows should be of oak because this resists water for the longest time, and have inside it a coating of turpentine and pitch, so that when it is not in use the part above which is out of the water does not come to open; and this type of bellows is turned by the weight of a man walking above on the steps.

It would also be extremely useful to cause it to turn by the force of a fall of water.

The base of the bellows below the tube *S T* remains fixed, and the rest turns there within, as a case would within its cover.

Use salt water so that it may not become foul in the bellows.

[*Machine for excavating earth. With drawing*]

Here the calculation of the power is not at present fixed.

But you, reader, have to understand that this has a use, which arises by means of the saving of time, which saving springs from the fact that the instrument which conveys the earth up from below is always in the act of carrying it and never turns back. The adversary says that in this case it takes as long to turn round in a useless circle as to turn back at the end of the forward action. But since the additional spaces of time that are interposed between the spaces of useful time are equal in this and in all other inventions, it is necessary to search here for a method whereby the time may be spent in as vigorous and effective a method of work as possible, which will be by inventing a machine that will take more earth; as will be shown on the reverse of this page.

The winch *n* as it turns causes a small wheel to revolve, and this small wheel turns the cogged wheel *f*, and this wheel *f* is joined to the angle of the boxes which carry the earth from the swamp and discharge themselves upon the barges. But the two cords *m f* and *m b* revolve round the pole *f*, and make the instrument move with the two barges against *m*, and these cords are very useful for this purpose.

The pole is so made as to descend to as great a depth as the wheel has to descend in order to deepen the water of the marsh.

Make it so that the buckets which are plunging with the mouth downwards have such an opening that the air cannot escape; it will also be a good thing that the covered exits to the buckets should be of terra cotta, so that they may be better able to pass beneath the water; and of copper would be best of all.

[*Magnifying glasses*]

Lens of crystal thickness, at the sides the twelfth part of an inch. This lens of crystal should be free from spots and very clear; and at the sides it ought to be the thickness of a twelfth of an inch, that is to say, of the one hundred and forty-fourth part of a braccio, and thin in the center according to the sight that it ought to serve for, that is to say, according to the proportion of those lenses which agree with it; and let it be worked in the same mold as these lenses. The width of the frame will be one-sixth of a braccio and its length one-quarter of a braccio; consequently it will be three inches long and two wide, that is to say, a square and a half. And this lens should be held at a distance of a third of a braccio from the eye when used, and it should be the same distance from the letter that you are reading. If it is farther away this letter will appear larger, so that the ordinary type of print will seem like a letter on an apothecary's chest.

This lens is suitable for keeping in a cabinet; but if you wish to keep it outside make it one-eighth of a braccio long and one-twelfth wide.

[*A pedometer. Figure*]

In order to know how far one goes in an hour, take the potter's wheel constructed as you see, and place above the instrument, of which the center may be upon a circular line which turns exactly five braccia, the diameter being one and $1\frac{2}{22}$ braccia. Then tightly close the instrument, have harmonic time, smear all the inside of the instrument with turpentine, turn the wheel uniformly and notice where the top layer of dust has stuck to the turpentine, and see how many revolutions the wheel has made and in how many beats of harmonic time. And if the wheel has made two revolutions in one beat of time, which amounts to ten braccia, that is to say, the three-hundredth part of a mile, you will be able to say that this instrument has moved a mile in three hundred beats of time, and that an hour is one thousand and eighty beats of time; which will make three miles an hour and one hundred and eighty three-hundredth parts.

[*A decoration*]

If you make small pipes after the manner of goose quills, which are opaque and white with a coating of black within and then transparent, and with sardonyx outside and then transparent; and let all the thick portion of the pipes be made up of these mixtures, and then moisten them and press them and leave them to dry in the press—if you press them flat they will give one effect, if you press them into a rectangle they will give another, and similarly if you press them into a triangle; but if you press them in front or folded in different ways you will also do well.

And if in the transparent part exposed to the sun you make with a small style a mixture of different colors, especially of black and white opaque, and yellow of burned orpiment, you can make very beautiful patterns and various small stains with lines like those of agate.

[Dress for carnival]

To make a beautiful garment, take fine cloth and give it a strong-smelling coat of varnish made of oil of turpentine; and glaze it with eastern [scarlet] kermes, having the stencil perforated and moistened to prevent it from sticking. And let this stencil have a pattern of knots, which should afterwards be filled in with black millet, and the background with white millet.

Take dust of oak-apple and vitriol and reduce it to a fine powder and spread this over the paper after the manner of varnish; then write on it with a pen dipped in the saliva and it will become as black as ink.

[Diagram]

To try again the wheel which continually revolves.

I have many weights attached to a wheel at various places: I ask you the center of the whole sum of the weight.

I take a wheel revolving on its axis, upon which are attached at various places weights of equal gravity, and I would wish to know which of these weights will remain lower than any of the others and at what stage it will stop. I will do as you see above, employing this rule for four sides of the circle, and that where you will see greater difference upon the arms of the balance, that is that experiment which will throw you the sum of one of the gravities more distant from the pole of the balance, that will go on and become stationary below; and if you want all the details, repeat the experiment as many times as there are weights attached to the wheel.

Moreover, you might set yourself to prove that by equipping such a wheel with many balances, every part, however small, which turned over as the result of percussion would suddenly cause another balance to fall, and by this the wheel would stand in perpetual movement. But by this you would be deceiving yourself; for as there are these twelve pieces and only one moves to the percussion, and by this percussion the wheel may make such a movement as may be one twentieth part of its circle, if then you gave it twenty-four balances the weight would be doubled and the proportion of the percussion of the descending weight diminished by half, and by this the half of the movement would be lessened. Consequently, if the first was one-twentieth of the circle this second would be one-fortieth, and it would always go in proportion, continuing to infinity.

As the attachment of the heavy body is farther from the center of the wheel, the revolving movement of the wheel round its pivot will become more difficult, although the motive power may not vary.

The same is seen with the time of clocks, for, if you place the two weights nearer or farther away from the center of the timepiece, you make the hours shorter or longer.

Whatever weight shall be fastened to the wheel, which weight may be the cause of the movement of this wheel, without any doubt the center of such weight will remain under the center of its axis.

And no instrument which turns on its axis that can be

constructed by human ingenuity will be able to avoid this result.

O speculators about perpetual motion, how many vain chimeras have you created in the like quest? Go and take your place with the seekers after gold.

[*With drawing*]

Lamp in which as the oil becomes low the wick rises.

And this proceeds from the fact that the wheel which raises the wick rests upon the oil. As the oil diminishes so the wheel descends, and as it descends it revolves by means of the thread that is wrapped round its axle, and the cogs of the wheel push the toothed pipe that receives the wick.

It will also do the same if *a*, the axle of the wheel, does not descend, and the only descent is that of the light object *b*, which floats upon the oil, for this light object descends at the same time as the surface of the oil, and causes the wheel to turn, and this by means of its cogs pushes up the aforesaid cogged pipe with a slow movement.

[*The mint of Rome. With drawings*]

This can also be made without a spring, but the screw above must always be joined to the part of the movable sheath.

No coins can be considered as good which have not the rim perfect; and in order to ensure the rim being perfect, it is necessary first that the coins should be absolutely round.

In order to make this, it is necessary first to make the coin perfect in weight, breadth and thickness; therefore, you must first have many plates made of this [uniform] breadth and thickness drawn through the same press, and these should remain in the form of strips, and from these strips you should stamp out the round coins after the manner in which sieves are made for chestnuts, and these coins are then stamped in the way described above.

The hollow of the mold should be uniformly and imperceptibly higher at the top than at the bottom.

This cuts the coins of perfect roundness, thickness and weight, and saves the man who cuts and weighs, and also saves the man who makes the coins round.

They pass therefore merely through the hands of the worker of the plate and the stamper, and they are very fine coins.

[*Siphon clock. Slow time fuse*]

A preparation of mercury drawn through very fine copper of the shape of a siphon, the sides through the length of which the liquid rises and falls being of imperceptible thickness, will be seen to form a timepiece after the manner of an hourglass, and this is the slowest and most graduated descent that can be made, so much so that it may happen that in an hour not one grain of the mercury passes from one vessel to the other.

And the surface of its container is sensitive by reason of the opacity of the mercury, the skin of this mercury becoming imperceptibly lowered with the descent that occurs as the siphon discharges itself; and by this means you will be able to create a fire which by means of percussion will generate itself at the end of a year or more, and this without any sound down to the moment of the creation of the fire.

[*Camp bed. With sketch*]

Four straps for the length and eight across.

And each of the straps to be buckled at one end and nailed at the other.

[*Movable bridge. With sketches*]

Bridge to draw horizontally with a windlass.

Let *a* be a pulley, *b* the windlass.

c n will be a pavement of flagstones which has a tube beneath it through which the chain passes.

This is the front of the said bridge.

Here is a bridge which carries with it little wheels, and another, better, which travels on small wheels that remain fixed in one position.

a b is the part of the bridge that projects out of the wall;
b c is the part that remains within.

[*Fittings of a stove*]

This is the lattice which comes between the eyes and the fire of the stove.

All the transparent part [*il netto*] has a breadth of a braccio and a quarter; and there are six thin boards, but it is better that they should be of thin brass.

The opening two braccia high and the transparent part one braccio and a quarter wide.

You should divide it in height in two parts, so as to be able at will to open below and not above, in order to warm the legs.

In the lower part you should use six boards, so that they are wider below than above, in order to be able to put the feet to warm; above, there should be eight, to be able to put the hands, which are narrower.

[*Diagram*]

To make a pair of compasses diminish or increase a portion of their measurement with equal proportion in each part:

Bind it spirally with a screw which has as much of it smooth as enters in the compasses and all the rest is carved spirally; and this screw may be changed at different places throughout the length of the compasses, because at different places there are holes equally distant from the extremities of these compasses, into which the screw can enter halfway as at *a*, a quarter as at *b*, and one-eighth as at *c*; and so it proceeds through the whole, and it is bound by the nut, *h*, of this screw.

Anyone who spends one ducat for the pair may take the instrument, and he will not be paying more than half a ducat as a premium to the inventor of the instrument and one grosso for the operator; but I have no wish to be an under-official.

[*To add water to white wine and so cause it to become red*]

Crush an oak-apple to a fine powder and stand it for eight days in white wine, and in the same way dissolve vitriol in water, and let the water and the wine settle well and become clear each of itself, and strain them well; and when you dilute the white wine with this water it will turn red.

[*With drawing*]

Dry or moist vapor bath, very small and portable, weighing twenty-five pounds.

[*With drawings*]

A method of ascertaining how far water travels in an hour. This is done by means of harmonic time, and it could be done by a pulse if the time of its beat were uniform; but musical time is more reliable in such a case, for by means of it, it is possible to calculate the distance that an object carried by this water travels in ten or twelve of these beats of time; and by this means it is possible to make a general rule for every level canal. But not for rivers, for when these are flowing underneath the surface they do not seem to be moving above.

[*Drawing: with note "lathe for potters"*]

How many miles an hour with a wind. And here one may see with the water of the mill which moves it how many revolutions the wheel, which is about five braccia, makes in an hour. And so you will make the true rule away from the sea, making the wheel go one, two and then three times in the hour; and by this means you will regulate it exactly, and it will be true and good.

[*Meat-roasting jack*]

Water which is blown through a small hole in a vessel in which it is boiled is blown out with fury and is entirely changed into steam, and by this means meat is turned to be roasted.

[*Drawing: wheel on shaft with counterpoise on suspended looped cord*]

In order to see how many miles a ship can go in an hour, have an instrument made which moves upon a smooth wheel together with this wheel, and so adjust the counterpoise that moves the wheel as to cause it to move for an hour; and you will be able to see how many revolutions this wheel makes in the hour. The revolution of the wheel may be five braccia, and it will make six hundred revolutions in a mile. And the glass should be varnished or soaped on the inside, so that the dust that falls from the hopper may attach itself to it; and the spot where it strikes will remain marked; and by this means you will see and be able with certainty [to discern] the exact height where the dust struck, because it will remain sticking there.

One may make of wood thin grained boards, which will seem like camlets and watered silks and with various fixed marks.

VIII

Earth, Air and Water

I · PHYSICAL GEOGRAPHY

THE streams of rivers move different kinds of matter which are of varying degrees of gravity, and they are moved farther from their position in proportion as they are lighter, and will remain nearer to the bottom in proportion as they are heavier, and will be carried a greater distance when driven by water of greater power.

But when this power ceases to be capable of subduing the resistance of the gravel, this gravel becomes firm and checks the direct movement of the water which led it to this place. Then the water, as it strikes on the gravel which has been increased in this manner, leaps back crosswise and strikes upon other spots to which it was unaccustomed, and takes away other deposits of soil down to their foundations. And so the places where first the said river used to pass are deserted and become silted up anew by a fresh deposit from the turbid waters, and these in due course become choked up in these same places.

Of the rivers greatly swollen by the falling down of the mountains along their sides, which bring about the formation of very great lakes at high altitudes:

The avalanches from the mountains falling down upon their bases, which have been worn away by the continuous currents of the rivers rushing precipitously at their feet with their swift waters, have closed up the mouths of the great valleys situated in the high places.

These are the causes why the surface of the water is raised by the creation of lakes, and why new streams and rivers are formed in high places.

I perceive that the surface of the earth was from of old entirely filled up and covered over in its level plains by the salt waters, and that the mountains, the bones of the earth, with their wide bases, penetrated and towered up amid the air, covered over and clad with much high-lying soil. Subsequently the incessant rains have caused the rivers to increase, and by repeated washing have stripped bare part of the lofty summits of these mountains, leaving the sight of the earth, so that the rock finds itself exposed to the air, and the earth has departed from these places. And the earth from off the slopes and the lofty summits of the mountains has already descended to their bases, and has raised the floors of the seas which encircle these bases, and caused the plain to be uncovered, and in some parts has driven away the seas from there over a great distance.

Here a doubt arises, and that is as to whether the Flood which came in the time of Noah was universal or not, and this would seem not to have been the case for the reasons which will now be given. We have it in the Bible that the said Flood was caused by forty days and forty nights of continuous and universal rain, and that this rain rose ten cubits above the highest mountain in the world. But consequently, if it had been the case that the rain was universal, it would have formed in itself a covering around our globe, which is spherical in shape; and a sphere has every part of its circumference equally distant from its center, and therefore on the sphere of water finding itself in the aforesaid condition, it becomes impossible for the water on its surface to move, since water does not move of its own accord unless to descend. How then did the waters of so great a Flood depart, if it is proved that they had no power of motion? If they departed, how did they move, unless they went upwards? At this point natural causes fail us, and therefore in order to resolve such a doubt we must needs either call in a miracle to our aid or else say that all this water was evaporated by the heat of the sun.

Of creatures which have their bones on the outside, like cockles, snails, oysters, scallops, *bouoli* and the like, which are of innumerable kinds:

When the floods of the rivers which were turbid with fine mud deposited this upon the creatures which dwelt beneath the waters near the ocean borders, these creatures became embedded in this mud; and finding themselves entirely covered under a great weight of mud, they were forced to perish for lack of a supply of the creatures on which they were accustomed to feed.

In course of time the level of the sea became lower, and as the salt water flowed away this mud became changed into stone; and such of these shells as had lost their inhabitants became filled up in their stead with mud. And consequently, during the process of change of all the surrounding mud into stone, this mud also which was within the frames of the half-opened shells—since by the opening of the shell it was joined to the rest of the mud—became also itself changed into stone. And therefore all the frames of these shells were left between two petrified substances, namely, that which surrounded them and that which they enclosed.

These are still to be found in many places, and almost all the petrified shellfish in the rocks of the mountains still have their natural frame round them, and especially those which were of a sufficient age to be preserved by reason of their hardness, while the younger ones, which were already in great part changed into chalk, were penetrated by the viscous and petrifying moisture.

All the creatures that have their bones within their skin, on being covered over by the mud from the inundations of rivers which have left their accustomed beds, are at once enclosed in a mold by this mud. And so in course of time, as the channels of the rivers become lower, these creatures being embedded and shut in within the mud, and the flesh and organs being worn away and only the bones remaining, and even these having lost their natural order of arrangement, they have fallen down into the base of the mold which has been formed by their impress. And as the mud becomes lifted above the level of the stream, the mud runs away, so that it dries and becomes first a sticky paste and then changes into stone, enclosing whatsoever it finds within itself and itself filling up every cavity; and finding the hollow part of the mold formed by these creatures, it percolates gradually through the tiny crevices in the earth through which the air that is within escapes away—that is laterally, for it cannot escape upwards since there the crevices are filled up by the moisture descending into the cavity, nor can it escape downwards, because the moisture which has already fallen has closed up the crevices. There remain the openings at the side, whence this air, condensed and pressed down upon by the moisture which descends, escapes with the same slow rate of progress as that of the moisture which descends there; and this paste as it dries becomes stone, which is devoid of weight, and preserves the exact shapes of the creatures which have there made the mold, and encloses their bones within it.

The creature that resides within the shell constructs its dwelling with joints and seams and roofing and the other various parts, just as man does in the house in which he dwells; and this creature expands the house and roof gradually in proportion as its body increases and as it is attached to the sides of these shells.

Consequently the brightness and smoothness which these shells possess on the inner side is somewhat dulled at the point where they are attached to the creature that dwells there, and the hollow of it is roughened, ready to receive the knitting together of the muscles by means of which the creature draws itself in when it wishes to shut itself up within its house.

When nature is on the point of creating stones, it produces a kind of sticky paste which, as it dries, forms itself into a solid mass together with whatever it has enclosed there, which, however, it does not change into stone but preserves within itself in the form in which it has found them. This is why leaves are found whole within the rocks which are formed at the bases of the mountains, together with a mixture of different kinds of things, just as they have been left there by the floods from the rivers which have occurred in the autumn seasons; and there the mud caused by the successive inundations has covered them over, and then this mud grows into one mass together with the aforesaid paste, and becomes changed into successive layers of stone which correspond with the layers of the mud.

And if you wish to say that the shells are produced by nature in these mountains by means of the influence of the stars, in what way will you show that this influence produces in the very same place shells of various sizes and varying in age, and of different kinds?

And how will you explain to me the fact of the shingle being all stuck together and lying in layers at different alti-

tudes upon the high mountains? For there there is to be
found shingle from divers parts carried from various countries to the same spot by the rivers in their course; and this
shingle is nothing but pieces of stone which have lost their
sharp edges from having been rolled over and over for a long
time, and from the various blows and falls which they have
met with during the passage of the waters which have brought
them to this spot.

And how will you account for the very great number of
different kinds of leaves embedded in the high rocks of these
mountains, and for the *aliga,* the seaweed, which is found
lying intermingled with the shells and the sand?

And in the same way you will see all kinds of petrified
things, together with ocean crabs, broken in pieces and
separated and mixed with their shells.

In this work of yours you have first to prove how the
shells at a height of a thousand braccia were not carried
there by the Deluge, because they are seen at one and the
same level, and mountains also are seen which considerably
exceed this level; and to inquire whether the Deluge was
caused by rain or by the sea rising in a swirling flood. And
then you have to show that neither by rain which makes the
rivers rise in flood nor by the swelling up of the sea could
the shells, being heavy things, be driven by the sea up the
mountains or be thrown there by the rivers contrary to the
course of their waters.

If you should say that the shells which are visible at the
present time within the borders of Italy, far away from the
sea and at great heights, are due to the Flood having deposited them there, I reply that, granting this Flood to have
risen seven cubits above the highest mountain, as he has
written who measured it, these shells which always inhabit

the area near the shores of the sea ought to be found lying on the mountain sides, and not at so short a distance above their bases, and all at the same level, layer upon layer.

Should you say also that the nature of these shells causes them to keep near the edge of the sea, and that as the sea rose in height the shells left their former place and followed the rising waters up to their highest level—to this I reply [that in forty days the shells cannot travel] that the cockle is a creature incapable when out of water of more rapid movement than the snail, or is even somewhat slower, since it does not swim, but makes a furrow in the sand, and supporting itself by means of the sides of this furrow will travel between three and four braccia in a day; and therefore with such a rate of motion it would not have traveled from the Adriatic Sea as far as Monferrato in Lombardy, a distance of two hundred and fifty miles, in forty days—as he has said who kept a record of this time.

And if you say that the waves carried them there—they could not move by reason of their weight except upon their base. And if you do not grant me this, at any rate allow that they must have remained on the tops of the highest mountains, and in the lakes which are shut in among the mountains, such as the lake of Lario or Como, and Lake Maggiore, and that of Fiesole and of Perugia and others.

As for those who say that these shells are found to exist over a wide area having been created at a distance from the sea by the nature of the locality and the disposition of the heavens, which move and influence the place to such a creation of animal life, to these it may be answered that, granted such an influence over these animals, it could not happen that they were in one line except in the case of animals of the same species and age; and not the old with the young, nor one with an outer covering and another without its covering, nor one broken and another whole, one filled with sea sand, and the fragments great and small of others inside the whole shells which stand gaping open; nor the claws of crabs without the rest of their bodies; nor with the shells of other species fastened on to them like animals crawling over them and leaving the mark of their track on the outside, where it has eaten its way like a worm in wood; nor would there be found among them bones and fishes' teeth which some call arrows and others serpents' tongues; nor would so many parts of different animals be found joined together, unless they had been thrown up there upon the borders of the sea.

And the Flood would not have carried them there because things heavier than water do not float upon the surface of the water, and the aforesaid things could not be at such heights unless they had been carried there floating on the waves, and that is impossible on account of their weight.

Where the valleys have never been covered by the salt waters of the sea, there the shells are never found; as is plainly visible in the great valley of the Arno above Gonfolina, a rock which was once united with Monte Albano in the form of a very high bank. This kept the river dammed up in such a way that before it could empty itself into the sea which was afterwards at the foot of this rock it formed two large lakes, the first of which is where we now see the city of Florence flourish together with Prato and Pistoia; and Monte Albano followed the rest of the bank down to where Serravalle now stands. In the upper part of the Val d'Arno as far as Arezzo, a second lake was formed and this emptied its waters into the above-mentioned lake. It was shut in at about where now we see Girone, and it filled all the valley above for a distance of forty miles. This valley received upon its base all the earth carried down by the turbid waters, and it is still to be seen at its maximum height at the foot of Prato Magno, for there the rivers have not worn it away.

Within this soil may be seen the deep cuttings of the rivers which have passed there in their descent from the great mountain of Prato Magno; in which cuttings there are no traces visible of any shells or of marine earth.

This lake was joined to that of Perugia.

A great quantity of shells may be seen where the rivers empty themselves into the sea, because in such places the water is not very salt on account of the mixture of the fresh water which unites with it. A proof of this is to be seen where the Apennines once emptied their rivers into the waters of the Adriatic, for there among the mountains in most parts a great quantity of shells are visible, together with bluish marine clay; and all the rocks which are broken away in such places are found to be full of shells.

We know that the Arno did the same when it fell from the rock of Gonfolina into the sea, which was not very far below it, because in those times it must have stood higher than the top of San Miniato al Tedesco, since in the highest summits of this [mountain] one sees the rocks full of shells and oysters within its banks. The shells did not extend in the direction of Val di Nievole because the fresh waters of the Arno did not extend so far.

How the shells were not carried from the sea by the Deluge, because the waters which came from the earth to the sea, although they drew the sea towards the earth, were those which smote its base, because the water which comes from the earth has a stronger current than that of the sea, and as a consequence is more powerful and enters beneath the other water of the sea, and stirs up the bottom and carries with it all the movable objects which are to be found in it such as the above-mentioned shells and other like things; and as the water which comes from the land is muddier than that of the sea, it is so much the more powerful and heavier than it. I do not see, therefore, in what way the said shells could have come to be so far inland unless they had been born there.

If you should tell me that the river Loire which passes

through France spreads itself over more than eighty miles of country when the sea is increased, because the country forms a great plain and the sea rises about twenty braccia, and that shells are sometimes found in this plain at a distance of eighty miles from the sea, the reply is that the flow and ebb in our Mediterranean seas does not cause so much variation, because in the Gulf of Genoa it does not vary at all, at Venice and in Africa only a little; and where it varies only a little, it covers but little of the country.

Refutation of such as say that the shells were carried a distance of many days' journey from the sea by reason of the Deluge.

I hold that the Deluge would not be able to carry up into the mountains objects native to the sea unless the sea had become so swollen as to form a flood so great that it even mounted above the height of these same places, and this process could not have occurred because it would have created a vacuum. And if you should say that the air would rush in there, we have already concluded that what is heavy cannot be supported on what is light, wherefore we conclude of necessity that this Deluge was caused by rain water; and if this was the case all this water flowed into the sea, and the sea does not flow up the mountains; and if it ran into the sea, it pushed the shells along the shore into the sea and did not draw them to itself. And if you should say that because the sea was raised by rain water it carried these shells to such a height, we have already stated that things heavier than water cannot float upon its surface, but remain at the bottom, and are not moved from there unless by pressure from the waves. And if you were to say that it was the waves which had carried them to these high places, we have proved that the waves when of great depth move in an opposite direction at their base to their movement above, this being shown by the turbidity of the sea arising from the soil that has been washed away near its shores.

An object lighter than water moves with its wave and it is left on the highest spot of the bank by the highest wave. An object heavier than water moves only when driven by its wave along the surface of its bed. And from these two conclusions, which in their places will be fully proved, we may conclude that the wave of the surface cannot carry shells because they are heavier than water; and consequently they will be driven by the lower wave when the wind comes from the land, because when the wind comes from the land, the wave at the bottom of the sea moves in the opposite direction to the course of the wind which is then prevailing; and this, moreover, will not cause the shells to be carried to the mountains, because the water at the bottom, which moves in the opposite direction to the wind, will be so much slower than the wave of the surface as it is deeper than the height of the wave. This is evident because if the wave of the surface is the height of one braccio and there are a hundred braccia of water below it, then without doubt the lower wave will be a hundred times slower than the upper wave, as is shown in the seventh proposition. The upper wave will never turn back on its base with any great force unless the depth of the water that is below the wave is equal to that of the wave.

The tiny wave which may be seen on the high seas traveling against the course of the wind will not pass over its base; that is, it will not touch it but will dissolve at contact with the surface wave. I hold that such movement of water, changing from its surface to its base, resembles that which takes place on the surface between two banks, seeing that if a third of the expanse of the river be moving towards the west, another third will move towards the east and the remainder to the west; and if there should be another similar part there, that would return to the east. The lateral movements of rivers will become slower in proportion as they are farther removed from the first current. As regards the friction created by water inside other water and moving more swiftly, whether it divides immediately, that is, whether the edges of this body of water are worn away or follow one after another—that is, the swifter portion carrying the less swift with it—I maintain that this is not the case, for if it carried with it more water than usual it would grow to such a size during its long course that it would be carrying with it all the water of the river.

The reason why the oysters are very seldom found dead on the shores of the sea is that usually they live fastened to the rocks at the bottom of the sea and are incapable of movement except in the half which is sensitive and light. The other valve is fixed to the stone, or if not fixed, nature has caused them to grow larger and so to become so heavy that the small amount of undulation which takes place in the vast depths of the sea cannot easily dislodge them. But the valve that has the power of movement is very light and performs the same function for it as the lid does for a chest. And when the oyster feeds, its food walks into the house of its own accord, for it consists of certain animalculae which feed round the shells of the dead ones and which consequently are found where there are a great many shells of dead oysters. If the Deluge had carried the shells for distances of three and four hundred miles from the sea, it would have brought them with the various different species mixed up, all heaped up together; but even at such distances from the sea we see the oysters all together and also the shellfish and the cuttle-fish and all the other shells which stand together in companies, found all together dead, and the single shells are found one at a distance from another, as we see them every day on the seashores.

And we find the oysters together in very large families,

among which some may be seen with their shells still joined together, which serves to indicate that they were left there by the sea and that they were still living when the straits of Gibraltar were cut through.

In the mountains of Parma and Piacenza, multitudes of shells and corals filled with wormholes may be seen still adhering to the rocks, and when I was making the great horse at Milan a large sack of those which had been found in these parts was brought to my workshop by some peasants, and among them were many which were still in their original condition.

Under the ground and down in the deep excavations of the stone quarries, timbers of worked beams are found which have already become black. They have been found during my time in the excavations made at Castel Fiorentino, and they were buried there before the sand deposited by the Arno in the sea which then flowed over the spot had been raised to such a height, and before the plains of the Casentino had been so much lowered by the removal of the earth which the Arno was continually washing away from them.

In Candia, in Lombardy, near to Allessandria della Paglia, while some men were engaged in digging a well for Messer Gualtieri, who has a house there, the skeleton of a very large ship was found at a depth of about ten braccia beneath the ground; and as the timber was black and in excellent condition, Messer Gualtieri thought fit to have the mouth of the well enlarged in such a way that the ends of the ship should be uncovered.

The red stone of the mountains of Verona is found with shells all intermingled which have become part of this stone, and their mouths have become sealed up by the cement of which the stone has been formed, and portions of them have remained separated from the rest of the mass of stone which enclosed them, because the outer covering of the shell intervened and thus prevented them from uniting; and in other cases this cement has petrified the old broken outer covering.

And if you should say that these shells have been and still constantly are being created in such places as these by the nature of the locality and through the potency of the heavens in those spots, such an opinion cannot exist in brains possessed of any extensive powers of reasoning, because the years of their growth are numbered upon the outer coverings of their shells; and both small and large ones may be seen, and these would not have grown without feeding or fed without movement, and here they would not be able to move.

How the northern bases of certain Alps are not yet petrified. This is seen clearly where the rivers which cut through them flow towards the north, for these cut through the strata of the living rock in the mountain heights; and where they unite with the plains these strata are all of clay that serves to make pots, as is seen in the Val di Lamona, where the river Lamona as it issues from the Apennines does these same things in its banks.

How the rivers have all sawn through and divided the members of the great Alps one from another. This is revealed by the arrangement of the stratified rocks, in which from the summit of the mountain down to the river one sees the strata on the one side of the river corresponding with those on the other. How the stratified rocks of the mountains are all in layers of mud deposited one above another by the floods of the rivers. How the different thicknesses of the strata of the rocks are created by the different floods of the rivers, that is, the greater and the less floods.

How between the various layers of the stone are still to be found the tracks of the worms which crawled about upon them when it was not yet dry. How all the marine clays still contain shells, and the shell is petrified together with the clay. Of the stupidity and ignorance of those who imagine that these creatures were carried to such places distant from the sea by the Deluge.

How another set of ignoramuses maintains that nature or the heavens have created them in these places through celestial influences; as though in those places one did not find the bones of fishes which have taken a long time to grow; as though one could not count on the shells of cockles and snails the number of the months and years of their lives, just as one can on the horns of bulls and wethers and in the ramification of plants when they have never been cut in any part. And since it has been shown by these signs that the length of their life is evident, it must needs be admitted that these animals could not live without the power of movement in order to seek their food; and we cannot see that they are equipped with any instrument for penetrating the earth or stone in which they find themselves enclosed. But how could one find in the shell of a large snail fragments and bits of many other sorts of shells of different kinds unless they had been thrown into it by the waves of the sea as it lay dead upon the shore, like the other light things which the sea casts up on the land?

Why do we find so many fragments and whole shells between the different layers of the stone unless they had been upon the shore and had been covered over by earth newly thrown up by the sea which then became petrified? And if the above-mentioned Deluge had carried them to these places from the sea, you would find the shells at the edge of one layer of rock only, not at the edge of many, where may be counted the winters of the years during which the sea multiplied the layers of sand and mud brought down by the neighboring rivers, and spread them over its shores. And if you should wish to say that there must have been many deluges in order to produce these layers and the shells among them, it would then become necessary for you to affirm that such a deluge took place every year. Further, as regards the fragments of these shells, it must be presumed that in such a locality there was a sea beach, where the shells were all cast up broken and divided and never in pairs as they are found in the sea when alive, with two valves which form a covering the one to the other. And within the layers of the banks of rivers and of seashores they are found broken; and on the edges of the rocks they are found infrequently and with the two valves together, like those which were left by the sea buried alive within the mud which afterwards dried up and in time became petrified.

And if you should say that the Deluge then rose with its waters above the mountains, the movement of the sea in its journey against the course of the rivers would have been so slow that it would not have been able to carry things heavier than itself floating in it; or if somehow it had had them floating in it, then as it subsided it would have left them strewn about in various places. But how are we to account for the fact of the corals being found every day round about Monferrato in Lombardy with wormholes in them, sticking to the rocks which have been left bare by the currents of the rivers? And the said rocks are all covered with stocks and families of oysters, which as we know do not move but always remain fixed by one of their valves to the rock, having the other open in order to feed upon the animalculae that are swimming about the waters and which while hoping to find good pasture become the food of the above-mentioned shells. Is it not found that the sand that is mixed with the seaweed has become petrified when the seaweed which has divided it has become less? And of this the Po affords instances every day in the debris of its banks.

At Alessandria della Paglia, in Lombardy, there is no other

stone from which to make lime except such as is made up of an infinite number of things native to the sea; but it is now more than two hundred miles distant from the sea.

In eighty-nine [the year 1489] there was an earthquake in the sea of Satalia near to Rhodes, and it opened the depths of the sea, and into the opening that was made, such a torrent of water was poured that for more than three hours the bed of the sea lay bare because of the water which had been lost from it, and then it closed up again to its former level. Whatever changes may occur in the weight of the earth, the surface of the sphere of waters will never cease to be equidistant from the center of the world.

The bosom of the Mediterranean received the principal waters of Africa, Asia and Europe; for they were turned towards it and came with their waters to the base of the mountains which surrounded it and formed its banks.

And the peaks of the Apennines stood up in this sea in the form of islands surrounded by salt water. Nor did Africa as yet, behind its Atlas Mountains, reveal the earth of its great plains, naked to the sky, some three thousand miles in extent; and on the shore of this sea stood Memphis; and above the plains of Italy where flocks of birds are flying today, fishes were once moving in large shoals.

[Instances and deductions as to the earth's increase]

Take a vase, fill it full of pure earth, and set it up on a roof. You will see how immediately the green herbs will begin to shoot up, and how these, when fully grown, will cast their various seeds; and after the children have thus fallen at the feet of their parents, you will see the herbs that have cast their seeds, becoming withered and falling back again to the earth, and within a short time becoming changed into the earth's substance and giving it increase. After this you will see the seeds springing up and passing through the same course, and so you will always see the successive generations, after completing their natural course, by their death and corruption giving increase to the earth. And if you let ten years elapse and then measure the increase in the soil, you will be able to discover how much the earth in general has increased, and then by multiplying you will see how great has been the increase of the earth in the world during a thousand years. Some may say that this instance of the vase which I have mentioned does not justify the deduction based upon it, because one sees in the case of these vases that for the prize of the flowers that are looked for, a part of the soil is frequently taken away, and its place is filled up with new rich soil; and I reply to them that, as the soil which is added there is a blend of rich fat substances and broken bits of all sorts of things, it cannot be said to be pure earth; and this mass of substances decaying and so losing in part their shape becomes changed into a rich ooze, which feeds the roots of the plants above them; and this is the reason why it may appear to you that the earth is lessened. But if you allow the plants that grow in it to die, and their seeds to spring up, then in time you will behold its increase.

For do you not perceive how, among the high mountains, the walls of ancient and ruined cities are being covered over and concealed by the earth's increase?

Nay, have you not seen how on the rocky summits of the mountains the live stone itself has in course of time swallowed up by its growth some column which it supported, and stripping it bare as with shears and grasping it tightly, has left the impress of its fluted form in the living rock?

This air which bounds and continually moves upon this terrestrial machine is mixed with moisture similar to that with which the earth is compounded, and the excess of this moisture falls back continually upon the earth once in twenty-four hours and then springs back raised a little by the heat of the sun and sustained by it so long as it remains in our hemisphere. Then, being left abandoned by it at its departure and still having weight, it falls back on the earth.

In summer this moisture is called dew, and in winter as the cold condenses it and freezes it, it is called hoar frost.

The wave travels beneath the surface[1] of the sea, and leaves behind itself all the foam which is produced in front of it.

The space of the surface of the water that intervenes between the waves· as they come to the shore is polished and smooth. And this comes about because the greatest wave is swifter than the lesser waves of which it is made up [in the univer]sal surface of the sea; and this greatest wave draws back the surface of the sea, and the first foam of the wave descends as it opens at the spot where the remainder is fleeing away.

And the figure of the foam which then remains behind in the wave is always triangular, and its angle is made up of the first foam and that in front of the course where the wave first descended.

The lowest parts of the world are the seas where all the rivers run.

The river never ceases its movement until it reaches the sea; the sea therefore is the lowest part of the world.

Water does not move from place to place unless it is drawn by a lower position. Lowness therefore serves as a magnet for water.

When the surface of the water consists of small shaded waves which form themselves into lines that meet in an angle, the fact shows that the bed of the river is not far away, and

---

[1] *La pelle,* literally "the skin" of the sea.

it is also produced by the sand thrown off by the water as it passes through a confined space, such as the arch of a bridge or the like. When the lines of its surface form a curved or crescent-shaped figure, this is a sign of its lack of depth, for it is caused by the sand carried by the greater current into the lesser, that is, by the less sluggish to the more sluggish, since both of them have but little speed or depth. When the surface of the water shows itself as a straight line, or just a little bent with tiny waves and these with but little sheen or brightness, there is very little depth there; and this is caused by two currents, one slower than the other, which join together again below the island that divides them higher up; for these have caused the sand which each bore with it to settle, because it is deposited at the point of their junction, since at this spot their movement ended.

Sometimes the waves are swifter than the wind, and sometimes the wind is much swifter than the wave; the ships prove this upon the sea. The waves can be swifter than the wind through having been commenced by the great winds, the wind then having ceased and the wave having still preserved a great impetus.

[*Influence of sun and moon on tides*]

That power shows itself greater which is impressed upon a lesser resistance. This conclusion is universal and we may apply it to the flow and ebb in order to prove that the sun or moon impresses itself more on its object, that is, on the waters, when these are of less depth. Consequently the shallow waters of swamps ought to receive with greater potency the cause of the flow and ebb, than the great depths of the ocean.

Every heap of sand, whether it be on level ground or sloping, will have its base twice the length of its axis.

The rivers make greater deposits of soil when near to populated districts than they do where there are no inhabitants, because in such places the mountains and hills are being worked upon, and the rains wash away the soil that has been turned up more easily than the hard ground which is covered with weeds.

The sea shuts itself in among the great valleys of the earth; and this earth serves as a cup for the sea; and the lips of the cup are the shores of the seas, and if these were taken away the sea would cover all the earth; but because every part of the earth that is uncovered is higher than the greatest height of the sea, this sea cannot flow over it, but merely contents itself with covering that earth which serves as its bed. Many, however, in ignorance of this thing, have presumptuously written how the surface of the water of the sea is higher than the highest mountain that can be found; as regards which thing, although they see the bank higher than the water, they are extremely blind who say that it is a miracle for the water in the midst of the sea to be higher than its shore or than the promontories which jut out over the sea. But this fallacy arises from the fact that they imagine a straight line of indefinite length extended above the middle of the sea, which without doubt will be higher than the said shores, because the earth is a sphere and its surface forms a curve, and the farther it is removed from its middle, the more it becomes remote from the said straight line; the fact of it becoming lower in this condition is that which has deceived them; and it is this reason which will be brought forward by the adversary. "That part of the water will be higher which is more remote from the center of the world."

The destruction of marshes will be brought about when turbid rivers flow into them.

This is proved by the fact that where the river flows swiftly it washes away the soil, and where it delays, there it leaves its deposit; and both for this reason and because water never travels so slowly in rivers as it does in the marshes of the valleys the movement of the waters there is imperceptible. But in these marshes the river has to enter through a long, narrow, winding channel, and it has to flow out over a large area of but little depth; and this is necessary because the water flowing in the river is thicker and more laden with earth in the lower than in the upper part; and the sluggish water of the marshes also is the same, but the variation between the lightness and heaviness of the upper and lower waters of the marshes far exceeds that in the currents of the rivers, in which the lightness of the upper part differs but little from the heaviness of the part below.

So the conclusion is that the marsh will be destroyed because it is receiving turbid water below, while above, on the opposite side of the same marsh, only clear water is flowing out; and consequently the bed of the marsh will of necessity be raised by means of the soil which is being continually discharged into it.

II · THE ATMOSPHERE

"THE air moves like a river and carries the clouds with it; just as running water carries all the things that float upon it."

Surface is the name of that division which the body of the air makes with the bodies which are enclosed within it. And it does not partake of the body by which it is surrounded, nor of that which it surrounds; on the contrary, it is the actual contact which these bodies make together.

Therefore, if these bodies are in continual contact, it is necessary that nothing should interpose between them, and consequently the surface, which is enclosed there, is nothing.

This surface has name and not substance because that which has substance has place. Not having place, it resembles nothingness, which has name without substance; consequently, the part of nothing not having anything except the name and not the substance, this part is equal to the whole; so that by this we conclude that the point and the line are equal to the surface.

Where flame cannot live, no animal that draws breath can live.

Excess of wind puts out flame, moderate wind nourishes it.

Drops are formed in the air through the mists or clouds by various movements, as when they encounter each other and become condensed or unite in the movement of the same cloud in the same direction, when one part of the cloud is swifter or slower than the other; for as the swifter part is behind the slower, it conquers it in its course and overtakes it, and condenses it and out of many small drops makes one large one, and this acquires weight and falls. But unless the drops are so formed as to be of considerable size, they are consumed by the friction they make with the air as they traverse it.

Just as the stone thrown into the water becomes the center and cause of various circles, and the sound made in the air spreads itself out in circles, so every body placed within the luminous air spreads itself out in circles and fills the surrounding parts with an infinite number of images of itself, and appears all in all and all in each *smallest* part.

The colors of the middle of the rainbow mingle with each other.

The bow itself is neither in the rain nor in the eye that

sees it, although it is produced by the rain, the sun, and the eye.

The rainbow is invariably seen by the eye which is situated between the rain and the body of the sun, and consequently when the sun is in the east and the rain in the west, the rainbow is produced upon the western rain.

I saw at Milan a thunderbolt strike the Torre della Credenza on its northern side. It traveled along it with a slow movement, and then all at once parted from the tower and carried with it and tore away a part of the wall, three braccia in breadth and length and two in depth. The wall was four braccia in width and was built of old bricks which were thin and small. It was torn away through the vacuum caused by the flame of the thunderbolt. I have found traces of the same power in the rocks of the high Apennines and especially in the rock of La Vernia. The same thing occurs with a cannon in the vacuum left by the flame.

Experience it is that shows how the air has darkness behind it and yet appears blue.

Make smoke of dry wood in a small quantity; let the rays of the sun fall upon this smoke, and behind it place a piece of black velvet, so that it shall be in shadow. You will then see that all the smoke which comes between the eye and the darkness of the velvet will show itself of a very beautiful blue color; and if instead of the velvet you put a white cloth, the smoke will become the color of ashes.

How water blown in the form of spray into a dark place, through which the solar rays pass, produces this blue ray; and especially when this water has been distilled; and how the thin smoke becomes blue. This is said in order to show how the blue color of the atmosphere is caused by the darkness that is above it; and the above-mentioned instances are offered for the benefit of anyone who cannot confirm my experience on Mon Boso.

III · THE NATURE OF WATER

OF the four elements, water is the second least heavy and the second in respect of mobility. It is never at rest until it unites with its maritime element, where, when not disturbed by the winds, it establishes itself and remains with its surface equidistant from the center of the world. It is the increase and humor of all vital bodies. Without it nothing retains its first form. It unites and augments bodies by its increase.

Nothing lighter than itself can penetrate it without violence.

It readily raises itself by heat in thin vapor through the air. Cold causes it to freeze. Stagnation make it foul. That is, heat sets it in movement, cold causes it to freeze, immobility corrupts it.

It assumes every odor, color and flavor, and of itself it has nothing. It percolates through all porous bodies. Against its fury no human defense avails, or if it should avail it is not for long. In its rapid course it often serves as a support to things heavier than itself. It can lift itself up by movement or bound, as far as it sinks down. It submerges with itself in headlong course things lighter than itself. The mastery of its course is sometimes on the surface, sometimes in the center, sometimes at the bottom. One portion rises over the transverse course of another, and but for this the surfaces of the running waters would be without undulations. Every small obstacle, whether on its bank or in its bed, will be the cause of the falling away of the bank or bed opposite to it. When the water is low it does more damage to the bank in its course than it does when it flows in full stream. Its parts do not weigh upon the parts placed beneath them. No river will ever keep its course in the same direction between its banks. Its upper parts do not impart weight to the lower.

If a drop of water falls into the sea when this is calm, it must of necessity be that the whole surface of the sea is raised imperceptibly, seeing that water cannot be compressed within itself like air.

Man has been called by the ancients a lesser world, and indeed the term is rightly applied, seeing that if man is compounded of earth, water, air and fire, this body of the earth is the same; and as man has within himself bones as a stay and framework for the flesh, so the world has the rocks which are the supports of the earth; as man has within him a pool of blood wherein the lungs as he breathes expand and contract, so the body of the earth has its ocean, which also rises and falls every six hours with the breathing of the world; as from the said pool of blood proceed the veins which spread their branches through the human body, in just the same manner the ocean fills the body of the earth with an infinite number of veins of water. In this body of the earth there is lacking, however, the sinews, and these are absent because sinews are created for the purpose of movement, and as the world is perpetually stable within itself no movement ever takes place there, and in the absence of any movement the sinews are not necessary; but in all other things man and the world show a great resemblance.

The movement of water within water proceeds like that of air within air.

Among irremediable and destructive terrors, the inundations caused by rivers in flood should certainly be set before every other dreadful and terrifying movement, nor is it, as some have thought, surpassed by destruction by fire. I find it to be the contrary, for fire consumes that which feeds it and is itself consumed with its food. The movement of water which is created by the slopes of the valleys does not end and die until it has reached the lowest level of the valley; but fire is caused by what feeds it, and the movement of water by its wish to descend. The food of the fire is disunited, and the mischief caused by it is disunited and separated, and the fire dies when it lacks food. The slope of the valley is continuous, and the mischief done by the destructive course of the river will be continuous until, attended by its valleys. it ends in the sea, the universal base and only resting place of the wandering waters of the rivers.

Write how the clouds are formed and how they dissolve, and what it is that causes vapor to rise from the water of the earth into the air, and the cause of mists and of the air becoming thickened, and why it appears more blue or less blue at one time than at another. Write in the same way of the regions of the air and the cause of snow and hail, and how water contracts and becomes hard in the form of ice, and of the new shapes that the snow forms in the air, and of the trees in cold countries with the new shapes of the leaves, and of the pinnacles of ice and hoarfrost that form new shapes of plants with strange leaves, the hoarfrost serving almost as the dew ready to nourish and sustain the said leaves.

[*What causes the eddies of water*]

All the movements of the wind resemble those of the water.

Universally all things desire to maintain themselves in their natural state. So moving water strives to maintain the course pursuant to the power which occasions it, and if it finds an obstacle in its path it completes the span of the course it has commenced, by a circular and revolving movement.

So when water pours out of a narrow channel and descends with fury into the slow-moving currents of mighty seas— since in the greater bulk there is greater power, and greater power offers resistance to the lesser—in this case, the water descending upon the sea beats down upon its slow-moving mass, and this cannot make a place for it with sufficient speed because it is held up by the rest of the water; and so the water that descends, not being willing to slacken its course, turns round after it has struck, and continues its first move-ment in circling eddies, and so fulfills its desire down in the depth; for in these same eddies it finds nothing more than its own movement, which is attended by a succession of circles one within the other; and by thus revolving in circles its course becomes longer and more continuous, because it meets with no obstacle except itself; and this motion eats away and consumes the banks, and they fall headlong in ruin. . . .

When a stone is thrown into still water it will create ripples that expand equally if the water is of uniform depth.

If two stones are thrown one near to the other within the space of a braccio, the circles of the water will increase equally one within the other without the one destroying the other.

But if the bottom is not level the circles will not expand in uniform movement except on the surface.

When an object of long shape is thrown into water it will create an oval undulation.

A round object thrown into running water will create an oval undulation in two movements.

Prove whether a triangle thrown into still water makes its wave of perfect roundness in the end.

[*The eddies at the bottom of water move in an opposite direction to those above*]

The reason of this is that, if the circles which above are large become reduced to a point as they are submerged, and then continue their movement in the direction in which it began, the water will at the bottom make a movement contrary to that above when it separates itself from its center.

Although the sounds which traverse the air proceed from their sources by circular movements, nevertheless the circles which are propelled by their different motive powers meet together without any hindrance and penetrate and pass across one another, always keeping their causes as their centers.

Since, in all cases of movement, water has great conformity with air, I will offer it as an example of the above-mentioned proposition. I say that, if at the same time you throw two small stones into a large lake of still water at a certain distance one from another, you will observe two distinct sets of circles form round the two points where they have struck; and as these sets of circles grow larger they come to meet together and the circles intersect one with another, always keeping as their centers the spots which were struck by the stones. The reason of this is that although some show of movement may be visible there, the water does not depart from its place because the openings made there by the stones are instantly closed; and the movement occasioned by the sudden opening and closing of the water makes a certain shaking which one would define as a quivering rather than a movement. That what I say may be more evident to you, just consider those pieces of straw which on account of their lightness float on the surface of the water and are not moved from their position by the wave that rolls beneath them as the circles widen. This disturbance of the water, therefore, being a quivering rather than a movement, the circles cannot break one another as they meet, for, as all the parts of water are of a like substance, it follows that these parts transmit the quivering from one to another without changing their place, for, as the water remains in its position, it can easily take this quivering from the parts near to it and pass it on to other parts near to it, its force meanwhile steadily decreasing until the end.

The winding courses of the water caused by the rebounds of the percussions which they make against the banks will cause the bed of the river below them to be more hollowed out than any other part; and in their percussions they will become of great depth; and the water that is whirled round near to these deep places will serve to undermine and destroy the banks against which it strikes.

One both clearly sees and recognizes that the waters which strike the banks of the rivers act in the same way as balls, which, when they are struck against walls, rebound from these at angles similar to those at which they strike, and proceed to strike against the opposite sides of the walls. So these waters, after having first struck against the one bank, leap back towards the opposite one and strike upon it and hollow it out with vigor, because there is a greater confluence of water in this spot. The reason of this is that the water which leaps back from one bank to another hollows out that part of the bed of the river which finds itself beneath it; and the other water of the river which cannot be received in this low part remains repulsed and thrown back somewhat by the direct course of the river. And having no way of escape, it returns to its natural course, that is, as the bed of the river finds itself lower under the winding ways made by the above-mentioned percussions of the waters, this second water, which has lost its adventitious means of escape, resumes its natural course, falls into the lower parts of the river and strikes the banks at the same spot as that which witnessed the percussion of the aforesaid rebounds. As this bank is thus assailed by two entirely different sets of percussions a larger hollow is caused in it, for, while the first strike the bank above, the others, descending more steeply, devour and lay it bare at its base, and this is the cause of the aforesaid destruction and subsidence of the banks.

[Why water is salt]

Pliny says in his second book, in the hundred and third chapter, that the water of the sea is salt because the heat of the sun scorches and dries up the moisture and sucks it up, and thereby greatly increases the salt savor of the sea.

But this cannot be admitted, because if the saltness of the sea were caused by the heat of the sun, there is no doubt that the lakes and pools and marshes would be more salt in proportion as their waters have less movement and depth; but, on the contrary, experience shows us that the waters of these marshes are entirely free from saltness. It is also stated by Pliny in the same chapter that this saltness might arise because, after the subtraction of every sweet and tenuous portion such as the heat readily draws to itself, the more bitter and coarser portion will be left behind, and in consequence the water on the surface is sweeter than that at the bottom. But this is contradicted by the reasons given above, whence it follows that the same thing would happen with marshes and other tracts of water which become dried up by the heat. It has also been said that the saltness of the sea is the sweat of the earth, but to this we may reply that then all the springs of water which penetrate through the earth would be salt.

The conclusion, therefore, is that the saltness of the sea is due to the numerous springs of water which, in penetrating the earth, find the salt mines, and dissolving parts of these carry them away with them to the ocean and to the other seas, from whence they are never lifted by the clouds which produce the rivers. So the sea would be more salt in our times than it has ever been at any time previously; and if it were argued by the adversary that in an infinite course of time the sea would become either dried up or congealed into salt, to this I reply that the salt is restored to the earth by the setting free of the earth which is raised up together with the salt it has acquired, and the rivers restore it to the earth over which they flow.

But—to express this better—if it be granted that the world is everlasting it must needs be that its population also will be everlasting; and that therefore the human race has perpetually been and will be consumers of salt; and if the whole mass of the earth were composed of salt it would not suffice for human food. And for this reason we are forced to conclude either that the substance of the salt is everlasting, as is the world, or that it dies and is renewed together with the men who consume it. But since experience teaches us that it does not die, as is shown from the fact of fire not consuming it, and from water becoming more salt in proportion as it is dissolved in it, and from the fact that when water evaporates the original quantity of salt remains, there must needs pass through human bodies, as urine or perspiration or the other excretions that are found there, as much salt as is brought every year into the cities. And therefore we may say that the rains which penetrate through the earth are what carry back underneath the foundations of cities and their peoples, through the passages of the earth, the saltness taken from the sea; and that the change in the position of the sea which was over all the mountains has left the salt in the mines that are to be found in these mountains.

As a third and last reason, we may say that salt is in all created things; and we may learn this from passing water through ashes and the refuse of things which have been burned, and from the urine of animals and the excretions which proceed from their bodies, and the earth into which by corruption all things are changed.

Where the channel of the water grows narrower, it digs its bed deeper and flowers more swiftly.

Iron which receives continually the impact of flowing water never rusts but is consumed by being burnished.

In proportion as the object dividing the water is more distant from the surface, it leaves less sand behind it.

That part of the bed or of the bank which projects with the sharpest angles into the straight course of the waters suffers most damage in the flow of the water.

The water of the mills ought to strike the blades of the wheels at right angles.

That water which flows with less slant will strike the wheel farther from the perpendicular of its fall.

That water which strikes farther from the perpendicular of its fall gives a less blow.

All the movements of streams of water which are equal in depth and declivity will be more swift at the surface than at the bottom, and more at the center than at the sides.

If the rock in a river projects above and divides the course of the water which joins after this rock, the interval that is found to exist between the rock and the reunion of the water will be the place where the sand becomes deposited.

But if the rock that divides the course of the waters is covered by the flowing waters only in its lower parts, the water that passes above will fall behind it and form a hollow at its feet and cause it to turn; and the water that falls head-long into this chasm turns in vortex upwards and downwards, for the uniting of the two streams of water which had been divided by the rock does not suffer the water immediately to pursue its journey.

If you throw sawdust down into a running stream, you will be able to observe where the water turned upside down after striking against the banks throws this sawdust back towards the center of the stream, and also the revolutions of the water and where other water either joins it or separates from it; and many other things.

As the water is driven up from the lower part of the vine towards its severed stems and afterwards falls back to its roots, penetrates these and rises again anew, so from the lowest depth of the sea the water rises to the tops of the mountains, and falls down through their burst veins and returns to the sea and rises again anew. Thus up and down, in and out, unresting, now with fortuitous, and now with natural motion, now in its liberty and now constrained by its mover, it goes revolving and, after returning in force to its mover, rises again anew and then falls anew; so as one part rises the other descends.

Thus from the lowest depths of the sea the water rises up to the summits of the mountains and falls down low through the burst veins, and at the same time other water is rising; so the whole element ranges about and makes its passage many times through the rivers that fall into the sea.

At one time it becomes changed to the loftiest clouds, and afterwards it is pent up within the deep caverns of the earth.

It has nothing of itself, but moves and takes everything, as is clearly shown when it is distilled.

Thus hither and thither, up and down, it ranges, never resting at all in quietude, always flowing to help wherever the vital humor fails.

Now taking away the soil, now adding to it, here depositing logs, there stones, here bearing sand, there mud, with nothing stable in bed or bank.

Now rushing on with headlong course, now descending in tranquillity, now showing itself with fierce aspect, now appearing bright and calm, now mingling with the air in fine spray, now falling down in tempestuous rain; now changed to snow or storms of hail, now bathing the air with fine rain; so also now turning to ice and now hot; never keeping any stability; now rising aloft in thin cloud, compressing the air where it shuts it in, so that it moves through the other air after the fashion of a sponge squeezed beneath the water, when what is enclosed within it is driven out through the rest of the water.

The heat that is poured into animated bodies moves the humors which nourish them.

The movement made by this humor is the conservation of itself and the vivification of the body which contains it.

Water is that which serves the vital humor of the arid earth; it is poured within it, and flowing with unceasing vigor through the spreading veins, it replenishes all the parts that depend of necessity on this humor.

And it flows from the vast depths of the mighty ocean in the deep wide caverns that lie hid within the bowels of the earth, whence through the spreading veins upwards against its natural course, in continual ascent to the high summits of the mountains, it returns through the burst veins to the deep.

Water is that which serves the vital humor of the arid earth; and the cause which moves it through the veins is just that which moves the humors in all the different species of animated bodies.

Whether the flow and ebb are caused by the moon or sun, or are the breathing of this machine of the earth. How the flow and ebb differ in different countries and seas.

How in the end the mountains will be leveled by the waters, seeing that they wash away the earth which covers them and uncover their rocks, which begin to crumble and are being continually changed into soil subdued alike by heat and frost. The waters wear away their bases and the mountains bit by bit fall in ruin into the rivers which have worn away their bases, and by reason of this ruin the waters rise in a swirling flood and form great seas.

The more powerful current will cleave asunder the less powerful and pass through the midle of it. Currents of equal power which clash together leap back from the site of their percussion. A whole mass of water in its breadth, depth and height is full of innumerable varieties of movements, as is shown on the surface of water of a moderate degree of turbulence, in which one sees continually gurglings and vortices, with various eddies formed of the more turbid water from the bottom that rises to the surface. How every seven years the waters of the Adige rise and then fall, and it makes a famine as it rises.

How the bottoms of rivers and ditches become trampled by big animals and this causes the muddy waters to escape and they thus leave in their course the soil in which they were loitering. How in the manner described above canals may be constructed through level lands. How to convey away the soil from canals which have become choked up with mud by the opening of certain sluices which are moved upwards by the canal.

How one ought to straighten rivers. How one ought so to provide that rivers do not sweep away other men's possessions. How one ought to maintain the beds of rivers. How one ought to maintain the banks. How the banks when broken should be repaired. How one ought to regulate the impetus of rivers in order to strike terror into the enemy so that he may not enter the valleys of this river to damage them.

How the river in order to be crossed by your army ought to be converted into many small branches. How one ought to ford rivers below the rows of horses so that they may protect the infantry from the rush of the water.

How by the use of wineskins an army is able to cross a river by swimming. How the shores of all the seas that touch one another are of equal height, and are the lowest part of the land which meets the air. Of the manner of swimming of fishes; of the way in which they leap out of the water, as may be seen with dolphins, for it seems a marvelous thing to make a leap upon something which does not stand firm but slips away.

Of the manner of swimming of animals of long shape, such as eels and the like. Of the way of swimming against the currents and great falls of rivers. Of the way which fishes swim when they are round in shape. How animals which do not have the hoof cleft asunder are not able to swim. How all the other animals which have feet with toes are by nature able to swim, except man. In what way a man ought to learn to swim. Of the way in which a man should rest upon the water. How a man ought to defend himself against the whirlpools or eddies of the waters which suck him down to the bottom. How a man when sucked down to the bottom has to seek the reflex current which will cast him out of the depths. How he ought to propel himself with his arms. How he ought to swim on his back.

How he can only remain under water for such time as he can hold his breath.

How by an appliance many are able to remain for some time under water. How and why I do not describe my method of remaining under water for as long a time as I can remain without food; and this I do not publish or divulge on account of the evil nature of men who would practice assassinations at the bottom of the seas by breaking the ships in their lowest parts and sinking them together with the crews who are in them; and although I will furnish particulars of others, they are such as are not dangerous, for above the surface of the water emerges the mouth of the tube by which they draw in breath, supported upon wineskins or pieces of cork.

How the waves of the seas continually consume their promontories and rocks. How the shores of the seas grow continually towards the center of the sea. The reason why the gulfs of the seas are created. The cause why the gulfs become filled up with earth or seaweed.

The cause why round about the shores of the seas there is found a large high bank called the mound of the sea.

Why the waves are higher when they touch the bottom nearer to the shore than they are on the high sea.

How at the mouths of certain valleys the gusts of wind strike down upon the waters and scoop them out in a great hollow, and carry the water up into the air in the shape of a column and of the color of cloud.

And this same thing I once saw taking place on a sandbank in the Arno, where the sand was hollowed out to a depth of more than a man's stature, and the gravel of it was removed and whirled a great distance apart, and assumed in the air the form of a mighty campanile; and the summit of it grew like the branches of a great pine, and then it bent on meeting the swift wind which passed over the mountains.

How the wave is least towards the approaching wind because the bank serves it as a shield.

How the water that finds itself between the percussions of the waves of the sea becomes changed into mist.

Of eddies wide at the mouth and narrow at the base.

Of eddies very wide at the base and narrow above.

Of eddies of the shape of a column.

Of eddies formed between two masses of water that rub together.

How the water that descends through the air breaks because the air through which it passes divides it. How the water which is divided as it descends continuously through the air has a medium of spray, which extends from one divided part to the other, and binds them up together. How all the volume of the water which descends through the air in continuous quantities is constrained to descend with equal movement, because where it made itself swifter it would separate itself from the part that was slower, and where it made itself slower it would be doubled and multiplied by the part that was swifter. How as great a weight of water is displaced as the weight of the thing that is supported by this water. How in the same slant, the water will make itself so much slower in its movement as it is lower upon its bed. How water made to gyrate in swift movement in a vessel by the hands of him who is whirling it round becomes extremely concave at the center.

Of the great difference there is when water is whirled in a vessel, according to whether the hand is held near to the center of this vessel or near the larger circle of the surface of the water. How the hand drawn frequently across the vessel up and down produces strange movements and surfaces of different heights. What water does when made to gyrate in an oval vessel. What water does when made to gyrate in a vessel with corners. What water does in a vessel that is struck from below. What water does in a vessel that is struck at the side. What water does in a vessel when the spot is struck on which it is standing.

Of the music of water falling into its vessel.

[*Of water*]

This wears away the lofty summits of the mountains. It lays bare and carries away the great rocks. It drives away the sea from its ancient shores, for it raises its base with the soil that it carries there. It shatters and devastates the high banks; nor can any stability ever be discerned in these which its nature does not suddenly bring to naught. It seeks out with its rivers every sloping valley where it may carry off or deposit fresh soil. Wherefore many rivers may be said to be those through which all the element has passed, and the sea has gone back many times to the sea, and no part of the earth is so high but that the sea has been at its foundations, and no depth of the ocean is so low but that the loftiest mountains have their bases there. And so it is sometimes sharp and sometimes strong, sometimes acid and sometimes bitter, sometimes sweet and sometimes thick or thin, sometimes it is seen bringing hurt or pestilence, sometimes health-giving, sometimes poisonous. So one would say that it suffers change into as many natures as are the different places through which it passes. And as the mirror changes with the color of its object, so it changes with the nature of the place through which it passes: health-giving, noisome, laxative, astringent, sulphurous, salt, incarnadined, mournful, raging angry, red, yellow, green, black, blue, greasy, fat, thin. Sometimes it starts a conflagration, sometimes it extinguishes one;

is warm and is cold; carries away or sets down, hollows out or raises up, tears down or establishes, fills up or empties, raises itself up or burrows down, speeds or is still, is the cause at times of life or death, of increase or privation, nourishes at times and at times does the contrary, at times has a tang of salt, at times is without savor, at times submerges the wide valleys with great floods. With time everything changes.

At times it goes twisting to the northern parts, eating away the base of its bank; at times it overthrows the bank opposite on the south; at times it turns towards the center of the earth, consuming the base which supports it; at times leaps up seething and boiling towards the sky; at times, revolving in a circle, it confounds its course; at times it extends on the western side, robbing the husbandmen of their tilth; at times it deposits the soil it has carried away in the eastern parts. And thus at times it digs out, and at times fills in where it has taken away and where it has made a deposit. Thus without any rest it is ever removing and consuming whatever borders upon it. So at times it is turbulent and goes ravening in fury; at times, clear and tranquil, it meanders playfully with gentle course among the fresh verdure. At times falls from the sky in rain or snow or hail; at times forms great clouds out of fine mist. At times moves of itself; at times by the force of others. At times gives increase to things that are born by its life-giving moisture. At times shows itself either fetid or full of pleasant odors. Without it nothing can exist among us. At times it is bathed in the hot element and dissolving into vapor becomes mingled with the atmosphere, and drawn upwards by the heat, it rises until having found the cold region it is pressed closer together by its contrary nature, and the minute particles become attached together.

And as when the hand under water squeezes a sponge which is well saturated, so that the water shut up in it as it escapes through the crevices is driven into the rest and drives this from its position by its wave, so it is with the cold which the warm moisture compresses, for when it has reduced it to a more solid form the air that is pent up within it breaks by force the weakest part, and hisses just as though it were coming out of bellows when they are pressed down by an insupportable weight. And thus in various positions it drives away the lighter clouds which form obstacles in its course.

Book of the various ways of leveling waters.

Book of how to divert rivers from places where they do damage.

Book of how to straighten the course of rivers which cover too much ground.

Book of how to divide rivers into many branches and make them fordable.

Book of how waters pass through seas with different movements.

Book of how to deepen the beds of rivers by different currents of water.

Book of how to control rivers so that the small beginnings of the damage they cause may not increase.

Book of the different movements of waters which pass through channels of different forms.

Book of how to prevent the small rivers diverting a larger one as their waters strike it.

Book of how to ascertain the lowest level in the current of the surface of rivers.

Book of the origin of rivers which flow from the lofty summits of the mountains.

Book of the variety of the movements of waters in their rivers.

A book of how to drive back armies by the fury of floods caused by the letting loose of waters.

A book of how to inundate armies by closing the outlets of the valleys.

A book to show how the waters bring down in safety logs hewn in the mountains.

A book of how boats are forced against the rush of the rivers.

A book of how to raise great weights by the simple increase of the waters.

A book of how to guard against the rush of rivers so that cities may not be struck by them.

Of the inequality in the hollow of a ship.

Book of the inequality of the curve of the sides of ships.

Book of the inequality in the position of the helm.

Book of the inequality in the keel of ships.

Book of the difference in the holes through which water is poured out.

Book of the water contained in vessels with air and of its movements.

Book of the motion of water through a syphon.

Book of the clashing together and concourse of water proceeding from different directions.

Book of the varying shapes of the banks along which the rivers pass.

Book of the various shoals formed below the locks of the rivers.

Book of the twistings and bendings of the currents of the rivers.

Book of the different places whence the waters of the rivers are derived.

Book of the shapes of the banks of the rivers and their permanence.

Book of the perpendicular fall of water upon various objects.

Book of the course of water when impeded in various positions.

Book of the various shapes of the obstacles which impede the course of the waters.

Book of the hollow or rotundity formed at the bottom round the various obstacles.

Book of how to conduct navigable canals over or beneath the rivers which intersect them.

IV · CANALS

EVERY large river may be led up the highest mountains on the principle of the siphon.

[*Plan on which are the words Florence, Prato, Pistoia, Serravalle, Lago, Lucca, Pisa*]

Let sluices be constructed in the Val di Chiana at Arezzo, so that in summer when there is a shortage of water in the Arno the canal will not become dried up, and let this canal be twenty braccia wide at the bottom and thirty at the surface and the general level two braccia or four, because two of these braccia serve the mills and the meadows. This will fertilize the country, and Prato, Pistoia and Pisa, together with Florence, will have a yearly revenue of more than two hundred thousand ducats, and they will supply labor and money for this useful work, and the Lucchesi likewise. Since the Lago di Sesto will be navigable, make it pass by way of Prato and Pistoia and cut through at Serravalle and go out into the lake, for then there will be no need of locks or supports, which are not permanent but require a constant supply of labor to work them and to maintain them.

And know that this canal cannot be dug for less than four denari per braccio, paying each laborer at the rate of four soldi per day. And the time of construction of the canal should be between the middle of March and the middle of June, because the peasants are not then occupied with their ordinary work, and the days are long and the heat does not prove exhausting.

A great weight may be deposited upon a ship without the use of windlasses, levers, ropes, or any force:

In order to deposit each very heavy weight that is all in one piece upon a floating barge, it is necessary to draw this weight to the shore of the sea, setting it lengthwise to the sea at the edge of the shore. Then a canal should be made to pass beneath this weight and to project as far beyond it as the half of the length of the barge which is to carry this weight. And in like manner the width of this canal should be regulated by the width of the barge, which should be filled with water and drawn beneath the weight. And then after the water has been bailed out, the ship will rise to such a height as to raise the said weight from the ground of itself. Thus laden it can then be drawn to the sea and led to the place that is prepared for it.

[*Of the canal of Martesana*]

By the making of the Martesana canal the amount of water in the Adda is lessened, owing to its being distributed over many districts in order to supply the meadows. A remedy for this would be to make many small channels, because the water which has been drunk up by the earth does no service to anyone, nor any injury because it has been taken from no one; and by the construction of such channels the water which before was lost returns again and is once more of service and use to mankind. And unless such

LEONARDO DA VINCI

channels have first been constructed it is not possible to make
these runlets in the lower-lying country. We should say,
therefore, that if such channels are made in the Martesana,
the same water, drunk in by the soil of the meadows, will
be sent back upon the other meadows by means of runlets,
this being water which had previously disappeared; and if
there were a scarcity of water at Ghiara d'Adda and in the
Mucca, and the inhabitants were able to make these channels,
it would be seen that the same water drunk in by the
meadows serves several times for this purpose.

[*Estimate for canal*]

The canal which is sixteen braccia in width at the bottom
and twenty at the top may be said to average eighteen braccia
over its whole width; and if it is four braccia in depth and
costs four denari per square braccio, it will cost per mile for
excavation alone nine hundred ducats, the square braccio
being calculated in ordinary braccia.

But if the braccia are such as are used to measure land,
of which every four are four and a half, and if the mile consists of three thousand ordinary braccia and these are converted into those used to measure land, then these three
thousand braccia lose a quarter, so that there remain two
thousand two hundred and fifty braccia. And therefore at
four denari the braccio, the miles comes out at six hundred
and seventy-five ducats; at three denari per square braccio,
the mile works out at five hundred and six and a quarter
ducats, and therefore the excavation of thirty miles of the
canal will work out at fifteen thousand one hundred and
eighty-seven and a half ducats.

Here there are, my lord, many gentlemen who will undertake this expense between them, if so be that they are allowed
to enjoy the use of the waters, the mills and the passage of

ships; and when the price shall have been repaid them, they
will give back the canal of the Martesana.

[*With drawing*]

To ensure that the mouths of the canals which hollow
themselves out from the rivers do not become filled up with
shingle, and also to prevent the shingle from remaining in
the middle of the dam that has been constructed against it,
it should be made with a transverse descent.

IX

Physics and Other Sciences

I · MOVEMENT AND WEIGHT

ALTHOUGH nature commences with reason and ends in experience, it is necessary for us to do the opposite, that is, to commence with experience and from this to proceed to investigate the reason.

Speak first of the movement, then of the weight, because it is produced by the movement, then of the force which proceeds from the weight and the movement, then of the percussion which springs from the weight, the movement and often from the force.

In equal movements made in equal time, the mover will always have more power than the thing which is moved. And the mover will be so much the more powerful than the thing moved, in proportion as the movement of this thing moved exceeds the length of movement of its mover; and the difference of the power of the mover over that of the thing moved will be so much less in proportion as the length of the movement made by the thing moved is less than the movement of this mover.

But observe, O reader, that in this case you must take count of the air, which becomes so much the more condensed in front of the thing moved as this thing moved is of greater speed; for this air is capable of being condensed in an infinite degree. This, however, could not happen with the movements made by things which are moved within water, for this is not capable of being condensed, as may be proved by placing it in a vessel with a narrow mouth, since for lack of the knowledge of some motive power you will not be able to place within it more than the natural capacity the vessel will contain. And it is just the contrary with the air, for if it is forced into a vessel with a very narrow mouth which contains a quantity of water, and the vessel is tilted at such an angle that the water shut up in it is between the mouth of the vessel and the air which has been condensed, the power of the condensed air drives the water of the vessel with such fury as to penetrate through the air for some distance, until the air that remains in the vessel can return to its first natural state.

But to return to our proposition, we may say that among movable things of the same gravity, that one will have the slower movement of which the front that cleaves the air takes up more space; and so conversely as it occupies less air, not, however, extending itself in such a degree of thinness as to cause its weight to fail, for where there is no weight there is no local movement through the air.

The impetus generated in still water has a different effect from that generated in still air. This is proved from the fact that water in itself is never compressed by means of any movement made below its surface, as the air is within itself when struck by a moving thing. And this we may readily learn from the bubbles with which the water is encumbered from its surface to its bed, which cluster round about as the water fills up the vacuum of itself that the fish leaves behind it as it penetrates; and the movements of this water strike and drive this fish, because water has weight within water only when it has movement, and this is the primary cause of the increase of movement for its mover.

I find that force is infinite together with time; and that weight is finite together with the weight of the whole globe of the terrestrial machine.

I find that the stroke of indivisible time is movement, and that this movement is of many varieties, namely natural, accidental and participating; and this participating movement ends its greatest power when it changes from the accidental to the natural, that is, in the middle of its course; and the natural is more powerful at the end than in any other place; the accidental is strongest in the third and weakest at the close.

Weight, force, a blow and impetus are the children of movement because they are born from it.

Weight and force always desire their death, and each is maintained by violence.

Impetus is frequently the cause why movement prolongs the desire of the thing moved.

Of water of uniform weight, depth, breadth and declivity, that portion is swifter which is nearest the surface; and this occurs because the water that is uppermost is contiguous to the air, which offers but little resistance through its being lighter than the water; and the water that is below is contiguous to the earth, which offers great resistance through being immovable and heavier than water. It follows that the part which is more distant from this base has less resistance than that above, which is contiguous to the air, for this is light and mobile.

Gravity and levity are accidental powers which are produced by one element being drawn through or driven into another.

No element has gravity or levity within its own element.

If all the bed of the sea were covered with men lying down, these men would sustain the whole of the element of water, consequently each man would find that he had a column of water a mile long upon his back. For if the whole sea is all supported upon its bed, each part of the bed sustains its part of the water.

Impetus at every stage of time becomes less by degrees, and the prolongation of its essence is caused by the air or the water, which closes up behind the movable thing, filling up the vacuum which the movable thing that penetrates it leaves of itself. And this air is more powerful to strike and compress the movable thing by direct percussion than is the air which is so placed as to resist the penetration of this movable thing by becoming compressed; and it is this compression of the air which diminishes the fury of the aforesaid impetus in the movable thing.

Impetus is the impression of local movement transmuted from the mover to the movable thing and maintained by the air or by the water as they move in order to prevent the vacuum.

The impetus of the movable thing within the water is different from the impetus of the movable thing within the air, and these differences result from the varieties of the aforesaid liquids, because air is condensable to infinity and water is not.

The impetus of the water is divided into two parts through its being of two natures, one of which is simple and the other complex. The simple is entirely beneath the surface of the water; the other is complex, that is, it is between the air and the water, as is seen with boats.

The simple impetus does not condense the water in front of the movement of the fish, but moves the water behind the movement of the fish with the same speed that the mover has; and the wave of the water that is over against it will never be swifter than its mover.

But the movement of the boat, called complex movement because it shares with the water and the air, is divided into three chief parts because this movement is carried on in three directions, namely, against the course of the river, in the direction of its current, and crosswise, that is, along the breadth of the river.

If the movement of the oar or of the wing be swifter than the water or the air driven by them, that amount of movement which is left in the water or the air is completed by the oar or the wing in an opposite movement.

But if the movement of this water or air be in itself swifter than that of the oar or wing, this oar and wing will not move against this water or air.

And if the movement of the water or of the air be in itself of the same swiftness as that of the oar or the wing that moves in it, then the oar and wing will follow the movement of the water and the air.

The compression which the flame produces of itself, which increases within the resisting wall of the mortar, is that which produces the impetuous movement of its ball; and this impetus cannot be created with less density of flame or less swiftness in its rate of increase. Such swiftness of increase cannot take place within a wall of less resistance than that of this mortar. It follows therefore that the expansion which the flame makes as it rushes out of the mortar into the air, losing this density and directness of course, causes a loss of as much density as it acquires in its expansion and it ceases to follow the flight of the ball to the extent to which it bends to the . . .

The movement of water within water acts as the movement of air within air.

Anything which descends freely acquires fresh momentum at every stage of its movement.

Movements are of [. . .] kinds, of which the first is called temporal, because it is concerned solely with the movement of time, and this embraces within itself all the others; the second is concerned with the life of things; the third is termed mental, and this resides in animated bodies; the fourth is that of the images of things which are spread through the air in straight lines: this class does not appear to be subject to time, for it is made indivisible in time and that which cannot be divided in the mind is not found among us; the fifth is that of sounds which proceed through the air, and this will be treated of later, as also of odors and savors, and this we may call movement of the senses; the other is called material movement, concerning which we shall make our treatise.

But we shall define movements merely as being of two kinds, of which one is material and the other incorporeal, because it is not perceptible to the visual sense, or we may say that the one is visible, the other invisible, although among the invisible movements there are a considerable number of material movements, such as the movement of Saturn, and as there would be with a number of wheels revolving. Wherefore we may say that the two kinds of movement are such that the one is that which is united with bodies, the other with the spirit. But among these movements, that of the images of things amid the air is swiftest, because it covers a great space at the same time as it is very brief, and this loses [. . .] through distance, because the air thickens; the second is that of the mind.

Of the movements of the senses we will only mention that of hearing because it operates in visible bodies, and works by means of time, as is shown in noises, peals of thunder, sounds and voices. Of smell, taste and touch we will not speak, because they do not form part of our subject.

Also one might speak of the influences of the planets and of God.

If a power moves a weight a certain distance in a certain time, the same power will move the half of this weight double the distance in the same time.

Or this whole power [will move] all the weight half the distance in half the time, or the whole power in the same time will move double the weight half the distance, or the whole power in half the time [will move] the whole weight half the distance.

Impetus is a power transmitted from the mover to the movable thing, and maintained by the wave of the air within the air which this mover produces; and this arises from the vacuum which would be produced contrary to the natural law if the air which is in front of it did not fill up the vacuum, so causing the air which is driven from its place by the afore-said mover to flee away. And the air that goes before it would not fill up the place from which it is divided if it were not that another body of air filled up the place from whence this air was divided; and so of necessity it follows in succession. And this movement would continue to infinity if the air were capable of being condensed to infinity.

[*A hymn to force*]

Force is all in the whole of itself and all in every part of itself.

Force is a spiritual capacity, an invisible power which is

implanted by accidental violence in all bodies that are withheld from their natural inclination.

Force is nothing else than a spiritual capacity, an invisible
power which is created and implanted by accidental violence
by sensible bodies in insensible ones, giving to these a
semblance of life; and this life is marvelous in its workings,
constraining and transforming in place and shape all created
things, running with fury to its own destruction, and producing different effects in its course as occasion requires.

Tarrying makes it great and quickness makes it weak.

It lives by violence and dies from liberty.

It transforms and constrains every body with change of
position and form.

Great power gives it great desire of death.

It drives away with fury whatever opposes its destruction.

Transmuter of various forms.

Lives always in hostility to whoever controls it.

Always sets itself against natural desires.

From small beginnings it slowly becomes larger, and
makes itself a dreadful and marvelous power.

And constraining itself it constrains everything.

. . . dwells in bodies which are kept away from their
natural course and use.

. . . willing consumes itself.

. . . force is all in all and all through all the body where
it is produced.

. . . Power [. . . *nza* (*potenza?*)] is only a desire of
flight.

Always it desires to grow weak and to spend itself.

Itself constrained it constrains every body.

Without it nothing moves.

Without it no sound or voice is heard.

Its true seed is in sentient bodies.

Weight is all in all its vertical obstacle and all in every
part of it.

If the oblique obstacle opposed to the weight is loosened and free, it will not make any resistance to this weight but will fall down with it in ruin.

Weight naturally passes to its desired position.

Every part of this force contains the whole opposite to weight.

And often they are victors one over the other.

They are in the grip of the same natural law, and the more powerful conquers the less.

Weight changes [its position] unwillingly and force is always on the point of fleeing.

Weight is corporeal and force is incorporeal.

Weight is material and force is spiritual.

If the one desires flight from itself and death, the other wishes for stability and permanence.

They are often producers one of another:

If weight brings forth force and force weight.

If weight conquers force and force weight.

And if they are of like nature they make long company.

If the one is eternal the other is fleeting.

There are two movements which can be made by a spherical heavy substance in the air, one of which is called simple, the other compound. Simple is that movement in which the surface of the movable thing moves as much as its center; compound is that in which the surface of the movable thing is in itself more swift than its center.

The compound movement is transformed into as many different aspects as there are different sides with which it strikes against the obstacles that are in its path.

The simple movement is changed into compound movement, if its movement is impeded in any part of its sides.

In a long course, compound movement made in the air resolves itself into simple movement; and the fact of this happening makes it more certain that the cause of the simple movement is also the cause of the compound movement; and this is shown in every wheel to which the revolving impulse is imparted, for it endures but little and is constantly growing less.

Every impression is preserved for a time in its sensitive object; and that which was of greater power will be preserved in its object for a longer time, and for a shorter time with the less powerful.

In this connection I apply the term sensitive to such object as by any impression is changed from that which was at first an insensitive object; that is, one which, while changing from its first state, preserves within itself no impression of the thing which has moved it. The sensible impression is that of a blow received upon a resounding substance, such as bells and suchlike things, or like the note in the ear, which, indeed, unless it preserved the impression of the notes, could never derive pleasure from hearing a voice alone; for when it passes immediately from the first to the fifth note the effect is as though one heard these two notes at the same time, and thus perceived the true harmony which the first makes with the fifth; but if the impression of the first note did not remain in the ear for an appreciable space of time, the fifth, which follows immediately after the first, would seem alone, and one note cannot create any harmony, and consequently any song whatsoever occurring alone would seem to be devoid of charm.

So, too, the radiance of the sun or other luminous body remains in the eye for some time after it has been seen; and the motion of a single firebrand whirled rapidly in a circle causes this circle to seem one continuous and uniform flame.

The drops of rain water seem continuous threads descending from their clouds; and so herein one may see how the eye preserves the impressions of the moving things which it sees.

The insensitive objects which do not preserve the impressions of the things which are opposite to them are mirrors, and any polished substance, which, so soon as ever the thing of which it bears the impression is removed from before it, becomes at once entirely deprived of that impression. We may, therefore, conclude that it is the action of the mover pressing against the body moved by it which moves this body in the direction in which it moves.

Among the cases of impressions being preserved in various bodies we may also instance the wave, the eddies of the water, the winds in the air, and a knife stuck into a table, which on being bent in one direction and then released, retains for a long time a quivering movement, all its movements being reciprocal one of another, and all may be said to be approaching towards the perpendicular of the surface where the knife is fixed by its point.

The voice impresses itself through the air without displacement of air, and strikes upon the objects and returns back to its source.

The concussion of liquid with solid bodies is of a different character from the above-mentioned cases of concussion; and the concussion of liquid with liquid also varies from the foregoing.

Of the concussion of solid with liquid, there is seen an example in the shores of the ocean, which receive the waters full on their rocks and hurl them against the steep crags; and oftentimes it happens that before the course of the wave is half completed, the stones carried by it return to the sea from whence they came; and their power of destruction is increased by the might of the wave which falls back from the lofty cliffs.

Force never has weight, although it often performs the function of weight.

The force is always equal to the weight which produces it. This is proved by the . . .

That body weighs less upon the air which rests upon a greater expanse of air. We may take as an example the gold from which money is made, which is extremely heavy, but which, when spread out in fine leaf for gilding, maintains itself upon the air with each slightest movement of this air.

A man about to give a great blow with his arms so places himself that all his power is on the opposite side to that of the place at which he intends to strike, for the thing which moves most exerts most power upon the thing that resists the movement.

Every impetuous movement bends towards the less resistance as it flies from the greater.

Every spherical body of thick and resisting surface, when moved by a like force, will make as much movement in the rebounds caused by its impact upon a concrete ground as if it were thrown freely through the air.

How admirable Thy justice, O Thou First Mover! Thou hast not willed that any power should lack the processes or qualities necessary for its results; for if a force have the capacity of driving an object conquered by it a hundred braccia, and this object while obeying it meets with some obstacle, Thou hast ordained that the force of the impact will cause a new movement which by divers rebounds will recover the entire amount of the distance it should have traversed.

And if you were to measure the track made by these bounds you will discover it to be of the same length as it would be if a similar object were impelled freely through the air by the same force.

You may make an experiment of this with a small glass ball as it strikes upon a surface of smooth polished stone. Take a long staff and mark it with different colors from end to end, and then give it to someone to hold, and set yourself at some distance away [to watch] the rebounds [and see] against the height of the staff to what colors the ball rises successively with each rebound, and make a note of them. If there are as many observers as the number of times the ball rebounds, each will keep it more easily in memory. But either have the staff fixed at the top or with the end in a hole, for if anyone held it with his hand he would interrupt the line of sight of the judge. Arrange that the first bound be made between two right angles, so that the ball may always fall in the same spot, because then the height of the rebounds against the staff may be more accurately discerned.

Then have this ball discharged by the same power in free course and make a note of the spot where it strikes; and measure it and you will find that the length of the second course is identical with the first.

Everything hit against a resisting object leaps back from this object at an angle equal to that of the percussion.

That thing which has most conformity with the element that surrounds it will issue forth from it with the slowest movement.

And the thing which is most unlike will separate itself from it with more impetuous movement.

Force I define as an incorporeal agency, an invisible power, which by means of unforeseen external pressure is caused by the movement stored up and diffused within bodies which are withheld and turned aside from their natural uses; imparting to these an active life of marvelous power, it constrains all created things to change of form and position, and hastens furiously to its desired death, changing as it goes according to circumstances. When it is slow its strength is increased, and speed enfeebles it. It is born in violence and dies in liberty; and the greater it is the more quickly it is consumed. It drives away in fury whatever opposes its destruction. It desires to conquer and slay the cause of opposition, and in conquering destroys itself. It waxes more powerful where it finds the greater obstacle. Everything instinctively flees from death. Everything when under constraint itself constrains other things. Without force nothing moves.

The body in which it is born grows neither in weight nor in form. None of the movements that it makes are lasting.

It increases by effort and disappears when at rest. The body within which it is confined is deprived of liberty. Often also by its movement it generates new force.

Every weight desires to descend to the center by the shortest way; and where there is the greater weight, there is the greater desire, and that thing which weighs the most if it is left free falls most rapidly. The less the slant of the opposing substance, the greater its resistance. But the weight passes by nature into all that supports it, and thus penetrating from support to support it grows heavier as it passes from body to body until it realizes its desire. Necessity draws it and abundance drives it away. It is all in all its vertical opposition and all in each of its degrees. And that opposition which slants the most will not offer resistance to its descent, but, being free, will fall together with it. In its function of pressing and making heavy it is like force. Weight is subdued by force, as force is by weight. One can see weight without force, but one cannot see force without weight. If weight has no neighbor it seeks one with fury, and force drives it away with fury. If weight desires an unchangeable position, force readily flies from it. If weight desires stability and force is always desirous of flight, weight of itself is without fatigue, while force is never exempt from it.

The more weight falls the more it increases and the more force falls the more it diminishes. If one is eternal, the other is mortal. Weight is natural and force is accidental. Weight desires stability and permanence, and force desires flight and death of itself. Weight, force and a blow resemble each other in respect of pressure.

I maintain that the displacement caused by the weight which falls is equal to the displacement caused by the force.

The body that receives the blow is not injured in the part opposite as it is in the part which is struck. The proof of this is shown when a stone is struck while lying in a man's hands, for the hand is not injured when it is holding the stone that is struck as much as it would be injured if it actually received the blow.

I ask, if a weight of a pound falling two braccia bury itself in the earth the depth of a hand, how deeply will it bury itself if it falls forty braccia, and how far a weight of two pounds will bury itself if it falls two braccia?

One may ask also, if the size of this weight be represented by a quantity *a* and then this quantity be doubled, its weight remaining the same and falling from the same height, how much greater impress the lesser bulk will make than the greater if the ground offer equal resistance?

A piece of wood separated from the rest by the blow of an ax will fly off from it at an equal angle to that of the blow.

Everything of a compact surface that falls upon a resisting object will have the line of its rebound at the same angle as the line of its incidence.

The force of the mover ought always to be in proportion to the weight of its movable thing and to the resistance of the medium in which the weight moves. But one cannot deduce the law of this action unless one first gives the quantity of the condensation of the air when struck by any movable thing whatever; and this condensation will be of greater or less density according to the greater or less speed of the mobile thing pressing on it, as is shown in the flight of birds, for the sound that they make with their wings in beating the air is deeper or more shrill according to whether the movement of the wings is slower or swifter.

The weight of every heavy thing suspended is all in the whole length of the cord that supports it and all in each part of it.

Every weight tends to fall towards the center by the shortest way.

The mover is always more powerful than the thing moved.

What is gravity and whether it is natural or accidental, and one may ask the same concerning levity.

The answer is that both are accidental powers because each always waits for its destruction and one is never born without the other or dies without the other. This is proved by the air which forms in the shape of a bubble or bladder at the bottom of the water, where the fact of its formation immediately creates its levity and creates the weight of the water that is above it. And as soon as the bubble arrives at the surface its levity dies, together with the gravity of the water that was above it.

The stone that descends through the water first makes the water heavy that closes up the beginning of the entrance made by the stone, and makes light the water that rises to fill up the space that the stone leaves as it descends, because that which moves upwards is light.

Whether the space of the water penetrated by the stone is filled by water descending or by water from the side or by water that is below.

Whether the air which clothes bodies with itself moves together with these bodies.

The air that clothes bodies with itself moves together with these bodies: this experience shows us when the horse runs along dusty roads.

Whether the movement of the air is as swift as its mover.

The air will never have swiftness equal to that of its mover; and this is shown us by the movements of the dust that I have already mentioned which follows the course of the horse, for after having moved a very short distance it turns back with an eddying movement and thereby consumes its impetus.

The air becomes condensed before bodies that penetrate it swiftly, acquiring so much more or less density as the speed is more violent or less.

A plank that is uniform in breadth, length, depth and weight will not preserve the slanting movement with which it started through the air that it penetrates for a long space, but will turn back and then again forward and so end its descent with a fluctuating movement. This springs from the fact that the uniform natural thickness of the air is destroyed because it is condensed under the right angle of the surface which strikes the air and cleaves it open. But on the opposite face of this plank it does the contrary in that it becomes rarefied, and as a consequence the rarefied air is of less resistance, and for this reason this surface shows itself heavier. The rarefaction acquired by the air that is behind this plank is much greater than the density that is produced in front of it. It may be proved why the air is condensed:

the air is condensed before the bodies that penetrate it, for when one pushes a part one does not push the whole of that which is in front. This is demonstrated by the flooding that is produced before the prow of a ship.

When the dusty table is struck at one side, observe the manner in which the movement of the dust commences to create the aforesaid hillocks, and how this dust rises to the top of the hillock.

The question is whether the weights descending in the pulleys give more or less of their weight to the pivots of the tackles as they descend than when they are stationary.

The staff most uniform in thickness bends with the most perfect curve.

The arrow shot from the center of the earth to the highest part of the elements will ascend and descend by the same straight line although the elements may be in a movement of circumvolution round their center.

An arrow shot from the prow of a ship in the direction in which the ship is moving will not appear to stir from the place at which it was shot if the ship's movement be equal to that of the arrow.

But if the arrow from such a ship be shot in the direction from whence it is going away with the above-mentioned rate of speed, this arrow will be separated from the ship with twice its movement.

The gravity which descends through the elements when they are in circumvolution always has its movement to correspond to the direction of the line that extends from the commencing point of the movement towards the center of the world.

The air that is compressed beneath the movable thing as it descends through it in a slanting position flees more from the upper than from the lower part of this movable thing.

Continuous tracts of air are as much rarefied on the one side as they are compressed on the other.

The rarefied part of the air offers so much less resistance as the compressed part offers more resistance. Therefore the back part of the movable thing, *b,* will descend with greater impetus than its front part, and this is the reason why the front *a,* which at the outset was below, at the end of the reflex movement is raised up.

Impetus is the impression of movement transmitted by the mover to the movable thing.

Impetus is a power impressed by the mover on the movable thing.

Every impression tends to permanence or desires permanence.

This is proved in the impression made by the sun in the eye of the spectator and in the impression of the sound made by the clapper as it strikes the bell.

Every impression desires permanence, as is shown by the image of the movement impressed upon the movable thing.

Every natural action is made in the shortest way: this is why the free descent of the heavy body is made towards the center of the world, because it is the shortest space between the movable thing and the lowest depth of the universe.

Such part of water as is in contact with the air will move according to the course of this air, although the water upon the bottom move in a contrary direction.

I ask why field lances or hunting whips have a greater movement than the arm. I say that this happens because the hand describes a much wider circle as the arm moves than does the elbow; and in consequence, moving at the same time the hand covers twice as much space as does the elbow, and therefore it may be said to be of a speed double that of the movement of the elbow, and so it sends things when thrown a greater distance from itself.

Corn tossed up with a sieve leaps up in the form of a pyramid.

The heavy body which descends freely with every degree of time acquires a degree of movement, and with every degree of movement it acquires a degree of speed.

Although the equal division of the movement of time cannot be indicated by degrees, as is the movement made by the bodies, nevertheless, the necessity of the case constrains me to make degrees after the manner in which they are made among musicians.

Let us say that in the first degree of time, it [i.e., the heavy body] acquires a degree of movement and a degree of speed, in the second degree of time it will acquire two degrees of movement and two of speed, and so it continues in succession, as has been said above.

[*Sketch*]

I wish to know how much higher one small cannon or carbine throws than another, and to do this I train my instrument according to the line *b c* in a firm manner, so that it will not alter its angle of elevation. This done, I shall insert so small a quantity of powder that the ball will be projected only two braccia away from the carbine, as *b s*, and I shall note where the ball falls, at *n*, then I shall double the charge of powder and see where it falls at *m*; and if I shall find that the base *m c* is double the base *n c*, I shall know that the height of the pyramid *h c* is double that of *s c*.

The weight that charges the crossbow has the same proportion to the weight of the arrow as the movement of the arrow of this crossbow has to the movement of its cord.

Here one ought to deduct three resistances made by the air, that is, the percussion of the bow of the crossbow made upon the air, and that of the cord; the third is that made against the arrow. And as the cord is thicker, so its arrow encompasses it the less.

A bow bends half a braccio and has power of one hundred and pulls two hundred braccia; and another has power of two hundred and opens a quarter of a braccio.

Which will discharge its arrow proportionately farther, the one or the other?

And if another opened a hundred times less and were a hundred times stronger, which would carry farthest in proportion with the said arrows?

[*Of the power of percussion*]

Many small blows cause the nail to enter into the wood, but if you join these blows together in one single blow, it will have much more power than it had separately in its parts. But if a power of percussion drives a nail entirely into a piece of wood, this same power can be divided into ever so many parts, and though the percussion of these occur on the nail for a long time, they can never penetrate to any extent in the said wood.

If a ten-pound hammer drives a nail into a piece of wood with one blow, a hammer of one pound will not drive the nail altogether into the wood in ten blows. Nor will a nail that is less than the tenth part [of the first] be buried more deeply by the said hammer of a pound in a single blow, although it may be in equal proportions to the first named, because what is lacking is that the hardness of the wood does not diminish the proportion of its resistance, that is, that it is as hard as at first.

Force is produced by dearth or profusion. It is the child of material movement, the grandchild of spiritual movement, the mother and source of gravity. This gravity is confined within the element of water and of earth, and this force is infinite, for by means of it infinite worlds could be set in motion if it were possible to make the instruments by which this force could be produced.

Force with material movement and weight with percussion are the four accidental powers in which all the works of mortals have their being and their end.

Force has its origin in spiritual movement, which courses through the limbs of sentient animals, thickening their muscles; and by this process of thickening, the muscles become contracted and so draw back the tendons which are connected with them, and from this originates the force that exists in men's limbs.

The quality and quantity of the force in a man will have the power of giving birth to other force, and this will be proportionately so much the greater according as the movement of the one is longer than that of the other.

Gravity and force, together with material movement and percussion, are the four accidental powers by which the human race in its marvelous and varied works seems to reveal itself as a second nature in this world; seeing that by the use of such powers all the visible works of mortals have their existence and their death.

Gravity is a power created by movement which transports one element into another by means of force, and this gravity has as much life as is the effort made by this element to regain its native place.

Force and gravity have much in common in all their powers, differing only in the movements of their birth and death. For simple gravity merely dies, that is, as it approaches its center. But force is born and dies in every movement.

The spirit of the sentient animals moves through the limbs of their bodies, and when it finds that the muscles in those it has entered are responsive, it sets itself to enlarge them; and as soon as they enlarge they shorten, and in shortening draw back the tendons which are joined to them. And from this arises the force and movement of human limbs. Consequently material movement springs from spiritual.

Every heavy body desires to lose its heaviness . . .

Gravity, force, together with percussion, are to be spoken of as producers of movement as well as being produced by it.

Of these three fortuitous powers, two have in their birth, their desire and their end one and the same nature.

When anyone wishes to make a bow carry a very long way, he should draw himself right up on one foot, raising the other so far from it as to create the necessary balance for his body, which is thrown forward on the first foot, and he should not have his arm fully extended. And so that he may be better equipped for the hard work, he should fit to the bow a piece of wood which as used in crossbows should go from the hand to the breast, and when he wishes to discharge the arrow, instantly at the same time he should leap forward and extend the arm that holds the bow and release the cord. And if by dexterity he does all this at the same moment it will travel a very long way.

The reason given for this is as follows: Know that as the leap forward is swift, it lends a degree of fury to the arrow; and the extending of the arm because it is swifter lends a second; the driving of the cord being also more swift gives a third. If the other arrows, therefore, are driven by three degrees of fury, and this by the dexterity shown is driven by six, it ought to travel double the distance. And I would remind you that you leave the bow relaxed, so that it will spring forward and remain taut.

If there are two men who hold a sheet by its borders, in which sheet there is a man who weighs two hundred pounds, and each pulls his end so much that the weight does not touch the ground, know that each of those who are pulling is holding up a weight as great as the man weighs who is in the middle, because he supports half the weight of the man in the center and half that of the man opposite who is pulling, so it appears that the weight in the center, being two hundred pounds, since each of those pulling has two hundred becomes four hundred pounds.

If a man with his whole strength throws a stone of four pounds twenty braccia, would he throw one of one pound eighty [M.S. eight] braccia or no? Would he throw one of half a pound one hundred and sixty braccia [MS. pounds] or no? And if he does not throw these to such a distance, what is the cause?

A man in running throws less of his weight on his legs than if he is standing still. And in like manner the horse when running is less conscious of the weight of the man whom he is carrying; consequently many look upon it as marvelous that when a horse is in a race it can support itself upon one foot only. Therefore we may say as regards weight in transverse movement that the swifter this is the less it weighs perpendicularly towards the center [of the earth].

The water that is moved from its place by reason of the ship weighs as much as the actual weight of this ship exactly.

I have ten measures of time and ten measures of force and ten measures of movement and ten of weight, and I wish to raise up this weight.

If I double the weight and not the force in the movement, it becomes necessary to double the time.

If I double the weight and not the time or the force, it becomes necessary to halve the movement.

If I double the weight and not the movement or the time, it becomes necessary to double the force.

If I halve the weight and not the movement or the time, the force is halved.

The center of any heavy body whatsoever will stand in a perpendicular line beneath the center of the cord on which it is suspended.

I ask, if you were to suspend a pole outside the center of its length, what degree of slant it would assume.

The pole which is suspended outside the center of its length by a single cord will assume such a slant as will make with its opposite sides, together with the perpendicular of the center of the cord that supports it, two equal acute angles or two equal obtuse angles.

[*Sketch*]

If the wheels are of equal height, the wagon will move with a sure degree of force. But if you change the two back wheels for wheels of greater height, it will move with greater ease. If, however, in the case of the first wheels you were to change the wheels in front for some less in height, in such a way that in the same manner the wheels in front were low and those behind high, the first movement will have been made more difficult.

A weight of one pound falls one braccio and gives a blow of a certain force; the question is asked, if a weight of half a pound were to fall double the height, or twice from the first height, or twice the weight from half the height, or four times from a quarter of the height, if it would produce the same result.

That thing which is entirely consumed by the long movement of its friction will have part of it consumed at the beginning of this movement.

This shows us that it is impossible to give or make anything of any absolute exactness, for if you desire to make a perfect circle of the movement of one of the points of the compasses, and you admit or confirm what is set forth above, namely, that in the course of long movement this point tends to become worn away, it is necessary to concede that if the whole be consumed in the whole of a certain space of time, the part will be consumed in the part of this time, and that the indivisible in the indivisible time may give a beginning to such consumption.

And thus the opposite point of these compasses, which turns in itself over the center of this circle, at every stage of movement is in process of being itself consumed and of consuming the place on which it rests; whence we may say that the end of the circle is not joined with its beginning, rather the end of such line is some imperceptible part nearer towards the center of such circle.

The pole which is suspended at its extremities by two cords divides its weight equally between these cords.

But if one of the cords remains fixed and the other moves towards it, weight moves from this fixed cord and joins itself to the weight of the movable one.

The more a cord is moved towards the center of the pole, the more weight is taken from the other cord.

The weight which is moved within the cords is in the same

proportion to the first weights as is the movement made by the cord to the remainder of the pole.

If the sea bears down with its weight upon its bed, a man who lay on this bed and had a thousand braccia of water on his back would have enough to crush him.

The desire of every heavy body is that its center may be the center of the earth.

When one is descending one takes short steps because the weight rests on the hinder foot, but when one is ascending one takes long steps because the weight is thrown on to the foot in front.

That wheel will revolve more easily which has its axis of less thickness.

II · MATHEMATICS

As I have shown, here at the side [diagram], various ways of squaring the circles, that is, by forming squares of a capacity equal to the capacity of the circle, and have given the rules for proceeding to infinity, I now begin the book called "De Ludo Geometrico," and I give also the method of the process to infinity.

Arithmetic is a mental science and forms its calculations with true and perfect denomination; but it has not the power in its continuing quantities which irrational or surd roots [*radici sorde*] have, for these divide the quantities without numerical denomination.

Surface is a flat figure which has length and breadth and is uniformly without depth.

Mechanics is the paradise of the mathematical sciences, because by means of it one comes to the fruits of mathematics.

All the pyramids made upon equal bases in parallel spaces are equal to each other.

The greatest pyramid that can be drawn from a cube will be the third of the whole cube.

[*To obtain the cube of the sphere*]

When you have squared the surface of the circle, divide the square into as many small squares as you please, provided that they are equal one to another, and make each square the base of a pyramid, of which the axis is the half diameter of the sphere of which you wish to obtain the cube; and let them all be equal.

If from two like wholes there be taken away like parts, there is the same proportion between part and part as there is between whole and whole.

It follows that if of these two circles the one is double the other, the quarter portion of the larger is double the quarter portion of the smaller.

And there is the same proportion between one remainder and the other as between one whole and the other.

And the same proportion between part and part as there is between remainder and remainder.

When two circles touch the same square at four points, one is double the other.

And also when two squares touch the same circle at four points, one is double the other.

The circle that touches the three angles of an equilateral triangle is triple the triangle that touches the three sides of the same triangle.

The diameter of the largest circle made in the triangle is equal to two-thirds the axis of the same triangle.

Every odd number multiplied by an odd number remains odd.

Every odd number multiplied by an even number becomes even.

Similarity does not imply equality.

Vitruvius, while measuring the mile by means of many complete revolutions of the wheels that move chariots, extended in his stadia many of the lines of the circumference of these wheels. He learned these from the animals that are movers of these chariots, but he did not recognize that that was the means of finding the square equal to a circle. This was first discovered by Archimedes the Syracusan, who found that the multiplication of half the diameter of a circle by half of its circumference made a rectilinear quadrilateral equal to the circle.

There is no certainty where one can apply neither any of the mathematical sciences nor any of those which are based upon the mathematical sciences.

Triangles are of three kinds, of which the first has three acute angles, the second a right angle and two acute angles, and the third an obtuse angle and two acute angles.

The triangle with three acute angles may be of three different shapes, of which the first has three equal sides, the second two equal sides and the third three unequal sides.

And the right-angled triangle may be of two kinds, i.e., with two equal sides and with three unequal sides.

The right-angled triangle with two equal sides is derived from the half of the square. And the right-angled triangle with three unequal sides is formed by the half of the long tetragon [rectangle], and the obtuse-angled triangle with two equal sides is formed by the half of the rhombus cut in its greatest length.

The square is the name applied to a figure of four equal sides which form within them four right angles, that is to say that the lines that compose the angles are equal to each other.

The long tetragon [rectangle] is a surface figure contained by four sides and four right angles; and although its opposite sides are equal it does not follow from this that the sides which contain the right angle may not be unequal between themselves.

The rhombus is of two kinds: the first is formed by the square and the second by the parallelogram; the first has its opposite angles equal and likewise all its sides equal; its only variation consists in that no side ends in equal angles but with an acute angle and an obtuse angle.

The boundaries of the line are points, the boundaries of the surface are lines and the boundaries of the body are surfaces.

That a straight line may be drawn from one point to another.

And this line may also be extended as much as one pleases beyond these points, but the boundaries of this line will always be two points.

That upon the same point one may make many circles.

All right angles are equal to each other.

Parallel lines are those upon which if a transversal line be drawn four angles are formed, which when taken within [on one side?] equal two right angles.

If two squared surfaces have the same proportion to each other as their squares, their sides will be corresponding, that is, commensurable in length.

And if there are two squared surfaces of which the sides are commensurable in length, it will follow that the proportion between them will be as that of their squares.

And if the squared surfaces are not in the same proportion one to another as are their squares, their sides will be incommensurable in length.

The rhomboid is the figure that is formed from the rhombus, but whereas the rhombus is formed from the square, the rhomboid is formed from the rectangle. It has the opposite sides and angles equal to each other but none of its angles is contained by equal sides.

Parallel or equidistant lines are those which when extended continuously in a straight line will never meet together in any part.

The things which are equal to the same thing are also equal to each other. And if to equal things one adds equal things the wholes will still be equal.

And if from equal things one takes away equal things the remainders will still be equal. And if from unequal things one takes away equal things the remainders will be unequal. And if two things are equal to another thing they will be equal to each other. And if there are two things which are each the half of the same thing, each will be equal to the other. And if one thing is placed over another and touches it so that neither is exceeded by the other, these things will be equal to each other. And every whole is greater than its part.

[*Geometrical paradox*]

If the angle is the contact of two lines, as the lines are terminated in a point an infinite number of lines may commence at this point, and conversely an infinite number of lines may end together at this point; consequently the point may be common to the beginning and the end of innumerable lines.

And here it seems a strange matter that the triangle is terminated in a point with the angle opposite to the base, and from the extremities of the base one may divide the triangle into an infinite number of parts; and it seems here that as the point is the common end of all the said divisions, the point as well as the triangle is divisible to infinity.

Every four angles made within the circle of all the space of the circle are equal to four right angles, whether the lines be curved and straight or all straight or all curved.

Every quantity of lines that intersect at the same point will form as many angles round this point as there are lines that proceed from it, and these angles joined together will be equal to four right angles.

The thing moved will never be swifter than its mover.

The boundary of one thing is the beginning of another.

The boundaries of two bodies joined together are interchangeably the surface the one of the other, as water with air.

A point has no part; a line is the transit of a point; points are the boundaries of a line.

An instant has no time. Time is made by the movement of the instant, and instants are the boundaries of time.

An angle is the contact of two lines which do not proceed in the same direction.

A surface is the movement of a line, and lines are the boundaries of a surface.

A surface has no body; the boundaries of bodies are surfaces.

[*Propositions*]

Every body is surrounded by an extreme surface.

Every surface is full of infinite points.

Every point makes a ray.

The ray is made up of infinite separating lines.

In each point of the length of any line whatever, there intersect lines proceeding from the points of the surfaces of the bodies and [these] form pyramids.

Each line occupies the whole of the point from which it starts.

At the extremity of each pyramid there intersect lines proceeding from the whole and from the parts of the bodies, so that from this extremity one may see the whole and the parts.

The air that is between bodies is full of the intersections formed by the radiating images of these bodies.

The images of the figures and colors of each body are transferred from the one to the other by a pyramid.

Each body fills the surrounding air by means of these rays of its infinite images.

The image of each point is in the whole and in the part of the line caused by this point.

Each point of the one object is by analogy capable of being the whole base of the other.

Each body becomes the base of innumerable and infinite pyramids.

That pyramid which is produced within more equal angles will give a truer image of the body from whence it is produced.

One and the same base serves as the cause of innumerable and infinite pyramids turned in various directions and of various degrees of length.

The point of each pyramid has in itself the whole image of its base.

The center line of the pyramid is full of the infinite points of other pyramids.

One pyramid passes through the other without confusion.

The quality of the base is in every part of the length of the pyramid.

That point of the pyramid which includes within itself all those that start upon the same angles will be less indicative of the body from whence it proceeds than any other that is shut up within it.

The pyramid with the most slender point will reveal less the true form and quality of the body from whence it starts.

That pyramid will be most slender which has the angles of its base most unlike the one to the other.

That pyramid which is shortest will transform in greatest variety the similar and equal parts of its base.

Upon the same quality of angles will start pyramids of infinite varieties of length.

The pyramid of thickest point, more than any other, will dye the spot on which it strikes with the color of the body from which it is derived.

If two circles intersect in such a way that the line of the circumference of the one is drawn over the center of the other as the other is of it, these circles are equal, and the straight lines which pass from the two points of intersection and from the center to the other intersect together within four right angles, and the circle made upon the two centers will remain divided in four equal parts by such said intersection, and there will be made a perfect square.

That body is said to be heavy which being free directs its movement to the center of the world by the shortest way.

That body is said to be light which being free flees from this center of the world; and each is of equal power.

Every continuous quantity is divisible to infinity.

If you multiply the number of the pounds that your body weighs by the number of the wheels that are situated in the tackle, you will find that the number of the total that results will be the complete quantity of pounds that it is possible to raise with your weight.

The line has not in itself any matter or substance but may more readily be called an incorporeal thing than a substance, and being of such condition it does not occupy space. Therefore the intersections of infinite lines may be conceived of as made at a point which has no dimensions, and as to thickness, if such a term can be employed, is equal to the thickness of one single line.

An angular surface becomes reduced to a point when it reaches its angle; or if the sides of this angle are produced in a straight line, then beyond this angle there is formed another surface, less or equal or greater than the first.

Every point is the head of an infinite number of lines, which combine to form a base, and suddenly from the said base by the same lines converge to a pyramid showing both its color and its form.

No sooner is the form created or compounded than suddenly of itself it produces infinite angles and lines; these lines spreading themselves in intersection through the air give rise to an infinite number of angles opposite to one another. With each of these opposite angles, given a base, will be formed a triangle alike in form and proportion to the greater angle; and if the base goes twice into each of the two lines of the pyramid it will be the same with the lesser triangle.

If into a vessel that is filled with wine as much water is made to enter as equals the amount of the wine and water which runs out of it, the said vessel can never be altogether deprived of wine. This follows from the fact that the wine, being a continuous quantity, is divisible to infinity, and therefore if in a certain space of time a particular quantity has poured away in another equal space of time half the quantity will have poured away, and in yet another a fourth of the quantity; and what is left is constantly being replenished with water; and thus always during each successive space of time the half of what remains will be poured out. Consequently, as it is capable of being divided to infinity, the continuous quantity of the aforesaid wine will be divided during an infinite number of spaces of time; and because the infinite has no end in time there will be no end to the number of occasions on which the wine is divided.

Archimedes has given the square of a polygonal figure, but not of the circle. Therefore Archimedes never found the square of any figure with curved sides; but I have obtained the square of the circle minus the smallest possible portion that the intellect can conceive, that is, the smallest point visible.

[*1509, April 28*]

Having for a long time sought to square the angle of two curved sides, that is the angle *e,* which has two curved sides

374

of equal curve—that is curve created by the same circle—now in the year 1509, on the eve of the calends of May, I have solved the proposition at ten o'clock on the evening of Sunday. I know therefore (as is shown on the reverse on this page, *A*) that the surface *a b* taken from its position and given the same value with the portion *c* as the rectilinear triangle *d c* corresponds exactly to the curvilinear triangle *e c,* I would call it the curvilinear triangle *a b d.* Therefore that square of the triangle *e* will be found in the rectilinear triangle *c d.*

Instrumental or mechanical science is the noblest and above all others the most useful, seeing that by means of it all animated bodies which have movement perform all their actions; and the origin of these movements is at the center of their gravity, which is placed in the middle with unequal weights at the sides of it, and it has scarcity or abundance of muscles, and also the action of a lever and counter-lever.

III · ASTRONOMY

THE sun does not move.

Omne grave tendit deorsum nec perpetuo potest sic sursum sustineri, quare jam totalis terra esset facta spherica.[1]

Make glasses in order to see the moon large.

The sun has substance, shape, movement, radiance, heat and generative power; and these qualities all emanate from itself without its diminution.

[1] Every heavy substance presses downwards, and thus cannot be upheld perpetually, wherefore the whole earth has been made spherical.

The solar rays, after penetrating the little holes which come between the various rounded particles of the clouds, take a straight and continuous course to the ground where they strike, illuminating with their radiance all the air through which they pass.

The moon has every month a winter and a summer.
And it has greater colds and greater heats and its equinoxes are colder than ours.

I find that those circles which at night seem to surround the moon, varying in circumference and in their degree of redness, are caused by the different degrees of thickness of the vapors which are situated at different altitudes between the moon and our eyes. And the circle that is larger and less red is in the first part lower than the said vapors; the second, being less, is higher and appears redder, because it is seen through two sets of vapors; and so the higher they are the smaller and the redder will they appear, for between the eye and them there will be more layers of vapors, and this goes to prove that where there appears greater redness, there is a greater quantity of vapors.

The moon is not luminous in itself, but it is well fitted to take the characteristics of light after the manner of the mirror or of water or any other shining body; and it grows larger in the east and in the west like the sun and the other planets, and the reason of this is that every luminous body grows larger as it becomes more remote.
It may be readily understood that every planet and star is farther away from us when in the west than when it is overhead by about three thousand five hundred [miles] according to the proof given at the side [of the page].[2] And

---

[2] Here the margin of the MS. contains a diagram representing the earth with the sun shown in two positions.

if you see the sun and moon reflected in water which is near at hand, it will seem to be the same size in the water as it does in the sky, while if you go away to the distance of a mile it will seem a hundred times as large. And if you see it reflected in the sea at the moment of its setting, the image of the sun will seem to you to be more than ten miles long, because it will cover in the reflection more than ten miles of sea. And if you were where the moon is, it would appear to you that the sun was reflected over as much of the sea as it illumines in its daily course, and the land would appear amid this water like the dark spots that are upon the moon, which when looked at from the earth presents to mankind the same appearance that our earth would present to men dwelling in the moon.

Some have said that vapors are given off from the moon after the manner of clouds, and are interposed between the moon and our eyes. If this were the case these spots would never be fixed as to either position or shape; and when the moon was seen from different points, even though these spots did not alter their position, they would change their shape, as does a thing which is seen on different sides.

Others have said that the moon is made up of parts, some more, some less transparent, as though one part were after the manner of alabaster, and another like crystal or glass. It would then follow that when the rays of the sun struck the less transparent part the light would stay on the surface, and consequently the denser part would be illuminated, and the transparent part would reveal the shadows of its obscure depths. Thus then they define the nature of the moon, and this view has found favor with many philosophers, and especially with Aristotle; but nevertheless it is false, since in the different phases which the moon and the sun frequently present to our eyes we should be seeing these spots vary, and at one time they would appear dark and at another light. They would be dark when the sun is in the west and the moon in the center of the sky, because the transparent hollows would then be in shadow, as far as the tops of their edges, since the sun could not cast its rays into the mouths of these same hollows; and they would appear bright at full moon, when the moon in the east faces the sun in the west; for then the sun would illumine even the lowest depths of these transparent parts, and in consequence as no shadow was created, the moon would not at such times reveal to us the above-mentioned spots. And so it would be, sometimes more, sometimes less, according to the change in the position of the sun to the moon, and of the moon to our eyes, as I have said above.

It has also been said that the spots on the moon are created in the moon itself, by the fact of its being of varying thinness or density. If this were so, then in the eclipses of the moon the solar rays could pierce through some part where it is thin, as has been stated, but since we do not see this result the aforesaid theory is false.

Others say that the surface of the moon is smooth and polished, and that, like a mirror, it receives within itself the reflection of the earth. This theory is false, since the earth, when not covered by the water, presents different shapes from different points of view; so when the moon is in the east it would reflect other spots than when it is overhead or in the west, whereas the spots upon the moon, as seen at full moon, never change during the course which it makes in our hemisphere. A second reason is that an object reflected in a convex surface fills only a small part of the mirror, as is proved in perspective. The third reason is that when the moon is full it faces only half the orb of the illuminated earth, in which the ocean and the other waters shine brightly, while the land forms spots amid this brightness; and consequently the half of our earth would be seen girded round about by the radiance of the sea, which takes its light from the sun, and in the moon this reflection would be the least part of that moon. The fourth reason is that one radiant body cannot be reflected in another, and consequently, as the sea derives its radiance from the sun, as does also the moon, it could not show the reflected image of the earth, unless one also saw reflected there separately the orb of the sun and of each of the stars which look down upon it.

The solar rays pass through the cold region of the air and do not change their nature. They pass through glasses filled with cold water and lose nothing of their nature thereby. And whatever may be the transparent place through which they pass, it is as though they passed through so much air.

And if you maintain that the cold rays of the sun are clothed with the heat of fire as they traverse its element, just as they assume the color of the glass they penetrate, it would follow that in penetrating the cold region they put on this mantle of cold after they have already put on the said mantle of heat, and thus the cold would counteract the heat, and therefore the solar rays would come to us deprived of heat, and as this is not confirmed by experience, such method of reasoning as to the sun being cold is vain.

But if you were to say that the cold through which the fiery rays of the sun pass somewhat modifies the excessive heat of these rays, it would follow from this that one would feel greater heat on the high peaks of the Caucasus, the mountain of Scythia, than in the valleys, because the mountain towers above the middle regions of the air, and no clouds are found there nor anything that grows.

And if you say that these solar rays thrust towards us the element of fire from whence they pass by local movement, this cannot be admitted because the local movement of such [a volume of] air cannot occur without the passing of a period of time, and this is greater in proportion as the sun is more on the horizon, for when there it is 3,500 miles farther away from us than when it is in the center of our heaven. If it acted thus it would cool the part of our horizon opposite to it, because it would carry away in its rays such part of the element of fire opposite to it as it penetrated.

If the lesser fire is attracted to and deflected by the greater fire, as one sees happen by experience, it must needs be that the sun draws the element of fire to itself rather than that it banishes it from itself and drives it towards us.

And the heat of the fire does not descend unless it follows burning matter, and in acting thus it is material and in consequence it is visible.

How if the moon is polished and spherical the image of the sun upon it is powerfully luminous, and is only on a small part of its surface.

You will see the proof of this by taking a ball of burnished gold and placing it in the darkness and setting a light at some distance from it. Although this illuminates about half the ball, the eye sees it reflected only on a small part of its surface, and all the rest of the surface reflects the darkness which surrounds it. For this reason it is only there that the image of the light is apparent, and all the rest remains invisible because the eye is at a distance from the ball. The same thing would happen with the surface of the moon if it were polished, glittering and solid, as are bodies which have a reflecting surface.

Show how if you were upon the moon or upon a star, our earth would appear to you to perform the same function for the sun as now the moon does. And show how the reflection of the sun in the sea cannot itself appear a sun as it does in a flat mirror.

My book attempts to show how the ocean with the other seas makes our world by means of the sunshine after the manner of a moon, and to the more remote worlds it appears a star; and this I prove.

Moon cold and moist.

Water is cold and moist.

Our sea has the same influence on the moon as the moon has on us.

The moon has no light of itself, but so much of it as the sun sees, it illuminates. Of this illuminated part we see as much as faces us. And its night receives as much brightness as our waters lend it as they reflect upon it the image of the sun, which is mirrored in all those waters that face the sun and the moon.

The crust or surface of the water of which the sea of the moon and the sea of our earth are composed is always wrinkled, whether little or much or more or less; and this ruggedness is the cause of the expansion of the innumerable images of the sun which are reflected in the hills and valleys and sides and crests of the innumerable furrows; that is, in as many different spots in each furrow as there are different positions of the eyes that see them. This could not happen if the sphere of water which in great part covers the moon were of uniform roundness, because then there would be an image of the sun for every eye, and its reflection would be distinct and the radiance of it would always be spherical in shape, as is clearly shown in the gilded balls placed on the summits of lofty buildings. But if these gilded balls were furrowed or made up of many small globules like mulberries, which are a black fruit composed of minute round balls, then each of the parts of this rounded mass visible to the sun and to the eye would reveal to the eye the radiance produced by the reflection of the sun. And thus in the same body there will be seen many minute suns and very often on account of their great distance they will blend one with another and seem continuous.

The luster of the new moon is brighter and more powerful than when it is full; and this is due to the fact that the angle of its incidence is much more obtuse in the new moon than in the full moon, where the angles are extremely acute, and the waves of the moon reflect the sun both on their hollows and on their crests, and the sides remain dark. But at the sides of the moon the troughs of the waves do not see the sun, for it only sees the crests of these waves, and in consequence the reflections are less frequent and more mingled with the shadows of the valleys. And this intermixture of shaded and luminous images all blending together comes to the eye with only a moderate amount of radiance, and at its edges it will be even darker, because the curve of the side of these waves will be insufficient to reflect the rays which it receives to the eye.

For which reason the new moon by its nature reflects the solar rays more towards the eye through these last waves than through any other place, as is shown by the figure of the moon striking with the rays *a* on the wave *b* and reflected in *b d* where the eye *d* is situated. And this cannot happen at full moon, where the solar ray standing in the west strikes the last rays of the moon in the east from *n* to *m,* and does not reflect towards the eye in the west; but leaps back to the east, slightly bending the direction of this solar ray; and so the angle of the incidence is very great.

The countless images which are reflected by the innumerable waves of the sea from the solar rays that strike upon these waves, cause a continuous and far-reaching splendor upon the surface of the sea.

The moon is an opaque and solid body, and if on the contrary it were transparent, it would not receive the light of the sun.

You have to prove how the earth performs all those same functions towards the moon which the moon does towards the earth.

The moon does not shine with its reflected light as does the sun, because the moon does not receive the light of the sun on its surface.

Between the sun and us there is darkness, and therefore the air appears blue.

Memorandum that I have first to show the distance of the sun from the earth and by means of one of its rays passing through a small hole into a dark place to discover its exact dimensions, and in addition to this by means of the sphere of water to calculate the size of the earth.

And the size of the moon I shall discover as I discover that of the sun, that is, by means of its ray at midnight when it is at the full.

To observe the nature of the planets, have an opening made in the roof and show at the base one planet singly. The reflected movement on this base will record the structure of the said planet. But arrange so that this base reflects only one at a time.

If you look at the stars without their rays—as may be done by looking at them through a small hole made with the extreme point of a fine needle and placed so as almost to touch the eye—you will perceive these stars to be so small that nothing appears less; and in truth the great distance gives them a natural diminution, although there are many there which are a great many times larger than the star which is our earth together with the water. Think, then, what this star of ours would seem like at so great a distance, and then consider how many stars might be set longitudinally and latitudinally amid these stars which are scattered throughout this dark expanse. I can never do other than blame those many ancients who said that the sun was no larger than it appears—among these being Epicurus; and I believe that such a theory is borrowed from the idea of a light set in our atmosphere equidistant from the center [of the earth]; whoever sees it never sees it lessened in size at any distance, and the reasons of its size and potency I shall reserve for the Fourth Book.

But I marvel greatly that Socrates should have spoken with disparagement of that body, and that he should have said that it resembled a burning stone, and it is certain that whoever opposes him in such an error can scarcely do wrong. I could wish that I had such power of language as should avail me to censure those who would fain extol the worship of men above that of the sun, for I do not perceive in the whole universe a body greater and more powerful than this, and its light illumines all the celestial bodies which are distributed throughout the universe.

All vital principle descends from it, since the heat there is in living creatures proceeds from this vital principle; and there is no other heat or light in the universe, as I shall show in the Fourth Book. And indeed those who have wished to worship men as gods—such as Jupiter, Saturn, Mars and the like—have made a very grave error, seeing that even if a man were as large as our earth he would seem like one of the least of the stars, which appears but a speck in the universe; and seeing also that these men are mortal and subject to decay and corruption in their tombs.

The stars are visible by night and not by day owing to our being beneath the dense atmosphere, which is full of an infinite number of particles of moisture. Each of these is lit up when it is struck by the rays of the sun, and consequently the innumerable radiant particles veil these stars; and if it were not for this atmosphere, the sky would always show the stars against the darkness.

A calculation of how many times the sun will go into its course in twenty-four hours:

Make a circle and set it to face south after the manner of sundials. Place a rod in the middle of it, so that its length is pointing to the center of the circle, and note the shadow made by the sun from this rod upon the circumference of the circle, and let us say that the breadth of the shadow is all *a n* (diagram). Now measure how many times this shadow will go into this circumference of the circle, and this will be the number of times that the solar body will go into its course in twenty-four hours. In this way one may see whether Epicurus was right in saying that the sun is as large as it seems to be, for as the apparent diameter of the sun is about a foot and as the sun would go a thousand times into its course in twenty-four hours, the length of its course would be a thousand feet, that is five hundred braccia, which is the sixth of a mile; so then the course of the sun between day and night would be the sixth part of a mile, and this venerable snail, the sun, would have traveled twenty-five braccia an hour.

[*The order of proving that the earth is a star*]

First explain the mechanism of the eye, then show how the scintillation of each star originates in the eye, and why the scintillation of one star is greater than that of another, and how the rays of the stars originate in the eye. I affirm that if the scintillation of the stars was as it appears, in the stars this scintillation would show itself as widely extended as the body of the star; and since it is larger than the earth, this movement made instantaneously would swiftly be found to cause the star to seem double in size. See afterwards how the surface of the air on the confines of the fire, and the surface of the fire at its boundary, is that in which the solar rays penetrating carry the resemblance of the heavenly bodies, large in their rising and setting and small when they are in the center of the sky.

[*An experiment in order to show how rays penetrate liquid bodies*]

Make two vessels each of parallel sides, the one four-fifths of the other and of equal height. Then fix one within the other as you see in the drawing, and cover the outside with color and leave an opening the size of a lentil, and allow a ray of the sun to enter there which makes its exit through another dark hole or by the window. Then observe whether the ray that passes within the water enclosed between the two vessels keeps the direction that it has outside or no; and from this deduce your rule.

In order to see how the solar rays penetrate this curve of the sphere of the air, have two balls made of glass, one twice as large as the other, and let them be as round as possible. Then cut them in half, place one inside the other, close them in front and fill them with water. Then let the solar ray pass within as you have done above, and observe whether the ray is bent or curved and from this deduce your rule. And in this way you can make an infinite number of experiments.

Observe as you place yourself with your eye in the center of the ball whether the light of a candle keeps its size or no.

Some say that the sun is not hot because it is not the color of fire but is much paler and clearer. To these we may reply that when liquefied bronze is at its maximum of heat it most resembles the sun in color, and when it is less hot it has more of the color of fire.

How the earth is not in the center of the circle of the sun, nor in the center of the universe, but is in fact in the center of its elements which accompany it and are united to it. And if one were to be upon the moon, then to the extent to which it together with the sun is above us, so far below it would our earth appear, with the element of water performing the same office as the moon does for us.

All your discourse points to the conclusion that the earth is a star almost like the moon, and thus you will prove the majesty of our universe; and thus you will make a discourse concerning the size of many of the stars according to the authorities.

Whether the friction of the heavens makes a sound or no:
Every sound is caused by the air striking a dense body, and if it is made by two heavy bodies one with another it is by means of the air that surrounds them; and this friction wears away the bodies that are rubbed. It would follow therefore that the heavens in their friction, not having air between them, would not produce sound. Had this friction really existed, however, in the many centuries that these heavens have revolved they would have been consumed by their own immense speed of every day. And if they made a sound it would not be able to spread, because the sound of the percussion made underneath the water is but little heard, and it would be heard even less or not at all in the case of dense bodies. Further, in the case of smooth bodies the friction does not create sound, and it would happen in a similar manner that there would be no sound in the contact or friction of the heavens. And if these heavens are not smooth at the contact of their friction, it follows that they are full of lumps and rough, and therefore their contact is not continuous, and if this is the case a vacuum is produced, which

it has been concluded does not exist in nature. We arrive therefore at the conclusion that the friction would have rubbed away the boundaries of each heaven, and in proportion as its movement is swifter towards the center than towards the poles, it would be more consumed in the center than at the poles; and then there would not be friction any more, and the sound would cease, and the dancers would stop, except that the heavens were turning one to the east and the other to the north.

Whether stars have light from the sun or in themselves:

It is said that they have light in themselves, since if Venus and Mercury had no light of their own, when they come between our eye and the sun they would darken as much of the sun as they cover from our eyes. This however is false, because it has been proved how a dark object placed against a luminous body is surrounded and entirely covered by the lateral rays of the remainder of this luminous body, and so it remains invisible. This is shown when the sun is seen through the ramification of leafless trees in the far distance; these branches do not conceal any part of the sun from our eyes. The same thing happens with the above-mentioned planets, for though they are themselves without light, they do not, as has been said, cover any part of the sun from our eyes.

It is said that the stars at night appear most brilliant in proportion as they are higher up, and that if they have no light of their own the shadow cast by the earth when it comes between them and the sun would come to darken them, since these stars neither see nor are seen by the solar body.

But those who say this have not considered that the pyramidal shadow of the earth does not reach many of the stars, and that in those which it does reach the pyramid is so diminished that it covers little of the body of the star, and all the rest is illuminated by the sun.

Explain the earth with its longer and shorter day in the north and in the south, and do the same for the moon and define them accurately.

Whether the rainbow is produced by the eye, that is its curve, or by the sun by means of the cloud:

The mirror does not take any images except those of visible bodies, and the images are not produced without these bodies; therefore if this arch is seen in the mirror, and the images converge there which have their origin in this rainbow, it follows that this arch is produced by the sun and by the cloud.

The rainbow is seen in the fine rains by those eyes which have the sun behind and the cloud in front; and a perpetually straight imaginary line which starts from the center of the sun and passes through the center of the eye will end in the center of the arch.

And this arch will never be seen by one eye in the same position as by the other eye; it will be seen in as many positions of the cloud where it is formed as there are eyes that see it.

Therefore this arch is all in all the cloud where it is produced, and all in each of the positions in which it may find itself, and so it will appear larger or smaller, half, whole, double, triple.

IV · BOTANY

"ALL seeds have the umbilical cord, which breaks when the seed is ripe. And in like manner they have matrix and secundina, as is seen in herbs and all the seeds which grow in pods."

When a tree has had part of its bark stripped off, nature in order to provide for it supplies to the stripped portion a far greater quantity of nutritive moisture than to any other part; so that because of the first scarcity which has been referred to, the bark there grows much more thickly than in any other place. And this moisture has such power of movement that after having reached the spot where its help is needed, it raises itself partly up like a ball rebounding, and makes various buddings and sproutings, somewhat after the manner of water when it boils.

When many grains or seeds are sown so that they touch and are then covered by a board filled with holes the size of the seeds and left to grow underneath it, the seeds as they germinate will become fixed together and will form a beautiful clump. And if you mix seeds of different kinds together, this clump will seem like jasper.

The branches of plants are found in two different positions: either opposite to each other or not opposite. If they are opposite to each other the center stem is not bent: if they are not opposite the center stem is bent.

The plants which spread out very much have the angles of the divisions which separate their ramifications more obtuse in proportion as their point of origin is lower down, that is, nearer to the thicker and older part of the tree; whereas in the newer part of the tree the angles of its ramifications are more acute.

The shadows on transparent leaves seen from beneath are the same as those on the right side of the leaf, for the shadow is visible in transparence on the under side as well as the part in light; but the luster can never be seen in transparence.

The lowest branches of the trees which have big leaves and

heavy fruits, such as coco palms, figs and the like, always bend towards the ground.

The branches always start above the leaf.

Young trees have more transparent leaves and smoother bark than old ones: the walnut especially is lighter in color in May than in September.

Universally almost all the upright parts of trees are found to bend somewhat, turning their convex part towards the south. And the branches are longer, thicker and more numerous towards the south than towards the north. This arises from the fact that the sun draws the sap towards that part of the surface of the tree which is nearest to it. This is evident in the trees which are frequently pollarded, for they renew their growth every three years. And one notices this unless the sun is screened off by other trees.

[*Symmetry of nature—ramifications of trees and water*]

All the branches of a tree at every stage of its height, united together, are equal to the thickness of its trunk.

All the ramifications of the waters at every stage of their length, being of equal movement, are equal to the size of their parent stream.

The leaf always turns its upper side towards the sky, so that it may be better able to receive over its whole surface the dew which drops down with the slow movement of the atmosphere; and these leaves are arranged on the plants in such a way that one covers another as little as possible, but they lie alternately one above the other, as is seen with the ivy which covers the walls. And this alternation serves two ends—that is, in order to leave spaces so that the air and the sun may penetrate between them, and the second purpose of it is that the drops which fall from the first leaf may fall onto the fourth, or onto the sixth in the case of other trees.

Trees 'finish' with a core; palm trees and the like always bend towards the ground.

The branch is always that above the last.

Young trees have more transparent bark and smoother bark than old ones; the walnut especially is lighter in color in May than in September.

Universally, almost all the upright parts of trees are found to bend somewhat turning their convex part towards the south. And the branches are longer, thicker and more numerous towards the south than towards the north. This arises from the fact that the sun draws the sap towards that part of the surface of the tree which is nearest to it. This is evident if the trees are not overshadowed by others.

[Summary of rules.—Ramification of trees confirmed]

All the branches of a tree at every stage of its height, united together are equal to the thickness of its trunk.

All the ramifications of the waters at every stage of their length, being of equal movement, are equal to the size of their parent stream.

The leafy boughs turn their upper side towards the sky that they may be better able to receive over all their surface the dew which drops down with the slow movement of the atmosphere. And these leaves are arranged on the plants in such a way that one covers another as little as possible, but they lie alternately one above the other as may be seen in the ivy which covers the walls. And this alternation serves two ends; that is, in order to leave spaces so that the air and sun may penetrate between them. The 2nd reason is that the drops which fall from the first leaf may fall onto the fourth or—in the case of other trees—

X

Sight and Sound

I · OPTICS

PREAMBLE to perspective—concerning the functions of the eye:

Consider now, O reader, what trust can we place in the ancients who have set out to define the nature of the soul and of life—things incapable of proof—while those things which by experience may always be clearly known and proved have for so many centuries either remained unknown or been wrongly interpreted.

The eye which thus clearly offers proof of its functions has even down to our own times been defined by countless writers in one way, but I find by experience that it acts in another.

I say that sight is exercised by all animals through the medium of light; and if against this anyone should instance the sight of nocturnal animals, I would say that these in exactly the same way are subject to the same law of nature. For, as one may readily understand, the senses, when they receive the images of things, do not send forth from themselves any actual power; but on the contrary the air which is between the object and its sense, serving as a medium, incorporates within itself the images of things, and by its own contact with the sense presents them to it, if the objects by either sound or smell project themselves to the eye or the nose by virtue of their incorporeal powers. Here the light is not necessary, nor is it made use of.

The forms of objects do not enter into the air as images unless they are luminous; this being so, the eye cannot receive the same from that air which does not contain them, but only touches their surface.

If you wish to speak of the many animals which hunt their prey by night, I answer that when that small amount of light sufficient for them to see their way fails them, they avail themselves of their powers of hearing and smell, which are not impeded by the darkness, and in which they are far in advance of man. If you watch a cat in the daytime leaping among a lot of pieces of crockery you will see that these will remain whole; but if it does the same by night it will break a considerable number. Night birds do not fly unless the moon is shining either full or in part, but their time of feeding is between the hour of sunset and the total darkness of the night.

No substance can be comprehended without light and shade; light and shade are caused by light.

All the images of the things set over against the eye converge in shining lines on the surface of the eye; and these intersect on the surface of the eye at equal angles.

The atmosphere is all in all and all in every part of it filled with the images of the bodies which are enclosed within it.

I find by experience that the black or almost black fringe of color [*colore crispo ovver rasposo*] which appears round the pupil serves for no other purpose except to increase or diminish the size of the pupil: to increase it when the eye is looking towards a dark place, to diminish it when it is looking at the light or at a luminous thing.

And you should make the experiment of holding a light near the eye, and make it when you are looking into the darkness and then turn the eye to this light, and you will be convinced by this experiment.

Why nature made the pupil convex, that is, raised up like part of a ball:

Nature has made the surface of the pupil situated in the eye convex in form, so that the surrounding objects may imprint their images at greater angles than could happen if the eye were flat.

The circle of the light which is in the middle of the white of the eye is by nature suitable to apprehend objects. This same circle has in it a point which seems black, and this is a nerve bored through it which goes within, to the seat of the powers charged with the power of receiving impressions and forming judgment, and this penetrates to the common sense. Now the objects which are over against the eyes act with the rays of their images after the manner of many archers who wish to shoot through the bore of a carbine, for the one among them who finds himself in a straight line with the direction of the bore of the carbine will be most likely to touch the bottom of this bore with his arrow. So the objects opposite to the eye will be more transferred to the sense when they are more in the line of the transfixing nerve.

That water which is in the light that surrounds the black center of the eye serves the same purpose as the hounds in the chase, for these are used to start the quarry and then the hunters capture it. So also with this, because it is a humor that derives from the power of the *imprensiva* and sees many things without seizing hold of them, but suddenly turns thither the central beam which proceeds along the line to the sense, and this seizes on the images and confines such as please it within the prison of the memory.

How the images of any object whatsoever which pass to the eye through some aperture imprint themselves on its pupil upside down and the understanding sees them upright:

The pupil of the eye which receives through a very small round hole the images of bodies situated beyond this hole always receives them upside down and the visual faculty always sees them upright as they are. And this proceeds from the fact that the said images pass through the center of the crystalline sphere situated in the middle of the eye; and in this center they unite in a point and then spread themselves out upon the opposite surface of this sphere without deviating from their course; and the images direct themselves upon this surface according to the object that has caused them, and from thence they are taken by the impression and transmitted to the common sense where they are judged. This may be proved thus: Let *a n* be the pupil of the eye *k h,* and let *p* be a small round hole made in the paper with the fine point of a stylus, and let *m b* be the object placed beyond this opening. I maintain that the upper part of this object cannot come to the upper part of the pupil of the eye through the straight line *m a* because at *v* its passage is impeded by the interposition of the paper. But this upper extremity *m* passes in a straight course through the hole to *n,* the lower part of the pupil, or you would say of the crystalline sphere, and from there it directs its course to the center of this sphere, then rises to the upper part of the opposite side, and from there, as has been said, it runs to the common sense.

Why the mirror in its images of objects changes the right side to the left and the left to the right:

The image of every object is changed in the mirror so that its right side is opposite to the left of the object reflected, and similarly the left to the right. This is of necessity the case because every natural action is performed by nature in the shortest manner and the briefest time possible. Let *a b* be a face which sends its image to the mirror *c d*, this face will have another face in this mirror turned towards it, so that it will have the left eye *c* opposite to the right *a* and similarly the right eye *d* will be opposite to the left eye *b*.

And if it should be urged by the opponent that the right eye of the image was opposite to the right of the object, we might project the lines from the right eye of the image to the right eye of the object and similarly from the left to the left, these lines being *a d* and *b c,* which are seen to intersect. And it is proved that in all cases of lines intersecting, the right extremity of the one is always opposite to the left extremity of the other, and this result is not produced by the shortest line because the diagonal of a square is always longer than its side, and here *a d* is the diagonal of the square *a b c d,* of which *a c* is one of its sides; and thus is concluded what was necessary in order to prove such a result.

And this effect in the mirror would be as though someone who was looking at you, someone, that is, who has the left eye opposite to your right, were as by a miracle transposing left and right, as is the case with letters used in stamping and with wax which takes the impress of the cornelian.

The pupil of the eye changes to as many different sizes as there are differences in the degrees of brightness and obscurity of the objects which present themselves before it.

In this case nature has provided for the visual faculty when it is irritated by excessive light by contracting the pupil of the eye, and by enlarging this pupil after the manner of the mouth of a purse, when it has had to endure varying degrees of darkness. And here nature works as one who having too much light in his habitation blocks up the window halfway or more or less according to the necessity, and who when the night comes throws open the whole of this window in order to see better within this habitation. Nature is here establishing a continual equilibrium, perpetually adjusting and equalizing by making the pupil dilate or contract in proportion to the aforesaid obscurity or brightness which continually presents itself before it. You will see the process in the case of the nocturnal animals such as cats, screech owls, long-eared owls and suchlike, which have the pupil small at midday and very large at night. And it is the same with all land animals and those of the air and of the water, but more, beyond all comparison, with the nocturnal animals.

And if you wish to make the experiment with a man, look intently at the pupil of his eye while you hold a lighted candle at a little distance away, and make him look at this light as you bring it nearer to him little by little, and you will then see that the nearer the light approaches to it the more the pupil will contract.

Whether the eye sees bright and dark things at the same time:

The crystalline humor which dwells within the pupil is condensed on meeting with shining things and becomes rarefied on meeting with dark things; and the truth of this is shown in closing the eye, for then the images retained which were of bright things seem dark and those of dark things seem bright; and this happens more with weak eyes than with those that are strong, and of this I will speak more fully in its place.

There follows the discourse concerning the eye of the nocturnal animals, which see better by night than by day. And this comes about because the size of the eyes is greater than the whole of the brain, especially in the case of the long-eared and short-eared owls, the white owls, the little owls and horned owls and such creatures, but it does not occur with man, who has a greater brain in proportion to the size of his eyes than any other animal that lives on land, and can see but little light after daytime.

There follows concerning the eye of the nocturnal animals, which see more by night than by day, and this arises in great part from the fact that, as was said before, there is a much greater difference between the size of the pupil when dilated and contracted than there is in the case of the animals which are active by day, for if the pupil of the man doubles its diameter at night, that is to say it is increased to four times what it is by day, the diameter of the pupil of the horned owl or the long-eared owl is increased to ten times what it is by day, which amounts to saying that the pupil is a hundred times as large as it is by day.

Furthermore, the ventricle situated in the brain of man called the *imprensiva* is more than ten times the whole of the eye of man, and of this the pupil in which the sight has its origin is less than a thousandth part; and in the case of the long-eared owl the pupil at night is considerably larger than the ventricle of the *imprensiva* situated in its brain. From this it follows that the *imprensiva* in man is greater in proportion to the pupil, it being in fact ten thousand times as great whereas in the case of the horned owl they are almost equal.

And this *imprensiva* of man in comparison with that of the long-eared owl is like a great room which receives the light through a small hole as compared with a small room which is entirely open. For within the great room there will be night at midday and in the small one which is open there will be day at midnight when the weather is not overcast. And herewith may be shown the workings of the most powerful causes by means of the anatomy of the eyes and the *imprensiva* of these two animals, namely of man and of the horned [long-eared?] owl.

That object will seem of greater radiance and size which is seen by a larger pupil. You may make an experiment of this with man's eyes by making as small a hole as possible in a sheet of paper and then bringing it as near as possible to the eye, and if you then look at a star through this hole you are making use of only a small part of the pupil, which sees this star with a wide space of sky round it and sees it so small that hardly anything can be less. And if you make the hole near the edge of the said paper you will be able to see the same star with the other eye at the same time and it will appear to you to be large, and thus in the said time you will see the one star twice with your two eyes and once it will be small and the other time large. Further, you will be able to see the whole body of the sun and with only a moderate amount of radiance, for the more its size is diminished, so in proportion is its radiance, as was set forth above. And from this it arises that the large pupils [*luce?*] see but little of the daylight because the excess of radiance impedes their vision.

This is proved in perspective, how things remote from the eye even when they are exceedingly large seem very small in bulk. And this may be seen without any elaborate demonstration if you raise your eyes to the sky when it is bedecked with stars, for you will see there many stars which are many times larger than the earth and yet appear very small on account of their great distance, and the light which you perceive in them is not their own but is merely an image of the sun reflected in them. For of themselves these stars have no light, but they have a surface like the watery sphere suitable for receiving and giving back the light of the sun which is reflected in them.

Sight and Sound

The pupil of the eye has a power of vision all in the whole and all in each of its parts; and an object placed in front of the eye which is less than its pupil does not occupy the place in the eye of any other distant object, and although it is compact it serves the function of a transparent object.

A proof of the manner in which glasses aid the sight:

Let *a b* be the glasses and *c d* the eyes, and suppose these to have grown old. Whereas they used to see an object at *e* with great ease by turning their position very considerably from the line of the optic nerves, but now by reason of age the power of bending has become weakened, and consequently it cannot be twisted without causing great pain to the eyes, so that they are constrained of necessity to place the object farther away, that is from *e* to *f*, and so see it better but not in detail. But through the interposition of the spectacles, the object is clearly discerned at the distance that it was when they were young, that is at *e*, and this comes about because the object *e* passes to the eye through various mediums, namely thin and thick—the thin being the air that is between the spectacles and the object, and the thick being the thickness of the glass of the spectacles—the line of direction consequently bends in the thickness of the glass, and the line is twisted, so that seeing the object at *e*, it sees it as though it were at *f*, with the advantage that the position of the eye with regard to its optic nerves is not strained and it sees it near at hand and discerns it better at *e* than at *f*, and especially the minute portions.

Every concave place will appear darker if seen from the outside than from within.

And this comes about because the eye that is outside in the air has the pupil much diminished, and that which is situated in a dark place has the pupil enlarged and with the lesser eyeball the power is diminished, and in like manner this power increases in proportion to the increase of its pupil, and when the pupil is of feeble power every small obscurity will appear dark, and as it grows in power every great obscurity will appear lit up.

Excess of light injures the eye, and in order to protect it from being injured in this way the visual faculty takes the help which anyone gets who shuts part of a window in order to lessen the excessive brightness which the sun produces in his dwelling.

Why the right object does not seem the left to the eye:

The images of the objects in the eye, when making their entry into the eye, deflect their rays in a way that is proved in perspective when these images pass from the density of the water to the thinness of the air. But to come back to the proposition that the right object does not appear the left in the eye, we see clearly by experiment that the images which penetrate into the vitreous humor by the pupil of the eye meet together in the sphere of the crystalline humor, as to which two considerations present themselves—namely, whether the visual faculty resides in it or at the extremity of the optic nerve, which extremity catches these images and transmits them to the common sense as do the nerves of the sense of smell; and if this faculty resides in the center of the crystalline humor it catches the images with its surface, and they are referred there from the surface of the pupil, where the objects are mirrored or reflected there from the surface of the uvea, which bounds and clothes the vitreous humor which has darkness behind its transparency, just as behind the transparency of the glass we find the darkness of the lead in order that objects may be the better mirrored in the surface of this glass. But if the visual faculty is in the center of the crystalline sphere, all the objects which are given it from the surface of the pupil of the eye will appear in the true position in which they are, and will not change from the right to the left and will seem larger, as is shown in perspective. And if this crystalline sphere takes these images reflected from the concavity of the uvea, it will take them upright although the uvea is a concave mirror, and it will take them upright because the center of the crystalline sphere is concentric with the center of the sphere of the uvea.

It is true that the images which pass to this uvea as they are outside the eye pass to it through the center of the crystalline sphere, and having arrived at the uvea they become inverted, as also are those which pass to the uvea without passing through this humor. We may surmise, therefore, admitting this visual faculty to reside at the extremity of the optic nerve, that from here it may be seen in the crystalline sphere that all the objects caught by it are upright, for it takes those that were inverted in the uvea and inverts them once again, and consequently this crystalline sphere presents the images upright which were given to it inverted. To such a master in optics one would perhaps say that the spherical surface of the crystalline sphere united to the sphere of the vitreous humor does not change its nature, and it is as though the whole were vitreous and that for this reason the vitreous sphere does not fulfill the same function as it would if it were surrounded by the air. The reply to this, however, is that this result cannot occur because a ball of crystal placed in water fulfills the same function as it does in air.

Of the intersection of the images of the objects received by the eye within the albugineous humor:

Experience which shows that the objects transmit their

images or likenesses intersected within the eye in the albugineous humor shows [what happens] when the images of the illuminated objects penetrate through some small round hole into a very dark habitation. You will then receive these images on a sheet of white paper placed inside this habitation somewhat near to this small hole, and you will see all the aforesaid objects on this paper with their true shapes and colors, but they will be less, and they will be upside down because of the said intersection.

These images if they proceed from a place that is lit by the sun will actually seem painted upon this paper, which should be very thin and seen in reverse; and the said hole should be made in a very thin sheet of iron. Let $a\ b\ c\ d\ e$ be the said objects lit by the sun, $o\ x$ be the façade of the dark habitation in which is the said hole at $n\ m,$ and $s\ t$ the said paper where the rays of the images of these objects inverted are cut, for as their rays are straight, a which is right becomes left at $k,$ and e which is left becomes right at $f,$ and so it is within the pupil.

I maintain that if the front of a building or some piazza or field which is illuminated by the sun has a dwelling over against it, and in that part of the front which does not face the sun you make a small round hole, all the objects which are lit by the sun will transmit their images through this hole, and will be visible inside the dwelling on the opposite wall, which should be made white. And they will be there exactly, but inverted; and if in different parts of the same wall you make similar holes you will produce the same effect in each.

Therefore the images of the illuminated objects are all everywhere on this wall and all in each of its smallest parts. The reason is this: We know clearly that this hole ought to give some light to this dwelling and the light which passes through it is caused by one or by many luminous bodies. If these bodies are of different colors and shapes, the rays which make their images will be of different colors and shapes and so also will be the representations on the wall.

Why objects as they come upon the small surface of the eye appear large arises from the fact that the pupil is a concave mirror; and so one sees, for example with a glass ball filled with water, that anything placed at the side either inside or outside appears larger.

Method of seeing the sun in an eclipse without causing suffering of the eye:

Take a sheet of paper and make holes in it with a knitting needle and look at the sun through these holes.

The movement of an object near a stationary object often causes this stationary object to seem to transform itself to the movement of the moving object and the moving object to seem stationary and fixed.

Every body that moves rapidly seems to color its path with the impression of its hue. The truth of this proposition is seen from experience; thus when the lightning moves among dark clouds the speed of its sinuous flight makes its whole course resemble a luminous snake. So in like manner if you wave a lighted brand, its whole course will seem a ring of flame. This is because the organ of perception acts more rapidly than the judgment.

The eye which is used to the darkness is hurt on suddenly beholding the light and therefore closes quickly, being unable to endure the light. This is due to the fact that the pupil, in order to recognize any object in the darkness to which it has grown accustomed, increases in size, employing all its force to transmit to the receptive part the image of things in shadow. And the light, suddenly penetrating, causes too large a part of the pupil which was in darkness to be hurt by the radiance which bursts in upon it, this being the exact opposite of the darkness to which the eye has already grown accustomed and habituated, and which seeks to maintain itself there, and will not quit its hold without inflicting injury upon the eye.

One might also say that the pain caused to the eye when in shadow by the sudden light arises from the sudden contraction of the pupil, which does not occur except as the result of the sudden contact and friction of the sensitive parts of the eye. If you would see an instance of this, observe and note carefully the size of the pupil when anyone is looking at a dark place, and then cause a candle to be brought before it, and make it rapidly approach the eye, and you will see an instantaneous contraction of the pupil.

If the object interposed between the background and the eye is less than the pupil of the eye, no part of the background will be covered by this object.

If all the images which come to the eye met in an angle, by the definition of the angle they would meet in a mathematical point which is proved to be indivisible. Then all things seen in the universe would seem one and that would be indivisible, and there would be no more space from one star to another which would be reckoned in such an angle.

And if experience shows us all things separated with spaces proportioned and definite, this power which imprints the images of objects is also itself divisible into as many larger and smaller parts as there are images of the things seen. We conclude therefore that the sense takes the images which are reflected on the surface of the eye, and then judges them within, and therefore they do not meet in a point, nor as a consequence in an angle.

If you bring your eye as near as you can to the surface of the sea, you will see the image of the sun in a wave of the water, and you will be able to measure it and you will find that it is very small.

If you bring your eye near the surface of the water of the sea or of a pool which is between your eye and the sun, you will find that the image of the sun on this surface shows itself very small. But if you retire a distance of several miles from this sea, you will perceive a proportionate increase in the image of the sun; and if the first image preserves the true shape and radiance of the sun as do mirrors, the second does not keep either the shape or the radiance of the sun but is a figure with broken contour lines and a lesser degree of radiance.

The figure of the image with contour lines broken and confused is formed by the blending of many images of the sun reflected to your eye by many waves of the sea, and the lesser degree of radiance springs from the fact that the shadowed and luminous images of the waves come to the eye all mingled together and consequently their light is affected by their shadows.

This, however, cannot happen with the surface of a single wave when you have approached very near to it with your eye.

Example of the enlargement and contraction of the pupil through the movement of the sun or other luminous body:

The darker the sky the greater the stars will seem, and if you light up the atmosphere these stars will show themselves less. And this change proceeds only from the pupil, which expands and contracts according to the clearness of the atmosphere which finds itself between the eye and the luminous body. Let the experiment be made with a candle placed above the head while you are looking at this star; afterwards proceed to lower this candle, little by little, until it is near the ray that comes from the star to the eye, and you will then see the star diminish so much that you will almost lose sight of it.

[*The structure and anatomy of the eye*]

The pupil of the eye is situated in the center in the eyeball [*luce*], which is of the shape of part of a sphere which takes the pupil at the center of its base. This *luce,* forming part of a sphere, takes all the images of the objects and transmits them by the pupil within to the place where the vision is formed.

In the anatomy of the eye, in order to be able to see the inside well without spilling its watery humor, you should place the complete eye in white of egg and make it boil and become solid, cutting the egg and the eye transversely so that no part of the middle portion may be poured out.

Again, it is possible for the same pupil to see the same object at the same time make two opposite movements without the pupil changing.

[*Diagram*]

That which is set forth above is seen by the pupil when it sees through a small hole made in the paper by the point of a needle, and keeping the eye close to it and interposing between the eye and the hole a very fine straw, which as you move it from right to left your eye will see in its true movement between the hole and it, in the true position in which this straw actually finds itself moving; and beyond this hole it will see it moving in the opposite direction to its true movement; so that at one and the same time it sees the true and the false movements separately the one from the other.

If you stand under water and look at something within the air you will see this thing out of its position, and it will be the same with a thing within the water seen from the air.

The intersections of the images at the entrance of the pupil do not mingle one in another in that space where this intersection unites them; and this is evident because if the rays of the sun pass through two panes of glass in contact one with another, the one of these being blue and the other yellow, the ray that penetrates them does not assume the hue of blue or yellow but of a most beautiful green. And the same process would occur with the eye if the images yellow and green in color should come to mingle one with the other at the intersection which they make within themselves at the entrance of the pupil, but as this does not happen such a mingling does not exist.

O marvelous Necessity, thou with supreme reason constrainest all effects to be the direct result of their causes, and by a supreme and irrevocable law every natural action obeys thee by the shortest possible process!

Who would believe that so small a space could contain the images of all the universe? O mighty process! What talent can avail to penetrate a nature such as these? What tongue will it be that can unfold so great a wonder? Verily, none! This it is that guides the human discourse to the considering of divine things.

Here the figures, here the colors, here all the images of every part of the universe are contracted to a point.

O what point is so marvelous!

O wonderful, O stupendous Necessity, thou by thy law

constrainest all effects to issue from their causes in the brief-est possible way!

These are the miracles . . . forms already lost, mingled together in so small a space, it can re-create and reconstitute by its dilation.

How it may be that from indistinct causes there may issue effects manifest and immediate, as are the images which have passed through the aforesaid natural point.

II · ACOUSTICS

THE note of the echo is either continuous or intermittent, it occurs singly or is united, is of brief or long duration, finite or endless in sound, immediate or far away.

It is continuous when the surface on which the echo is produced is uniformly concave. The note of the echo is inter-mittent when the place which produces it is broken and interrupted. It is single when it is produced in one place only. It is united when it is produced in several places. It is either brief or long-continuing, as when it goes winding round within a bell which has been struck, or in a cistern or other hollow space, or in clouds wherein the note recurs at fixed distances in regular intervals of time, ever uniformly growing fainter, and is like the wave that spreads itself out in a circle over the sea.

The sound often seems to proceed from the direction of the echo, and not from the place where the real sound is; and similarly it happened at Ghiera d'Adda, when a fire which broke out there caused in the air twelve lurid reflec-tions upon twelve clouds, and the cause was not perceived.

Whether the whole circle made in the air by the sound of a man's voice carries with it all the word spoken, since the part of this circle having struck upon another man's ear does not leave the part of this speech in this ear but the whole:

What has been said is shown in the case of light, and you would be able to say whether the whole of the light illumines the whole of a building, since the part of this building would not be illumined merely by a part of this light.

If you wish to dispute the point and say that this light illumines the said part of the habitation not with the whole but with its part, I will give you the instance of one or two mirrors set in different positions on this spot; each part of this mirror will have within itself the whole of the said light. This shows therefore that this light is all in all and all in every part of this habitation; and it is the same with the voice in its circle.

"That sound which remains or seems to remain in the bell after it has received the stroke is not in the bell itself but in the ear of the listener, and the ear retains within itself the image of the stroke of the bell which it has heard, and only loses it by slow degrees, like that which the impression of the sun creates in the eye, which only by slow degrees becomes lost and is no longer seen."

[*A proof to the contrary*]

If the aforesaid proposition were true, you would not be able to cause the sound of the bell to cease abruptly by touching it with the palm of the hand, especially at the beginning of its strength, for surely if it were touched it would not happen that as you touched the bell with the hand the ear would simultaneously withhold the sound; whereas we see that if after the stroke had taken place the hand is placed upon the thing which is struck the sound suddenly ceases.

The rumbling of the cannon is caused by the impetuous fury of the flame beaten back by the resisting air, and that quantity of the powder causes this effect because it finds itself ignited within the body of the cannon; and not perceiving itself in a place that has capacity for it to increase, nature guides it to search with fury a place suitable for its increase, and breaking or driving before it the weaker obstacle it wins its way into the spacious air; and this not being capable of escaping with the speed with which it is attacked, because the fire is more volatile than the air, it follows that as the air is not equally volatile with the fire it cannot make way for it with that velocity and swiftness with which the fire assails it, and therefore it happens that there is resistance, and the resistance is the cause of a great roar and rumbling of the cannon.

But if the cannon were to be moved against the oncoming of an impetuous wind, it would be the occasion of a greater roar made by reason of the greater resistance of the air against the flame, and so it would make a less rumbling when moved in the line of the wind because there would then be less resistance.

[Whether the sound lies in the hammer or in the anvil]

I say that because the anvil is not suspended it cannot resound. The hammer resounds in the jump that it makes after the blow, and if the anvil were to re-echo the sound made on it by every small hammer as does the bell with every different thing which strikes it with the same depth of tone, so would the anvil when struck by each different hammer. And as therefore you hear different notes with hammers of different sizes, it follows that the note is in the hammer and not in the anvil.

Why the thing which is not suspended does not sound and when suspended every slight contact takes away the sound from it:

The bell when struck makes a sudden tremor and the sudden tremor causes it instantly to strike the circumscribing air, which instantly resounds.

On being impeded by any slight contact, it does not make the tremor or strike and so the air does not resound.

If the bird suddenly beats the air, ought this to resound or no:

I maintain it does not, because as the air penetrates through the thing that beats it it does not receive the blow and consequently it cannot make sound.

The voice after it has struck on the object will return to the ear by a line at a slant equal to that of the line of the incidence, that is, the line which carries the voice from its cause to the place where this voice can reform itself; and this voice acts in the manner of a thing seen in a mirror which is all in all the mirror and all in the part of it. Let us say, therefore, that the mirror is *a b* and the thing seen is *c*; just as *c* sees all the parts of the mirror, so all the parts of the mirror see *c*; therefore *c* is all in all the mirror because it is in all its parts; and it is all in the parts because it sees itself in as many different parts as there are different positions of spectators . . .

Let us take the sun as an example. If you should walk along the bank of a river and watch the sun's reflection in it, for so long a time as you walk along the bank of the river it will seem that the sun moves with you, and this because the sun is all in the whole and all in the part.

Whether many tiny voices joined together will make as much sound as one large one. I maintain they will not; for if you were to take ten thousand voices of flies all together, they would not carry as far as the voice of a man; and if such voice of a man were split up into ten thousand parts, no one of these parts would be equal to the size of the voice of a fly.

Whether a sound that is double another will be heard twice as far. I maintain that it will not, for if it were so two men shouting would be heard twice as far as one; but experience does not confirm this.

If you cause your ship to stop, and place the head of a long tube in the water, and place the other extremity to your ear, you will hear ships at a great distance from you.

You can also do the same by placing the head of the tube upon the ground, and you will then hear anyone passing at a distance from you.

I say that the note of the echo is cast back to the ear after it has struck, just as the images of objects strike the mirror and are thence reflected to the eye. And in the same way as these images fall from the object to the mirror and from the mirror to the eye at equal angles, so the note of the echo will strike and rebound within the hollow where it has first struck, at equal angles to the ear.

If flies made with their mouths the sound that is heard when they fly, then since it is very long and sustained they would need a great pair of bellows for lungs in order to drive out so great and so long a wind, and then there would be a long silence in order to draw into themselves an equal volume of air; therefore where there was a long duration of sound there would be a long intermission.

That the sound which flies make proceeds from their wings you will see by cutting them a little, or better still by smearing them a little with honey in such a way as not entirely to prevent them from flying, and you will see that the sound made by the movement of the wings will become hoarse and the note will change from high to deep to just the same degree as the fly has lost the free use of its wings.

XI

Tales, Fables and Prophecies

I · TALES

DEAR Benedetto—To give you the news of the things here from the east, you must know that in the month of June there appeared a giant who came from the Libyan desert. This giant was born on Mount Atlas, and was black, and he fought against Artaxerxes with the Egyptians and Arabs, the Medes and Persians; he lived in the sea upon the whales, the great leviathans and the ships. When the savage giant fell by reason of the ground being covered over with blood and mire, it seemed as though a mountain had fallen; whereat the country [shook] as though there were an earthquake, with terror to Pluto in Hell, and Mars fearing for his life fled for refuge under the side of Jove.

And from the violence of the shock he lay prostrate on the level ground as though stunned; until suddenly the people, believing that he had been killed by some thunderbolt, began to turn about his great beard; and like a flock of ants that range about hither and thither furiously among the brambles beaten down by the ax of the sturdy peasant, so these are hurrying about over his huge limbs and piercing them with frequent wounds.

At this the giant, being roused and perceiving himself to be almost covered by the crowd, suddenly, on feeling himself smarting from their stabs, uttered a roar which seemed as though it were a terrific peal of thunder, and set his hands on the ground and lifted up his awe-inspiring countenance;

and then placing one of his hands upon his head, he perceived it to be covered with men sticking to the hairs after the fashion of tiny creatures which are sometimes harbored there, and who, as they clung to the hairs and strove to hide among them, were like sailors in a storm who mount the rigging in order to lower the sail and lessen the force of the wind; and at this point he shook his head and sent the men flying through the air after the manner of hail when it is driven by the fury of the winds, and many of these men were found to be killed by those who fell on them like a tempest. Then he stood erect, trampling upon them with his feet.

[*Note: This and the pieces that follow seem parts of a fantastic tale written in the form of letters.*]

The black visage at first sight is most horrible and terrifying to look upon, especially the swollen and bloodshot eyes, set beneath the awful lowering eyebrows, which cause the sky to be overcast and the earth to tremble.

And believe me there is no man so brave but that, when the fiery eyes were turned upon him, he would willingly have put on wings in order to escape, for the face of infernal Lucifer would seem angelic by contrast with this.

The nose was turned up in a snout with wide nostrils, and sticking out of these were quantities of large bristles, beneath which was the arched mouth, with the thick lips, at whose extremities were hairs like those of cats, and the teeth were yellow; and from the top of his instep he towered above the heads of men on horseback.

And as his cramped position had been irksome, and in order to rid himself of the importunity of the throng, his rage turned to frenzy, and he began to let his feet give vent to the frenzy which possessed his mighty limbs, and entering in among the crowd he began by his kicks to toss men up in the air, so that they fell down again upon the rest, as though there had been a thick storm of hail, and many were those who in dying dealt out death. And this barbarity continued until such time as the dust stirred up by his great feet, rising up in the air, compelled his infernal fury to abate, while we continued our flight.

Alas, how many attacks were made upon this raging fiend to whom every onslaught was as nothing. O wretched folk, for you there avail not the impregnable fortresses, nor the lofty walls of your cities, nor the being together in great numbers, nor your houses or palaces! There remained not any place unless it were the tiny holes and subterranean caverns where after the manner of crabs and crickets and creatures like these you might find safety and a means of escape. Oh, how many wretched mothers and fathers were deprived of their children! How many unhappy women were deprived of their companions! In truth, my dear Benedetto, I do not believe that ever since the world was created there has been witnessed such lamentation and wailing of people, accompanied by so great terror. In truth, the human species in such a plight has need to envy every other race of creatures; for though the eagle has strength sufficient to subdue the other birds, they yet remain unconquered through the rapidity of their flight, and so the swallows through their speed escape becoming the prey of the falcon, and the dolphins also by their swift flight escape becoming the prey of the whales and of the mighty leviathans; but for us wretched mortals there avails not any flight, since this monster when advancing slowly far exceeds the speed of the swiftest courser.

I know not what to say or do, for everywhere I seem to find myself swimming with bent head within the mighty throat and remaining indistinguishable in death, buried within the huge belly.

The preaching and persuasion of faith.

The sudden inundation down to its end.

The ruin of the city.

The death of the people and their despair.

The pursuit of the preacher and his liberation and benevolence.

Description of the cause of this fall of the mountain.

The havoc that it made.

The avalanche.

The finding of the prophet.

His prophecy.

The inundation of the lower parts of western Armenia, the channels in which were formed by the cutting of Mount Taurus.

How the new prophet showed that this destruction occurred as he had foretold.

Description of Mount Taurus and of the river Euphrates. To the Devatdar of Syria, lieutenant of the sacred Sultan of Babylon:[1]

The recent unforeseen event which has occurred in these our northern parts, which I am certain will strike terror not only into you but into the whole world, shall be revealed to you in its due order, showing first the effect and then the cause.

Finding myself in this part of Armenia in order to discharge with devotion and care the duties of that office to which you have appointed me, and making a beginning in those parts which seem to me to be most suitable for our purpose, I entered into the city of Calindra, which is near to

[1] Some scholars believe this to be a draft of an actual letter, which indicates that Leonardo traveled to Armenia in the service of an Oriental potentate. The chances are, however, that it is a fragment of an intended romance.

our borders. This city is situated on the seacoast of that part of the Taurus range which is separated from the Euphrates and looks westward to the peaks of the great Mount Taurus. These peaks are of such a height that they seem to touch the sky, for in the whole world there is no part of the earth that is higher than their summit, and they are always struck by the rays of the sun in the east four hours before day. And being of exceedingly white stone this shines brightly and performs the same office for the Armenians of these parts as the beautiful light of the moon would in the midst of the darkness; and by reason of its great height it outstretches the highest level of the clouds for a space of four miles in a straight line.

This peak is visible from a great part of the west, illuminated by the sun after its setting during the third part of the night. And it is this which among you in calm weather has formerly been thought to be a comet, and seems to us in the darkness of the night to assume various shapes, sometimes dividing into two or three parts, sometimes long and sometimes short. And this proceeds from the fact that the clouds on the horizon come between part of this mountain and the sun, and by their cutting these solar rays the light of the mountain is broken by various spaces of clouds and therefore its brightness is variable in shape.

Why the mountain shines at its summit half or a third of the night, and seems a comet after sunset to those who dwell in the west, and before sunrise to those who dwell in the east.

Why this comet seems variable in shape, so that at one time it is round, at another long, at another divided into two or three parts, at another united, and sometimes invisible and sometimes becoming visible again.

I am not justly to be accused of idleness, O Devatdar, as your strictures seem to intimate, but your unbounded affection which has caused you to confer these benefits upon me has constrained me to employ the utmost care in seeking out and diligently investigating the cause of so momentous and so startling an occurrence, and for this time was necessary.

In order now to make you well acquainted with the cause of so great an effect, it is necessary that I shall describe the nature of the place, and then I will proceed to the event, by which process I believe you will be fully satisfied.

Do not distress yourself, O Devatdar, at my delay in replying to your urgent request, because the matters about which you have asked me are of such a nature as cannot well be expressed without lapse of time, and especially because in wishing to expound the cause of so great an effect it is necessary to describe exactly the nature of the place, and you will afterwards be able by means of this easily to satisfy yourself as to the above-mentioned request.

I will omit any description of the shape of Asia Minor, or of what seas or lands they are which determine the aspect of its surface, knowing as I do your diligence and care in your studies to be such that you will already have acquired this knowledge; I pass on, therefore, to furnish you with an account of the true shape of Mount Taurus, which has been the scene of so surprising and destructive a catastrophe, for this may serve to advance our purpose.

It is this Mount Taurus which, according to many, is said to be the ridge of the Caucasus, but, wishing to be quite clear about this, I set myself to interrogate some of the inhabitants of the shores of the Caspian Sea; and they inform me that although their mountains bear the same name, these are of greater height, and they confirm this, therefore, to be the true Mount Caucasus, since Caucasus in the Scythian tongue means "supreme height." And in fact nothing is known of the existence either in the east or the west of any mountain of so great a height, and the proof of this is that the inhabitants of those countries which are on the west see the sun's rays illuminating part of its summit for a fourth part of the longest night, and similarly with the countries which are on the east.

The shadow of this ridge of the Taurus is so high that in the middle of June when the sun is at the meridian it reaches to the borders of Sarmatia, which are twelve days' journey, and in mid-December it extends as far as the Hyperborean Mountains, which are a month's journey to the north. And the side that faces the way the wind blows is full of clouds and mists, because the wind, which is cleft in twain as it strikes against the rock and closes up again beyond it, carries with it in this way the clouds from all parts and leaves them where it strikes, and it is always full of thunderbolts through the great number of clouds which are gathered there, and this causes the rock to be all fissured and filled with huge débris.

This mountain at its base is inhabited by a very opulent people; it abounds in most beautiful springs and rivers; it is fertile and teems with everything that is good and especially in those parts which have a southern aspect. After an ascent of about three miles, you come to where begin the forests of great firs and pines and beeches and other similar trees; beyond for a space of another three miles you find meadows and vast pastures, and all the rest as far as the beginning of the peak of Taurus is eternal snow, for this never disappears in any season, and it extends at this height for about fourteen miles in all. From the point where the peak begins for about a mile the clouds never pass, so that they extend for about fifteen miles with a height of about five in a straight line. As far beyond or thereabouts we find the summit of the peaks of Taurus, and here from about halfway upwards we commence to find the air grow warm, and there is no breath of wind to be felt and nothing can live there very long. Nothing is brought forth there except some birds of prey, which nest in the deep gorges of the Taurus and descend below the clouds to seek their prey upon the grassy hills. It is all bare rock from above where the clouds are, and the rock is of a dazzling whiteness, and it is not possible to go to the lofty summit because the ascent is rough and dangerous.

As I have in my letters rejoiced with you many times over your prosperous fortunes, so I know now that you as a friend will share my sorrow at the miserable condition to which I am reduced; for the fact is that in these last days I have had so many anxieties, so many fears, dangers and losses, as have also the wretched country-folk, that we have come to envy the dead.

And certainly I for my part cannot imagine that since first the elements by their separation made order out of chaos, they can ever have united their force or rather their frenzy to work such destruction to mankind, as has now been seen and experienced by us; so that I cannot imagine what could further increase so great a misfortune as this that we have experienced in a space of ten hours. First we were assailed and buffeted by the might and fury of the winds, and then followed the avalanches from the great snow-covered mountains which have choked up all these valleys, and caused a great part of this city to fall in ruins. And, not content with this, the tempest has submerged with a sudden deluge of water all the lower parts of the city; and beyond all this there was added a sudden storm of rain and a furious hurricane, laden with water, sand, mud, and stones all mingled together with roots, branches and stumps of various trees; and every kind of thing came hurtling through the air and descended upon us, and finally a great fire—which did not seem to be borne by the wind but as though carried by thirty thousand devils—has burnt up and destroyed all this country and has not yet ceased. And the few of us who remain are left in such a state of dismay and fear that, like those who are half-witted, we scarce dare to hold speech one with another, but giving up even the attempt at work we stay huddled together in the ruins of some of the churches, men and women small and great all mingled together like herds of goats; and but for certain people having helped us with provisions we should all have died of hunger. Now you can understand the state we are in; and yet all these evils are as nothing by comparison with those which threaten us within a brief space of time.

I know that you as a friend will have a fellow-feeling for my misfortunes, even as I in my former letters have shown myself glad at your prosperity.

A priest while going the round of his parish on the Saturday before Easter, in order to sprinkle the houses with holy water as was his custom, coming to the studio of a painter, and there beginning to sprinkle the water upon some of his pictures, the painter turning round with some annoyance asked him why he sprinkled his pictures in this manner. The priest replied that it was the custom and that it was his duty to act thus, that he was doing a good deed and that whoever did a good deed might expect a recompense as great or even greater; for so God had promised that for every good deed which we do on the earth we shall be rewarded a hundredfold from on high. Then the painter, having waited until the priest had made his exit, stepped to the window above and threw a large bucket of water down onto his back, calling out to him: "See, there is the reward that comes to you a hundred-

fold from on high as you said it would, on account of the
good deed you did me with your holy water with which you
have half ruined my pictures."

The Franciscan friars at certain seasons have periods of
fasting, during which no meat is eaten in their monasteries,
but if they are on a journey, as they are then living on alms-
giving, they are allowed to eat whatever is set before them.
Now a couple of these friars traveling under these conditions
chanced to alight at an inn at the same time as a certain
merchant, and sat down at the same table, and on account
of the poverty of the inn nothing was served there except one
roasted cockerel. At this the merchant, as he saw that it
would be scant fare for himself, turned to the friars and said:
"On days like these, if I remember rightly, you are not permitted in your monasteries to eat any kind of meat." The
friars on hearing these words were constrained by their rule
to admit without any attempt at argument that this was indeed the case; so the merchant had his desire and devoured
the chicken, and the friars fared as best they could.

Now, after having dined in this wise, all three table companions set out on their journey together, and having gone a
certain distance they came to a river of considerable breadth
and depth, and as they were all three on foot, the friars by
reason of their poverty and the other from niggardliness, it
was necessary according to the custom of the country that
one of the friars who had no shoes and stockings should
carry the merchant on his shoulders; and consequently the
friar having given him his clogs to hold took the man on his
back. But as it so happened the friar when he found himself
in the middle of the stream bethought himself of another of
his rules, and coming to a standstill after the manner of
St. Christopher raised his head towards him who was weigh-

ing heavily upon him and said: "Just tell me, have you any money about you?" "Why you know quite well that I have," replied the other. "How do you suppose a merchant like me could travel about otherwise?" "Alas!" said the friar. "Our rule forbids us to carry any money on our backs." And he instantly threw him into the water.

As the merchant was conscious that this was done as a jest and out of revenge for the injury he had done them, he smiled pleasantly and pacifically, and blushing considerably from shame he endured their revenge.

II · FABLES

THE laurel and the myrtle, on seeing the pear tree being cut down, cried out with a loud voice: "O pear tree, where are you going? Where is the pride that you had when you were laden with ripe fruit? Now you will no longer make shade for us with your thick foliage." Then the pear tree replied: "I am going with the husbandman who is cutting me down and who will take me to the workshop of a good sculptor, who by his art will cause me to assume the form of the god Jove, and I shall be dedicated in a temple and worshipped by men in place of Jove. While you are obliged to remain always maimed and stripped of your branches which men shall set around me in order to do me honor."

The ape on finding a nest of small birds approached them with great joy, but as they were already able to fly he could only catch the smallest. Filled with joy he went with it in his hand to his hiding place; and having commenced to look at the tiny bird he began to kiss it; and in his uncontrollable affection he gave it so many kisses and turned it over and squeezed it, until he took away its life. This is said for those who by being too fond of their children bring misfortune upon them.

The unhappy willow—on finding herself unable to enjoy the pleasure of seeing her slender boughs attain to such a height as she desired, or even point towards the sky, because she was continually being maimed and lopped and spoiled for the sake of the vine or any other tree which happened to be near—summoned up all her faculties and by this means opened wide the portals of her imagination, remaining in continual meditation, and seeking in the world of plants for one wherewith to ally herself which could not need the help of her branches. So continuing for a time with her imagination at work, the thought of the gourd suddenly presented itself to her mind, and all her branches quivered in her intense joy, for it seemed to her that she had found the right companion for the purpose she desired, because the gourd is by nature more fitted to bind others than to be bound herself. After coming to this conclusion she lifted up her branches towards the sky and waited, on the lookout for some friendly bird to serve as the intermediary of her desire. Among the rest she descried the magpie near to her and said to him: "O gentle bird, by the refuge you have lately found among my branches at dawn, when the hungry, cruel and rapacious falcon has wished to devour you—by that rest you have often found in me when your wings craved rest—by those delights you have enjoyed among my branches in amorous dalliance with your companions—I entreat you to go and seek out the gourd and obtain from her some of her seeds, telling her that I will care for whatever is born from them as though they were my own offspring, and in like manner use all such words as may incline her to the like purpose, though to you who are a master of language there is no need for me to give instruction. If you will do this I am content to let your nest be in the fork of my boughs together with all your family without payment of any rent." So the magpie, after stipulating with the willow for certain further conditions, the most important being that she should never admit upon her boughs any snake or polecat, cocked his tail and lowered his head, and casting himself loose from the bough let himself float on his wings; and beating about with these in the fleeting air, seeking hither and thither, and guiding himself by using his tail as a rudder, he came to a gourd, and after courteously saluting her obtained by a few polite words the seeds for which he sought. On taking these back to the willow he was welcomed with joyful looks; and then scraping away with his foot some of the earth near the willow he planted the grains with his beak round about her in a circle.

These soon began to grow, and as the branches increased and opened out they began to cover all the branches of the willow, and their great leaves shut away from it the beauty of the sun and the sky. And all this evil not sufficing, the gourds next began to drag down to the ground in their rude grip the tops of the slender boughs, twisting them and distorting them in strange shapes. Then the willow, after shaking and tossing herself to no purpose to make the gourds loose their hold, and vainly for days cherishing such idle hopes, since the grasp of the gourds was so sure and firm as to forbid such thoughts, seeing the wind pass by, forthwith commended herself to it. And the wind blew hard; and it rent open the willow's old and hollow trunk, tearing it in two parts right down to its roots; and as they fell asunder she vainly bewailed her fate, confessing herself born to no good end.

The spider, having found a bunch of grapes, which because of its sweetness was much visited by bees and various sorts of flies, fancied that it had found a spot very suitable for its wiles. And after having lowered itself down by its fine thread and entered its new habitation, there day by day, having ensconced itself in the tiny holes made by the spaces between the various grapes in the bunch, like a robber it assaulted the wretched animals which were not on their guard against it. But after some days had passed, the keeper of the vineyard cut this bunch off and placed it with the others, and it was pressed with them. And the grapes, therefore, served as trap and snare for the deceiving spider as well as for the flies whom he had deceived.

The fig tree, standing near to the elm, and perceiving that her boughs bore no fruit themselves, yet had the hardihood to keep away the sun from her own, unripe figs, rebuked her, saying: "O elm, are you not ashamed to stand in front of me? Only wait until my children are fully grown and you will see where you will find yourself." But when her offspring were ripe a regiment of soldiers came to the place, and they tore off the branches of the fig tree in order to take her figs, and left her all stripped and broken.

And as she thus stood maimed in all her limbs, the elm questioned her, saying: "O fig tree, how much better was it to be without children than to be brought by them to so wretched a pass?"

Once upon a time the razor emerging from the handle which served it as a sheath, and placing itself in the sun, saw the sun reflected on its surface, at which thing it took great pride, and turning it over in its thoughts, it began to say to itself: "Am I to go back any more to that shop from which I have just now come away? No, surely! It cannot be the pleasure of the gods that such radiant beauty should stoop to such vile uses! What madness would that be which should induce me to scrape the lathered chins of rustic peasants and to do such menial service? Is this body made for actions such as these? Certainly not! I will go and hide myself in some retired spot, and there pass my life in tranquil ease."

And so having hidden itself away for some months, returning one day to the light and coming out of its sheath, it perceived that it had acquired the appearance of a rusty saw, and that its surface no longer reflected the sun's radiance. In vain with useless repentance it bemoaned its irreparable hurt, saying to itself: "Ah, how much better would it have been to have let the barber use that lost edge of mine that had so rare a keenness! Where now is the glittering surface? In truth the foul insidious rust has consumed it away!"

The same thing happens with minds which in lieu of exercise give themselves up to sloth; for these like the razor lose their keen edge, and the rust of ignorance destroys their form.

A stone of considerable size, only recently left uncovered by the waters, stood in a certain spot perched up at the edge of a delightful copse, above a stony road, surrounded by plants bright with various flowers of different colors, and looked upon the great mass of stones which lay heaped together in the road beneath. And she became filled with longing to let herself down there, saying within herself: "What am I doing here with these plants? I would fain dwell in the company of my sisters yonder;" and so letting herself fall she ended her rapid course among her desired companions. But when she had been there for a short time she found herself in continual distress from the wheels of the carts, the iron hoofs of the horses and the feet of the passers-by. One rolled her over, another trampled upon her; and at times she raised herself up a little as she lay covered with mud or the dung of some animal, and vainly looked up at the place from whence she had departed as a place of solitude and quiet peace.

So it happens to those who, leaving a life of solitude and contemplation, choose to come and dwell in cities among people full of infinite wickedness.

As the painted butterfly was idly wandering and flitting about through the darkened air a light came within sight, and thither immediately it directed its course, and flew round about it in varying circles marveling greatly at such radiant beauty. And not contented merely to behold, it began to treat it as was its custom with the fragrant flowers, and directing its flight it approached with bold resolve close to the light, which thereupon consumed the tips of its wings and legs and the other extremities; and then dropping down at the foot of it, it began to consider with astonishment how this accident had been brought about; for it could not so much as entertain a thought that any evil or hurt could possibly come to it from a thing so beautiful; and then having in part regained the strength which it had lost, it took another flight and passed right through the body of the flame, and in an instant fell down burned into the oil which fed the flame, preserving only so much life as sufficed it to reflect upon the cause of its destruction, saying to it: "O accursed light! I thought that in you I had found my happiness! Vainly do I lament my mad desire, and by my ruin I have come to know your rapacious and destructive nature."

To which the light replied: "Thus do I treat whoever does not know how to use me aright."

This is said for those who, when they see before them these carnal and worldly delights, hasten towards them like the butterfly, without ever taking thought as to their nature, which they know after long usage to their shame and loss.

The flint on being struck by the steel marveled greatly and said to it in a stern voice: "What arrogance prompts you to annoy me? Trouble me not, for you have chosen me by mistake; I have never done harm to anyone." To which the steel made answer: "If you will be patient you will see what a marvelous result will issue forth from you."

At these words the flint was pacified and patiently endured its martyrdom, and it saw itself give birth to the marvelous element of fire which by its potency became a factor in innumerable things.

This is said for those who are dismayed at the outset of their studies, and then set out to gain the mastery over themselves and in patience to apply themselves continuously to those studies, from which one sees result things marvelous to relate.

III · PROPHECIES

[*Of cannon which come forth out of a pit and from a mold*]
There shall come forth from beneath the ground that which by its terrific report shall stun all who are near it, and cause men to drop dead at its breath, and it shall devastate cities and castles.

[*Of dreaming*]
It shall seem to men that they see new destructions in the sky, and the flames descending therefrom shall seem to have taken flight and to flee away in terror; they shall hear creatures of every kind speaking human language; they shall run in a moment, in person, to divers parts of the world without movement; amidst the darkness they shall see the most radiant splendors. O marvel of mankind! What frenzy has thus impelled you! You shall hold converse with animals of every species, and they with you in human language. You shall behold yourselves falling from great heights without

suffering any injury; the torrents will bear you with them as they mingle in their rapid course.

[*Of ants*]

Many communities there will be who will hide themselves and their young and their victuals within gloomy caverns, and there in dark places will sustain themselves and their families for many months without any light either artificial or natural.

[*Of bees*]

And many others will be robbed of their store of provisions and their food, and by an insensate folk will be cruelly immersed and drowned. O justice of God! why dost thou not awake to behold thy creatures thus abused?

[*Of sheep, cows, goats and the like*]

From countless numbers will be stolen their little children, and the throats of these shall be cut, and they shall be quartered most barbarously.

[*Of nuts, olives, acorns, chestnuts and the like*]

Many children shall be torn with pitiless beatings out of the very arms of their mothers, and flung upon the ground and then maimed.

[*Of funeral rites and processions and lights and bells and followers*]

The greatest honors and ceremonies shall be paid to men without their knowledge.

[*The olives which drop from the olive trees give us the oil which makes light*]

There shall descend with fury from the direction of the sky that which will give us nourishment and light.

[*Of brick kilns and lime kilns*]

At the last the earth will become red after being exposed to fire for many days, and the stones will become changed to ashes.

[*Of wantonness*]

And they will go wild after the things that are most beautiful to seek after, to possess and make use of their vilest parts; and afterwards, having returned with loss and penitence to their understanding, they will be filled with great admiration for themselves.

[*Of dreaming*]

Men shall walk without moving, they shall speak with those who are absent, they shall hear those who do not speak.

[*Of feathers in beds*]

Flying creatures will support men with their feathers.

[*Of extinguishing the light when one goes to bed*]

Many by forcing their breath out too rapidly will lose the power of sight, and in a short time all power of sensation.

[*Of oxen which are eaten*]

The masters of the estates will eat their own laborers.

[*Of beating the bed to remake it*]

To such a pitch of ingratitude shall men come that that which shall give them lodging without any price shall be loaded with blows, in such a way that great parts of the inside of it shall be detached from their place, and shall be turned over and over within it.

[*Of the precious metals*]

There shall come forth out of dark and gloomy caves that which shall cause the whole human race to undergo great afflictions, perils and death. To many of those who follow it, after much tribulation it will yield delight; but whosoever pays it no homage will die in want and misery. It shall bring to pass an endless number of crimes; it shall prompt and incite wretched men to assassinate, to steal and to enslave; it shall hold its own followers in suspicion; it shall deprive free cities of their rank: it shall take away life itself from many; it shall make men torment each other with many kinds of subterfuge, deceits and treacheries.

O vile monster! How much better were it for men that thou shouldst go back to hell! For this the vast forests shall be stripped of their trees; for this an infinite number of creatures shall lose their lives.

[Of fire]

From small beginnings shall arise that which shall rapidly become great; and it shall have respect for no created thing, but its power shall be such as to enable it to transform almost everything from its natural condition.

[Of the dead who are taken to be buried]

The simple folk will carry a great number of lights to light up the journeys of all those who have wholly lost the power of sight. O human folly! O madness of mankind! These two phrases stand for the commencement of the matter.

[Of the dowries of maidens]

And whereas at first young maidens could not be protected from the lust and violence of men, either by the watchfulness of parents or by the strength of walls, there will come a time when it will be necessary for the fathers and relatives of these maidens to pay a great price to whoever is willing to marry them, even although they may be rich and noble and exceedingly beautiful. Herein it seems certain that nature desires to exterminate the human race, as a thing useless to the world and the destroyer of all created things.

[*Of the cruelty of man*]

Creatures shall be seen upon the earth who will always be fighting one with another, with very great losses and frequent deaths on either side. These shall set no bounds to their malice; by their fierce limbs a great number of the trees in the immense forests of the world shall be laid level with the ground; and when they have crammed themselves with food it shall gratify their desire to deal out death, affliction, labors, terrors and banishment to every living thing. And by reason of their boundless pride they shall wish to rise towards heaven, but the excessive weight of their limbs shall hold them down. There shall be nothing remaining on the earth or under the earth or in the waters that shall not be pursued and molested or destroyed, and that which is in one country taken away to another; and their own bodies shall be made the tomb and the means of transit of all the living bodies which they have slain. O earth! what delays thee to open and hurl them headlong into the deep fissures of thy huge abysses and caverns, and no longer to display in the sight of heaven so savage and ruthless a monster?

The water of the sea shall rise above the high summits of the mountains towards the sky, and it shall fall down again onto the dwellings of men: that is, as clouds.

Feathers shall raise men towards heaven even as they do birds: that is, by letters written with their quills.

Men will pursue the thing they most fear: that is, they will be miserable lest they should fall into misery.

You shall behold the bones of the dead by their rapid movement directing the fortunes of their mover: the dice.

Oxen shall by their horns protect the fire from death: the lantern.

The forests will bring forth young who will become the cause of their death: the handle of the hatchet.

Men will deal rude blows to that which is the cause of their life: they will thrash the grain.

The skins of animals will make men rouse from their silence with loud cries and oaths: balls for playing games.

The wind which passes through the skins of animals will make men leap up: that is, the bagpipes, which cause men to dance.

[*Of crucifixes which are sold*]
I see Christ again sold and crucified, and his saints suffering martyrdom.

[*Of the shadow cast by man at night with a light*]
There shall appear huge figures in human shape, and the nearer to you they approach the more will their immense size diminish.

Those will be drowned who give light for divine service: the bees which make the wax of the candles.

The great rocks of the mountains will dart forth fire, such that they will burn up the timber of many vast forests and many beasts both wild and tame:

The flint of the tinder-box, which makes a fire that consumes all the loads of faggots of which the forests are cleared, and with this the flesh of beasts is cooked.

The oxen will become in great part the cause of the destruction of cities; and so also will horses and buffaloes: they draw the guns.

[*Of leather bottles*]
The goats will carry wine to the cities.

[*Of shoemakers*]
Men will take a pleasure in seeing their own works worn out and destroyed.

XII

Personalia and Letters

I · PERSONALIA

'O LEONARDO, why do you toil so much?'

In the earliest recollections of my infancy it seemed to me when I was in the cradle that a kite came and opened my mouth with its tail, and struck me within upon the lips with its tail many times.

The Medici created and destroyed me. (*Li medici mi creorono e disstrussono.*)[1]

Note as to the moneys I have had from the King on account of my salary from July, 1508, until April, 1509. First 100 crowns, then another 100, then 70, then 50 and then 20, and then 200 francs, a franc being worth 48 soldi.

Find Ligny (*Ingil*)[2] and tell him you will wait for him at

[1] This interpretation is due to Gerolamo Calvi, who considers the note to have been written in the last years of Leonardo's life, either when on the point of departing from Rome or in France. His patron Giuliano de' Medici had died and the Medici Pope, Leo X, had failed to give him any employment commensurate with his powers. He thus sets in terse antithesis this destruction of his hopes and the fact that Lorenzo il Magnifico was his first patron. The latter statement is confirmed by the testimony of the Anonimo Gaddiano: *"stette da giovane col Magnifico Lorenzo de' Medici, et dandolj provisione per se il faceva lavorare nel giardino sulla piaza disan Marcho dj Firenze, et haveva 30 annj, che dal detto Magnifico Lorenzo fu mandato al duca di Milano."*

The sentence has also been held to refer to the medical profession, to whom on occasion he alludes with marked asperity. In MS. F 96 v. he characterizes them as 'destroyers of life.' In Arundel MS. 147 v. he speaks of men being chosen to be doctors for diseases about which they do not know.

[2] In MS. the letters of these words, presumably for reasons of secrecy, were scrambled.

Rome (*a morra*),[2] and will go with him to Naples (*in lo panna*).[2] See that you make the donation (*e no igano dal*),[2] and take the book of Vitolone, and the measurements of the public buildings. Have two trunks covered ready for the muleteer; bedspreads will do very well for the purpose; there are three of them but you will leave one at Vinci. Take the stoves from the Grazie. Get from Giovanni Lombardo the [model of] the theatre of Verona. Buy some tablecloths and towels, hats, shoes, four pairs of hose, a great coat of chamois hide, and leather to make new ones. The turning-lathe of Alessandro. Sell what you cannot carry. Get from Jean de Paris the method of coloring in tempera, and the way of making white salt, and tinted papers either single or with many folds, and also his box of colors. Learn how to work flesh tints in tempera. Learn how to melt gum into lacquer-varnish. Take seed of . . . (*fotteragi*), of white cudweed and of garlic from Piacenza. Take the "De Ponderibus." Take the works of Leonardo of Cremona. Carry the charcoal-burner which belongs to Giannino. Take the seed of lilies, of common lady's mantle, and of watermelon. Sell the boards of the scaffolding. Give the stove to whoever stole it. Learn leveling, how much soil a man can dig out in a day.

If liberty is dear to you, may you never discover that my face is love's prison.

Finally through anger he has wounded the image of his God; think if I had found him.

Say on, Sandro![3] How does it strike you? I tell you what is true, and I have not made a success of it.

[3] The reference may be to Sandro Botticelli.

And many hate their fathers and break off friendships when they are reproved for their vices; instances to the contrary have no weight with them, nor has any human counsel.

EXPENSES FOR CATERINA'S[4] BURIAL

For three pounds of wax	s.	27
For the bier	s.	8
Pall upon the bier	s.	12
Carrying and setting up of cross	s.	4
For the carrying of the dead	s.	8
For four priests and four clerks	s.	20
Bell, book, sponge	s.	2
For the gravediggers	s.	16
To the ancient	s.	8
For the license and the officials	s.	1
		106
For the doctor		5
Sugar and candles	s.	12
		123

I have so many words in my mother tongue that I ought rather to complain of the lack of a right understanding of things, than of a lack of words with which fully to express the conception that is in my mind.

I have wasted my hours.[5]

---

[4] Caterina was Leonardo's mother.

[5] Note written on the right-hand lower corner of a page that contains mathematical and architectural drawings, and others anatomical of the generative functions, with acoustical note and memoranda.

Tell me if anything similar was ever made: you understand, and that is enough for the present.[6]

On one occasion above Milan, over in the direction of Lake Maggiore, I saw a cloud shaped like a huge mountain made up of banks of fire, because the rays of the sun which was then setting red on the horizon had dyed it with their color. This great cloud drew to itself all the little clouds which were round about it. And the great cloud remained stationary, and it retained the light of the sun on its apex for an hour and a half after sunset, so enormous was its size.

The duke lost his State, his personal possessions and his liberty, and none of his enterprises have been completed.[7]

On the twenty-third day of April, 1490, I commenced this book and recommenced the horse.

Giacomo came to live with me on St. Mary Magdalene's Day, 1490, when ten years of age. Thievish, lying, obstinate, greedy.

The second day I had two shirts cut out for him, a pair of hose and a doublet, and when I put money aside to pay for these things he stole the money from the wallet, and it was never possible to make him confess, although I was absolutely convinced.   4 lire.

On the following day I went to supper with Giacomo Andrea, and the other Giacomo had supper for two and did mischief for four, for he broke three flagons, spilt the wine, and after this came to supper where I . . .

Item, on the seventh day of September he stole a style worth twenty-two soldi from Marco, who was with me. It

[6] This is on the same page with reduction of periphery of quadrant to straight line and calculation of spheres.

[7] Leonardo's laconic epitaph upon the fallen fortunes of Lodovico Sforza, ruler of Milan until his overthrow by the French.

was of silver, and he took it from his studio. After the said Marco had searched for it a long time he found it hidden in the box of the said Giacomo. 2 lire 1 soldo.

Item, on the twenty-sixth day of the following January when I was in the house of Messer Galeazzo da Sanseverino in order to arrange the pageant at his tournament, and certain of the pages had taken off their clothes in order to try on some of the costumes of the savages who were to appear in this pageant, Giacomo went to the wallet of one of them as it lay on the bed with the other effects, and took some money that he found there. 2 lire 4 soldi.

Item, a Turkish hide had been given me in the same house by the Master Agostino of Pavia in order to make a pair of boots, and this Giacomo stole it from me within a month and sold it to a cobbler for twenty soldi, and with the money as he has himself confessed to me he bought aniseed comfits. 2 lire.

Item, further on the second day of April, Giovanni Antonio chanced to leave a silver style upon one of his drawings, and this Giacomo stole it from him, and it was worth twenty-four soldi. 1 lira 4 soldi.

The first year: a cloak, 2 lire; 6 shirts, 4 lire; 3 doublets, 6 lire; 4 pairs of hose, 7 lire 8 soldi; a suit of clothes lined, 5 lire; 24 pairs of shoes, 6 lire 5 soldi; a cap, 1 lira; laces for belt, 1 lira.

When I was at sea in a position equally distant from a level shore and a mountain, the side on which the shore was, seemed much farther off than that of the mountain.[8]

Nor does the tempestuous sea make so loud a roaring

[8] In the sketch that accompanies this note a vessel is seen proceeding from a mountainous shore to one more low-lying. Its major interest is in the biographical question it raises. That Leonardo was himself once at sea in a position equally distant between a level and a mountainous shore, both visible at once, is here clearly stated.

when the northern blast beats it back in foaming waves between Scylla and Charybdis, nor Stromboli nor Mount Etna when the pent-up, sulphurous fires, bursting open and rending asunder the mighty mountain by their force, are hurling through the air rocks and earth mingled together in the issuing belching flames. . . .

And drawn on by my eager desire, anxious to behold the great abundance of the varied and strange forms created by the artificer nature, having wandered for some distance among the overhanging rocks, I came to the mouth of a huge cavern before which for a time I remained stupefied, not having been aware of its existence, my back bent to an arch, my left hand clutching my knee, while with the right I made a shade for my lowered and contracted eyebrows; and I was bending continually first one way and then another in order to see whether I could discern anything inside, though this was rendered impossible by the intense darkness within. And after remaining there for a time, suddenly there were awakened within me two emotions, fear and desire, fear of the dark threatening cavern, desire to see whether there might be any marvelous thing therein.

O powerful and once living instrument of constructive nature, thy great strength not availing thee, thou must needs abandon thy tranquil life to obey the law which God and time ordained for all-procreative nature! To thee availed not the branching, sturdy dorsal fins wherewith pursuing thy prey thou wast wont to plough thy way, tempestuously tearing open the briny waves with thy breast.

O how many times the frightened shoals of dolphins and big tunny-fish were seen to flee before thy insensate fury; and thou, lashing with swift, branching fins and forked tail, didst create in the sea sudden tempest with loud uproar and foundering of ships; with mighty wave thou didst heap up the open shores with the frightened and terrified fishes, which thus escaping from thee were left high and dry when the sea abandoned them, and became the plenteous and abundant spoil of the neighboring peoples.

O time, swift despoiler of created things! How many kings, how many peoples hast thou brought low! How many changes of state and circumstance have followed since the wondrous form of this fish died here in this hollow winding recess? Now, destroyed by time, patiently it lies within this narrow space, and, with its bones despoiled and bare, it is become an armor and support to the mountain which lies above it.

II · LETTERS

[*Draft of letter to Lodovico Sforza, Duke of Milan,* 1482]

Most Illustrious Lord, having now sufficiently seen and considered the proofs of all those who count themselves masters and inventors of instruments of war, and finding that their invention and use of the said instruments does not differ in any respect from those in common practice, I am emboldened without prejudice to anyone else to put myself in communication with your Excellency, in order to acquaint you with my secrets, thereafter offering myself at your pleasure effectually to demonstrate at any convenient time all those matters which are in part briefly recorded below.

1. I have plans for bridges, very light and strong and suitable for carrying very easily, with which to pursue and at times defeat the enemy; and others solid and indestructible by fire or assault, easy and convenient to carry away and place in position. And plans for burning and destroying those of the enemy.

2. When a place is besieged I know how to cut off water from the trenches, and how to construct an infinite number of bridges, mantlets, scaling ladders and other instruments which have to do with the same enterprise.

3. Also if a place cannot be reduced by the method of bombardment, either through the height of its glacis or the strength of its position, I have plans for destroying every fortress or other stronghold unless it has been founded upon rock.

4. I have also plans for making cannon, very convenient and easy of transport, with which to hurl small stones in the manner almost of hail, causing great terror to the enemy from their smoke, and great loss and confusion.

5. Also I have ways of arriving at a certain fixed spot by caverns and secret winding passages, made without any noise even though it may be necessary to pass underneath trenches or a river.

6. Also I can make armored cars, safe and unassailable, which will enter the serried ranks of the enemy with their artillery, and there is no company of men at arms so great that they will not break it. And behind these the infantry will be able to follow quite unharmed and without any opposition.

7. Also, if need shall arise, I can make cannon, mortars and light ordnance, of very beautiful and useful shapes, quite different from those in common use.

8. Where it is not possible to employ cannon, I can supply catapults, mangonels, *trabocchi* and other engines of wonderful efficacy not in general use. In short, as the variety of circumstances shall necessitate, I can supply an infinite number of different engines of attack and defense.

9. And if it should happen that the engagement was at sea, I have plans for constructing many engines most suitable

either for attack or defense, and ships which can resist the fire of all the heaviest cannon, and powder and smoke.

10. In time of peace I believe that I can give you as complete satisfaction as anyone else in architecture in the construction of buildings both public and private, and in conducting water from one place to another.

Also I can execute sculpture in marble, bronze or clay, and also painting, in which my work will stand comparison with that of anyone else whoever he may be.

Moreover, I would undertake the work of the bronze horse, which shall endue with immortal glory and eternal honor the auspicious memory of the Prince your father and of the illustrious house of Sforza.

And if any of the aforesaid things should seem impossible or impracticable to anyone, I offer myself as ready to make trial of them in your park or in whatever place shall please your Excellency, to whom I commend myself with all possible humility.

Dearest Father:

On the last of the past month I had the letter you wrote to me which in a brief space caused me pleasure and also sorrow. I was pleased at learning from it that you were in good health, for which God be praised. I was filled with sorrow at hearing of your discomfort.

My most beloved brother:[1]

This is sent merely to inform you that a short time ago I received a letter from you from which I learned that you have had an heir, which circumstance I understand has afforded you a great deal of pleasure. Now in so far as I had judged you to be possessed of prudence I am now entirely

---

[1] Reference is to Domenico, who was born in 1484.

convinced that I am as far removed from having an accurate judgment as you are from prudence; seeing that you have been congratulating yourself in having created a watchful enemy, who will strive with all his energies after liberty, which can only come into being at your death.

[*The following is one of several drafts of a letter to Leonardo's patron, Giuliano de' Medici*]

So greatly did I rejoice, most Illustrious Lord, at your much-wished-for restoration to health that my own malady almost left me. But I greatly regret that I have been unable to satisfy the desires of your Excellency, entirely through the malice of that German rogue, as regards whom I have left nothing undone which I thought might give him pleasure. And firstly because I invited him to take up his abode and have meals with me, so that I could always see what work he was doing and could easily correct his errors, and moreover he would acquire Italian and so be able to speak it easily without an interpreter, and most important of all the moneys due to him could always be paid before the time, as always has been. Then he asked that he might have the models finished in wood just as they were to be in iron, and wished to carry them away to his own country. But this I refused, telling him that I would give him a drawing of the width, length, thickness and outline of what he had to, and so we remained at enmity.

The second thing was that in the room where he slept he made himself another workshop with new screw-vices and instruments, and there worked for others. Afterwards he went to dine with the Swiss of the Guard where there are plenty of idlers, but he beat them all at it. Then he used to go out and more often than not two or three of them went together with guns to shoot birds among the ruins, and this went on until the evening.

Finally I discovered that it was this master Giovanni who made mirrors who had brought all this about and this for two reasons; first because he had said that my coming here had deprived him of the countenance and favor of your Lordship which always . . . , and the other reason is because he says the room of this iron-worker would suit him for working at mirrors, and he has given proof of this, for besides setting him against me he has made him sell all his effects and leave his workshop to him, and he has established himself there now with a number of assistants making many mirrors to send to the fairs.

[Draft of a letter apparently written by Leonardo to demonstrate his fitness to repair the Cathedral at Milan]

My Lords, Fathers, Deputies:

You know that medicines when well used restore health to the sick, and he who knows them well will use them well when he also knows what man is, and what life and the constitution are, and what health is. Knowing these well he will know their opposites, and being thus equipped he will be nearer to devising a remedy than anyone else. In just the same way a cathedral in need of repair requires a doctor-architect who understands well what a building is, and on what rules the correct method of construction is based, and from whence these rules are derived, and into how many parts they are divided, and what are the causes which hold the structure together, and make it permanent, and what the nature of weight is and what the desire of strength, and how these should be interwoven and bound up together, and what effect their union produces. Whoever shall have a true knowledge about the above-named things will satisfy you both by his intelligence and his work.

So for this reason I shall endeavor without disparaging and without defaming anyone to satisfy you partly by arguments and partly by demonstration, sometimes revealing the effects from the causes, sometimes confirming the reasoning from experience, fitting with them certain of the principles of the architects of old time and the evidence of the buildings they constructed and [showing] what were the reasons of their destruction or their permanence.

And I shall show at the same time what is the first [law] of weight, and what and how many are the causes which bring ruin to buildings, and what is the condition of their stability and permanence.

But in order not to be diffuse to your Excellencies I will speak first of the invention of the first architect of the cathedral, and will show you clearly what was his purpose, confirming this by the building which has been commenced, and when I have made you understand this you will be able clearly to recognize that the model which I have constructed possesses in itself that symmetry, that harmony and that regularity which belongs to the building already begun.

What a building is, and where the rules of sound construction derive their origin, and what and how many are the parts that belong to these. . . .

Either I or some other who may expound it better than I, choose him, and set aside all partiality.

[*Fragment of a letter to Lodovico Sforza*]

I regret very much that the fact of my having to gain my living should have prevented me from continuing the work which your Highness has entrusted to me: but I hope that within a short time I shall have earned so much as to be able with a tranquil mind to satisfy your Excellency, to whom I commend myself. If your Highness thought that I had money, you were deceived, for I have had six mouths to feed for thirty-six months, and I have had fifty ducats.

Letters

[*The Commissioners of Buildings at Piacenza were apparently about to undertake the construction of bronze doors
for the cathedral*]

Illustrious Commissioners of Buildings! hearing that your
Excellencies have resolved upon the construction of certain
great works in bronze, I propose to offer you certain counsels
on the subject. First, then, take care not to act so swiftly and
hastily in awarding the commission that by your speed you
put it out of your power to make a good choice both of
subject and of a master, as Italy has a number of men of
capacity. Some fellow, that is, who by his incompetence may
afterwards afford occasion to your successors to cast blame
on yourselves and your generation, judging that this age was
poorly equipped either with men of good judgment or good
masters, seeing that other cities and especially the city of the
Florentines were almost at this very same time enriched with
such beautiful and great works in bronze, among these being
the gates of their baptistery. Florence indeed, like Piacenza,
is a place of resort, where many visitors congregate, and
these when they see its beautiful and stately works of art
form the impression that the city must have worthy inhabitants, seeing that these works serve as evidence of this; but
they form quite a different impression if they see a great
expenditure in metal wrought so poorly that it would be less
of a reproach to the city if the doors were of plain wood,
for then the material would have cost little and, therefore,
would not seem to require a great degree of skill.

Now, the parts principally sought for in cities are their
cathedrals, and, as one approaches these, the first objects
which meet the eye are their doors by which one enters into
the churches.

Beware, gentlemen of the Commission, lest the too great
speed, whereby you desire, with such swiftness as I perceive

451

you use, to allot the commission for so important a work, may become the reason why what was intended for the honor of God and of men may prove a great dishonor to your judgment and to your city, where, as it is a place of distinction and of resort, there is an innumerable concourse of visitors. This disgrace would befall you if by your negligence you put your trust in some braggart who, by his subterfuges or by the favor here shown him, were to be awarded such a commission by you as should bring great and lasting shame both to him and to you.

I cannot help feeling angry when I reflect upon the sort of men who have made me a confidant of their desire to embark upon such an undertaking, without giving a thought to their capacity for it—not to say more.

One is a maker of pots, another of cuirasses, a third makes bells and another collars for them, another even is a bombardier; yet another is in the Duke's household and boasts that he is by way of being an intimate acquaintance of Messer Ambrogio Ferrere, and that he has some influence and has made certain promises to him, and if this does not satisfy you he will get on his horse and ride off to the Duke, and will get such letters from him that you will never be able to refuse him the work.

But consider to what straits the poor masters who by study have made themselves competent to execute such works are reduced, when they have to contend against fellows like these! What hope have they of being able to look for reward for their talent!

Open your eyes and try to ensure that your money is not so spent as to purchase your own shame. I can assure you that from this district you will get nothing except the works of hard, mean or clumsy masters. There is not a man who is capable—and you may believe me—except Leonardo the

Florentine, who is making the bronze horse of the Duke Francesco; and you can leave him out of your calculations altogether, for he has a work to do which will last him the whole of his life, and indeed I doubt whether he will ever finish it, so great it is.

Most Illustrious, most Reverend, and my Unique Lord, the Lord Ippolito, Cardinal of Este, My Supreme Lord, at Ferrara.

Most Illustrious and Most Reverend Lord,

A few days ago I arrived from Milan, and finding that one of my elder brothers refuses to carry out the provisions of a will made three years ago when our father died—as also no less because I would not seem to myself to fail in a matter that I consider most urgent—I cannot forbear to request of your most Reverend Highness a letter of commendation and favor to Ser Raphaello Hieronymo, who is now one of the members of our illustrious Signoria before whom my case is being tried; and more particularly it has been referred by his Excellency the Gonfaloniere to the said Ser Raphaello, so that his Lordship may be able to reach a decision and bring it to completion before the coming of the festival of All Saints.

And therefore, my Lord, I beseech you, as earnestly as I know how and am able, that your Highness will write a letter to the said Ser Raphaello in that happy and engaging manner that you have the art of, commending to him Leonardo Vincio, your most humble servant, as I call myself and always wish to be; requesting and urging that he may be desirous not only to do me justice but to do so with kindly urgency; and I have no doubt at all from many reports that have reached me that inasmuch as Ser Raphaello is most kindly disposed to your Highness the matter will then proceed *ad votum.* And this I shall attribute to the letter of your most Reverend Highness, to whom once more I commend myself. *Et bene valeat.*

   Florence, 18 September, 1507.
      E.V.R.D.
                        Your most humble servant,
                              Leonardus Vincius, *pictor.*

My Illustrious Lord [Antonio Maria], the affection which your Excellency has always shown to me and the benefits which I have received from you are continually in my thoughts.

I have a suspicion that the small response I have made for the great benefits which I have received from your Excellency may have made you somewhat incensed with me; and that is the reason why I have never had any reply to the many letters that I have written to your Excellency. I am now sending Salai to you to explain to your Lordship that I am almost at the end of my litigation with my brothers, and that I hope to be with you this Easter, and to bring with me two pictures of the Madonna of different sizes, which I have begun for the Most Christian King or for whomsoever else it shall please you. I shall be very glad to know on my return there where I am to have my lodging, because I would not wish to give any more trouble to your Lordship, and further whether seeing that I have been engaged in work for the Most Christian King, my salary is to continue or not. I am writing to the President of that water which the king granted me, of which I was not given possession on account of the scarcity in the canal due to the great drought, and to the fact of the outlets not having been regulated; he promised me however that as soon as this was done I should be put in possession; so that I beseech you if you should happen to meet the said President not to think it irksome, now that these outlets are regulated, to remind him to have me put in possession of this water, since I am given to understand that in great measure it rests with him. Nothing else occurs to me. I am always at your commands.

Dear Messer Francesco:

I am sending Salai to you in order to learn from his Excellency the President what conclusion has been reached in the matter of the regulation of the water, since at my departure the order for the outlets of the canal had been set in hand; because the illustrious President promised me that my claim should be settled so soon as ever this adjustment had been made. It is now a considerable time since I learned that the canal was set in working order and likewise its outlets, and I wrote immediately to the President and to you, and then repeated my letters, but have never had any reply. Will you, therefore, have the kindness to write and inform me what has taken place, and unless it is actually on the point of settlement, will you for my sake be so kind as to exert a little pressure on the President and also on Messer Girolamo da Cusano, to whom please commend me, and also offer my respects to his Excellency?

Good day to you, Messer Francesco, God knows why when I have written you so many letters you have never made me a single reply. Just wait until I come to you, by God, for I will make you write so much that you will perhaps be sorry for it.

The Best of the World's Best Books
COMPLETE LIST OF TITLES IN
THE MODERN LIBRARY

For convenience in ordering use number at right of title

ADAMS, HENRY	The Education of Henry Adams 76
AIKEN, CONRAD (Editor)	A Comprehensive Anthology of American Poetry 101
AIKEN, CONRAD (Editor)	20th-Century American Poetry 127
ALEICHEM, SHOLOM	Selected Stories of 145
ANDERSON, SHERWOOD	Winesburg, Ohio 104
AQUINAS, ST. THOMAS	Introduction to St. Thomas Aquinas 259
ARISTOTLE	Introduction to Aristotle 248
ARISTOTLE	Politics 228
ARISTOTLE	Rhetoric and Poetics 246
AUGUSTINE, ST.	The Confessions of 263
AUSTEN, JANE	Pride and Prejudice and Sense and Sensibility 264
BACON, FRANCIS	Selected Writings of 256
BALZAC	Droll Stories 193
BALZAC	Père Goriot and Eugénie Grandet 245
BEERBOHM, MAX	Zuleika Dobson 116
BELLAMY, EDWARD	Looking Backward 22
BENNETT, ARNOLD	The Old Wives' Tale 184
BERGSON, HENRI	Creative Evolution 231
BLAKE, WILLIAM	Selected Poetry & Prose of 285
BOCCACCIO	The Decameron 71
BOSWELL, JAMES	The Life of Samuel Johnson 282
BRONTË, CHARLOTTE	Jane Eyre 64
BRONTË, EMILY	Wuthering Heights 106
BROWNING, ROBERT	Selected Poetry of 198
BUCK, PEARL	The Good Earth 15
BURCKHARDT, JACOB	The Civilization of the Renaissance in Italy 32
BURK, JOHN N.	The Life and Works of Beethoven 241
BUTLER, SAMUEL	Erewhon and Erewhon Revisited 136
BUTLER, SAMUEL	The Way of All Flesh 13
BYRNE, DONN	Messer Marco Polo 43
BYRON, LORD	The Selected Poetry of 195
BYRON, LORD	Don Juan 24
CAESAR, JULIUS	The Gallic War and Other Writings of 295
CALDWELL, ERSKINE	God's Little Acre 51
CALDWELL, ERSKINE	Tobacco Road 249
CANFIELD, DOROTHY	The Deepening Stream 200
CARROLL, LEWIS	Alice in Wonderland, etc. 79
CASANOVA, JACQUES	Memoirs of Casanova 165
CELLINI, BENVENUTO	Autobiography of Cellini 150
CERVANTES	Don Quixote 174
CHAUCER	The Canterbury Tales 161
CHEKHOV, ANTON	Best Plays by 171
CHEKHOV, ANTON	The Short Stories of 50
CICERO	The Basic Works of 272
COLERIDGE	Selected Poetry and Prose of 279

COMMAGER, HENRY STEELE
& NEVINS, ALLAN   A Short History of the United States 235
CONFUCIUS   The Wisdom of Confucius 7
CONRAD, JOSEPH   Lord Jim 186
CONRAD, JOSEPH   Nostromo 275
CONRAD, JOSEPH   Victory 34
COOPER, JAMES FENIMORE   The Pathfinder 105
CORNEILLE & RACINE   Six Plays of Corneille and Racine 194
CORVO, FREDERICK BARON   A History of the Borgias 192
CRANE, STEPHEN   The Red Badge of Courage 130
CUMMINGS, E. E.   The Enormous Room 214
DANA, RICHARD HENRY   Two Years Before the Mast 236
DANTE   The Divine Comedy 208
DA VINCI, LEONARDO   The Notebooks of 156
DEFOE, DANIEL   Moll Flanders 122
DEFOE, DANIEL   Robinson Crusoe and A Journal of the
                                     Plague Year 92
DEWEY, JOHN   Human Nature and Conduct 173
DICKENS, CHARLES   David Copperfield 110
DICKENS, CHARLES   Pickwick Papers 204
DICKENS, CHARLES   A Tale of Two Cities 189
DICKINSON, EMILY   Selected Poems of 25
DINESEN, ISAK   Out of Africa 23
DINESEN, ISAK   Seven Gothic Tales 54
DONNE, JOHN   Complete Poetry and Selected Prose of
                                     12
DOS PASSOS, JOHN   Three Soldiers 205
DOSTOYEVSKY, FYODOR   The Best Short Stories of 293
DOSTOYEVSKY, FYODOR   The Brothers Karamazov 151
DOSTOYEVSKY, FYODOR   Crime and Punishment 199
DOSTOYEVSKY, FYODOR   The Possessed 55
DOUGLAS, NORMAN   South Wind 5
DOYLE, SIR ARTHUR CONAN   The Adventures and Memoirs of Sher-
                                     lock Holmes 206
DREISER, THEODORE   Sister Carrie 8
DUMAS, ALEXANDRE   Camille 69
DUMAS, ALEXANDRE   The Three Musketeers 143
DU MAURIER, DAPHNE   Rebecca 227
ELLIS, HAVELOCK   The Dance of Life 160
EMERSON, RALPH WALDO   Essays and Other Writings 91
FAULKNER, WILLIAM   Absalom, Absalom! 271
FAULKNER, WILLIAM   Go Down, Moses 175
FAULKNER, WILLIAM   Light in August 88
FAULKNER, WILLIAM   Sanctuary 61
FAULKNER, WILLIAM   The Sound and the Fury and As I Lay
                                     Dying 187
FIELDING, HENRY   Joseph Andrews 117
FIELDING, HENRY   Tom Jones 185
FLAUBERT, GUSTAVE   Madame Bovary 28
FORESTER, C. S.   The African Queen 102
FRANCE, ANATOLE   Penguin Island 210
FRANKLIN, BENJAMIN   Autobiography, etc. 39
FREUD, SIGMUND   The Interpretation of Dreams 96
FROST, ROBERT   The Poems of 242
GALSWORTHY, JOHN   The Apple Tree
                                     (in Great Modern Short Stories 168)
GAUTIER, THEOPHILE   Mlle. De Maupin and
                                     One of Cleopatra's Nights 53

GEORGE, HENRY	Progress and Poverty 36
GOETHE	Faust 177
GOGOL, NIKOLAI	Dead Souls 40
GOLDSMITH, OLIVER	The Vicar of Wakefield and other Writings 291
GRAVES, ROBERT	I, Claudius 20
GUNTHER, JOHN	Death Be Not Proud 286
HACKETT, FRANCIS	The Personal History of Henry the Eighth 265
HAGGARD, H. RIDER	She and King Solomon's Mines 163
HARDY, THOMAS	Jude the Obscure 135
HARDY, THOMAS	The Mayor of Casterbridge 17
HARDY, THOMAS	The Return of the Native 121
HARDY, THOMAS	Tess of the D'Urbervilles 72
HART & KAUFMAN	Six Plays by 233
HARTE, BRET	The Best Stories of 250
HAWTHORNE, NATHANIEL	The Scarlet Letter 93
HEGEL	The Philosophy of 239
HELLMAN, LILLIAN	Four Plays by 223
HENRY, O.	Best Short Stories of 4
HERODOTUS	The Persian Wars 255
HOFFENSTEIN, SAMUEL	The Complete Poetry of 225
HOMER	The Iliad 166
HOMER	The Odyssey 167
HORACE	The Complete Works of 141
HOWELLS, WILLIAM DEAN	The Rise of Silas Lapham 277
HUDSON, W. H.	Green Mansions 89
HUGHES, RICHARD	A High Wind in Jamaica 112
HUGO, VICTOR	The Hunchback of Notre Dame 35
HUXLEY, ALDOUS	Antic Hay 209
HUXLEY, ALDOUS	Brave New World 48
HUXLEY, ALDOUS	Point Counter Point 180
IBSEN, HENRIK	Six Plays by 6
IRVING, WASHINGTON	Selected Writings of 240
JAMES, HENRY	The Bostonians 16
JAMES, HENRY	The Portrait of a Lady 107
JAMES, HENRY	The Turn of the Screw 169
JAMES, HENRY	Washington Square 269
JAMES, HENRY	The Wings of the Dove 244
JAMES, WILLIAM	The Philosophy of William James 114
JAMES, WILLIAM	The Varieties of Religious Experience 70
JEFFERS, ROBINSON	Roan Stallion; Tamar and Other Poems 118
JEFFERSON, THOMAS	The Life and Selected Writings of 234
JOYCE, JAMES	Dubliners 124
KAFKA, FRANZ	Selected Stories of 283
KANT	The Philosophy of 266
KAUFMAN & HART	Six Plays by 233
KEATS	The Complete Poetry and Selected Prose of 273
KIPLING, RUDYARD	Kim 99
KOESTLER, ARTHUR	Darkness at Noon 74
LAOTSE	The Wisdom of 262
LAWRENCE, D. H.	The Rainbow 128
LAWRENCE, D. H.	Sons and Lovers 109
LAWRENCE, D. H.	Women in Love 68
LEWIS, SINCLAIR	Dodsworth 252
LEWIS, SINCLAIR	Cass Timberlane 221
LONGFELLOW, HENRY W.	Poems 56

LOUYS, PIERRE	Aphrodite 77
LUDWIG, EMIL	Napoleon 95
MACHIAVELLI	The Prince and The Discourses 65
MALRAUX, ANDRÉ	Man's Fate 33
MANN, THOMAS	Death in Venice (in Great German Short Novels and Stories 108)
MARQUAND, JOHN P.	The Late George Apley 182
MARX, KARL	Capital and Other Writings 202
MAUGHAM, W. SOMERSET	The Best Short Stories of 14
MAUGHAM, W. SOMERSET	Cakes and Ale 270
MAUGHAM, W. SOMERSET	The Moon and Sixpence 27
MAUGHAM, W. SOMERSET	Of Human Bondage 176
MAUPASSANT, GUY DE	Best Short Stories 98
MAUROIS, ANDRÉ	Disraeli 46
McCORD, DAVID (Editor)	What Cheer: An Anthology of Humorous and Witty Verse 190
MEAD, MARGARET	Coming of Age in Samoa 126
MELVILLE, HERMAN	Moby Dick 119
MEREDITH, GEORGE	The Egoist 253
MEREDITH, GEORGE	The Ordeal of Richard Feverel 134
MEREJKOWSKI, DMITRI	The Romance of Leonardo da Vinci 138
MICHENER, JAMES A.	Selected Writings of 296
MILTON, JOHN	The Complete Poetry and Selected Prose of John Milton 132
MOLIÈRE	Eight Plays by 78
MONTAIGNE	Selected Essays of 218
MORIER, JAMES	The Adventures of Hajji Baba of Ispahan 289
NASH, OGDEN	The Selected Verse of Ogden Nash 191
NEVINS, ALLAN & COMMAGER, HENRY STEELE	A Short History of the United States 235
NEWMAN, CARDINAL JOHN H.	Apologia Pro Vita Sua 113
NIETZSCHE, FRIEDRICH	Thus Spake Zarathustra 9
NOSTRADAMUS	Oracles of 81
ODETS, CLIFFORD	Six Plays of 67
O'HARA, JOHN	Appointment in Samarra 42
O'HARA, JOHN	Selected Short Stories of 211
O'NEILL, EUGENE	The Emperor Jones, Anna Christie and The Hairy Ape 146
O'NEILL, EUGENE	The Long Voyage Home: Seven Plays of the Sea 111
PALGRAVE, FRANCIS (Editor)	The Golden Treasury 232
PARKER, DOROTHY	The Collected Short Stories of 123
PARKER, DOROTHY	The Collected Poetry of 237
PARKMAN, FRANCIS	The Oregon Trail 267
PASCAL, BLAISE	Pensées and The Provincial Letters 164
PATER, WALTER	Marius the Epicurean 90
PATER, WALTER	The Renaissance 86
PEPYS, SAMUEL	Passages from the Diary of 103
PERELMAN, S. J.	The Best of 247
PLATO	The Republic 153
PLATO	The Works of Plato 181
POE, EDGAR ALLAN	Selected Poetry and Prose 82
POLO, MARCO	The Travels of Marco Polo 196
POPE, ALEXANDER	Selected Works of 257
PORTER, KATHERINE ANNE	Flowering Judas 284
PORTER, KATHERINE ANNE	Pale Horse, Pale Rider 45
PROUST, MARCEL	The Captive 120
PROUST, MARCEL	Cities of the Plain 220

PROUST, MARCEL	The Guermantes Way 213
PROUST, MARCEL	The Past Recaptured 278
PROUST, MARCEL	Swann's Way 59
PROUST, MARCEL	The Sweet Cheat Gone 260
PROUST, MARCEL	Within a Budding Grove 172
RACINE & CORNEILLE	Six Plays by 194
READE, CHARLES	The Cloister and the Hearth 62
REED, JOHN	Ten Days that Shook the World 215
RENAN, ERNEST	The Life of Jesus 140
RICHARDSON, SAMUEL	Clarissa 10
ROSTAND, EDMOND	Cyrano de Bergerac 154
ROUSSEAU, JEAN JACQUES	The Confessions of 243
RUSSELL, BERTRAND	Selected Papers of Bertrand Russell 137
SAKI	The Short Stories of 280
SANTAYANA, GEORGE	The Sense of Beauty 292
SCHOPENHAUER	The Philosophy of Schopenhauer 52
SCHULBERG, BUDD	What Makes Sammy Run? 281
SHAKESPEARE, WILLIAM	Tragedies, 1, 1A—complete, 2 vols.
SHAKESPEARE, WILLIAM	Comedies, 2, 2A—complete, 2 vols.
SHAKESPEARE, WILLIAM	Histories, 3 Histories, Poems, 3A } complete, 2 vols.
SHAW, BERNARD	Four Plays by 19
SHAW, BERNARD	Saint Joan, Major Barbara, and Androcles and the Lion 294
SHELLEY	The Selected Poetry & Prose of 274
SMOLLETT, TOBIAS	Humphry Clinker 159
SPINOZA	The Philosophy of Spinoza 60
STEINBECK, JOHN	In Dubious Battle 115
STEINBECK, JOHN	The Grapes of Wrath 148
STEINBECK, JOHN	Of Mice and Men 29
STEINBECK, JOHN	Tortilla Flat 216
STENDHAL	The Red and the Black 157
STERNE, LAURENCE	Tristram Shandy 147
STEWART, GEORGE R.	Storm 254
STOKER, BRAM	Dracula 31
STONE, IRVING	Lust for Life 11
STOWE, HARRIET BEECHER	Uncle Tom's Cabin 261
STRACHEY, LYTTON	Eminent Victorians 212
SUETONIUS	Lives of the Twelve Caesars 188
SWIFT, JONATHAN	Gulliver's Travels, A Tale of a Tub, The Battle of the Books 100
SYMONDS, JOHN A.	The Life of Michelangelo 49
TACITUS	The Complete Works of 222
TENNYSON	Selected Poetry of 230
THACKERAY, WILLIAM	Henry Esmond 80
THACKERAY, WILLIAM	Vanity Fair 131
THOMPSON, FRANCIS	Complete Poems 38
THOREAU, HENRY DAVID	Walden and Other Writings 155
THUCYDIDES	The Complete Writings of 58
THURBER, JAMES	The Thurber Carnival 85
TOLSTOY, LEO	Anna Karenina 37
TROLLOPE, ANTHONY	Barchester Towers and The Warden 41
TROLLOPE, ANTHONY	The Eustace Diamonds 251
TURGENEV, IVAN	Fathers and Sons 21
TWAIN, MARK	A Connecticut Yankee in King Arthur's Court 162
VEBLEN, THORSTEIN	The Theory of the Leisure Class 63
VIRGIL	The Aeneid, Eclogues & Georgics 75

VOLTAIRE   Candide and Other Writings 47
WALPOLE, HUGH   Fortitude 178
WALTON, IZAAK   The Compleat Angler 26
WARREN, ROBERT PENN   All The King's Men 170
WEBB, MARY   Precious Bane 219
WELLS, H. G.   Tono Bungay 197
WELTY, EUDORA   Selected Stories of 290
WHARTON, EDITH   The Age of Innocence 229
WHITMAN, WALT   Leaves of Grass 97
WILDE, OSCAR   Dorian Gray, De Profundis 125
WILDE, OSCAR   The Plays of Oscar Wilde 83
WILDE, OSCAR   Poems and Fairy Tales 84
WORDSWORTH   Selected Poetry of 268
YEATS, W. B. (Editor)   Irish Fairy and Folk Tales 44
YOUNG, G. F.   The Medici 179
ZIMMERN, ALFRED   The Greek Commonwealth 207
ZOLA, EMILE   Nana 142

MISCELLANEOUS   An Anthology of Irish Literature 288
                           The Arabian Nights' Entertain-
                              ments 201
                           Best Amer. Humorous Short Stories 87
                           Best Russian Short Stories 18
                           Best Spanish Stories 129
                           A Comprehensive Anthology of Ameri-
                              can Poetry 101
                           The Consolation of Philosophy 226
                           Eight Famous Elizabethan Plays 94
                           Eighteenth-Century Plays 224
                           Famous Ghost Stories 73
                           The Federalist 139
                           Five Great Modern Irish Plays 30
                           Fourteen Great Detective Stories 144
                           Great German Short Novels and Stories
                              108
                           Great Modern Short Stories 168
                           Great Tales of the American West 238
                           The Greek Poets 203
                           The Latin Poets 217
                           The Making of Man: An Outline of
                              Anthropology 149
                           The Making of Society: An Outline of
                              Sociology 183
                           Medieval Romances 133
                           New Voices in the American Theatre
                              258
                           Outline of Abnormal Psychology 152
                           Outline of Psychoanalysis 66
                           Restoration Plays 287
                           Seven Famous Greek Plays 158
                           The Short Bible 57
                           Six Modern American Plays 276
                           Twentieth-Century Amer. Poetry 127